Astronomy

REGION OF ORION

The photograph was made with a small lens with an exposure of ten hours. It covers nearly one twentieth of the whole sky. The Hyades, in Taurus, are near the upper right corner. Sirius appears at the lower left. Faintly luminous nebulosity is abundant in the vicinity of Orion. (*Photographed by Edwin Hubble, Mount Wilson Observatory*)

Astronomy

A Textbook for University and College Students

by

ROBERT H. BAKER, Ph.D.

Professor of Astronomy in the University of Illinois
Author of *An Introduction to Astronomy*

FOURTH EDITION

NEW YORK

D. VAN NOSTRAND COMPANY, Inc.

250 FOURTH AVENUE

PREFACE TO THE FOURTH EDITION

Occasional revisions have kept "Astronomy" abreast of the times and have been guided by experience in its use in the classroom. In this new edition the book is almost entirely rewritten and is considerably rearranged. Its purpose and general level remain unchanged. It is a textbook for introductory courses in astronomy requiring no special preparation in mathematics or physics.

Among the new features the reader will find a brief treatment of celestial navigation. Spectrum analysis is introduced earlier, so that its applications in the planetary system may be mentioned. The presentation of sidereal astronomy is somewhat more orderly; it includes the results of recent inquiries, as for example the newer ideas about stars with extended atmospheres. The Chapters are shorter than before and their number is increased, suggesting more frequent reviews. New review questions and problems appear at the ends of the Chapters.

The author's thanks are due to many colleagues, particularly to Dr. Bart J. Bok for suggesting many features of the revision and for his critical reading of the entire manuscript.

ROBERT H. BAKER

University of Illinois Observatory,
June, 1945.

PREFACE TO THE FIRST EDITION

This book is intended for use as a text in introductory college courses in astronomy. In its preparation, the author has kept in mind the requirements of his own classes, in which many of the students have had little previous acquaintance with physical science, and limited preparation in elementary mathematics.

It is believed that the book can be read with understanding, in general, by students of this description, and that the treatment is sufficiently mature to afford a profitable introduction to astronomy to those who are more advanced in preparation. It is believed also that the inclusion of the most recent discoveries and viewpoints and the excellence of the illustrations will make this book acceptable for general reading and reference.

In the preparation of this book the author has consulted original sources wherever it was possible, particularly in the more recent developments. He has drawn freely from many scientific publications. The photographs which are reproduced in this book have been generously furnished by institutions and individuals in various parts of the world.

Grateful acknowledgment is made to Professor Frank Schlesinger for reading parts of the manuscript and for helpful comments, and to the late Professor Ralph H. Curtiss for reading and criticizing other parts. The author is deeply indebted to Professor Philip Fox who read all the manuscript and suggested many improvements.

ROBERT H. BAKER

University of Illinois Observatory,
May, 1930.

CONTENTS

Astronomy

INTRODUCTION

Astronomy, the "science of the stars," is concerned not merely with the stars, but with all the celestial bodies which together comprise the known physical universe. It deals with planets and their satellites, with comets and meteors, with stars and the interstellar material, with star clusters, the system of the Milky Way, and the other systems which lie beyond the Milky Way.

The most comprehensive of the sciences, astronomy is also regarded as the oldest of all. People of ancient times were attentive watchers of the skies. They were attracted by the splendor of the celestial scenery, as we are today, and by its mystery which entered into their religions and mythologies. Astrology, the pseudo-science which held that the destinies of nations and individuals were revealed by the stars, furnished at times another motive for the study of the heavens.

Still another incentive to the early cultivation of astronomy was its usefulness in relation to ordinary pursuits. The daily rotation of the heavens provided means of telling time. The cycle of the moon's phases and the westward march of the constellations with the changing seasons were convenient for calendar purposes. The pole of the heavens in the north, around which the Dippers wheel, and whose place is now marked roughly by the star at the end of the Little Dipper's handle, served as a guide to the traveler on land and sea. These are some of the ways in which the heavens have been useful to man from the earliest times to the present.

But the value of astronomy must not be measured in terms of economic applications. Astronomy is concerned primarily with an aspiration of mankind, which is fully as impelling as the quest for survival and material welfare, namely, the desire to know about the universe around us and our relation to it. The importance of this service is clearly demonstrated by the widespread public interest in astronomy, and by the generous financial support which has promoted the construction and effective operation of great telescopes in rapidly increasing numbers. Nowhere in the college curricula can the value of learning for its own sake be more convincingly presented than in the introductory courses in astronomy.

It is the purpose of astronomy to furnish a description of the physical universe, in which the characteristics and relationships of its various parts are clearly shown. At present, the picture is incomplete. Doubtless it will remain incomplete always, subject to improvements in the light of new explorations and viewpoints. The advancing years will bring additional grandeur and significance to our view of the universe, as they have in the past.

The Sphere of the Stars. As early as the sixth century B.C., Greek philosophers regarded the earth as a globe standing motionless in the center of the universe. The boundary of the universe was a spherical shell, on whose inner surface the stars were set. This *celestial sphere* was supported by an inclined axis through the earth, on which the sphere rotated daily, causing the stars to rise and set. Within the sphere of the stars seven celestial bodies moved around the earth; they were the sun, the moon, and the five bright planets.

For more than two thousand years thereafter, this view of the universe, the universe of appearances, remained practically unchanged. The chief problem of astronomy was to account for the motions of the seven wandering bodies, so that their places in the heavens could be predicted for the future. The outstanding solution of the problem, on the basis of the central, motionless earth, was the Ptolemaic system.

Copernicus, in the sixteenth century, proposed the theory that the planets revolve around the sun rather than the earth, and that the earth is simply one of the planets. The rising and setting of the stars was now ascribed to the daily rotation of the earth. The new theory placed the sun and its family of planets sharply apart from the stars. With its gradual acceptance, the stars came to be regarded as remote suns, at different distances from us and in motion in different directions. The ancient sphere of the stars remained only as a convention; and the way was prepared for explorations into the star fields, which have led to the more comprehensive view of the universe that we hold today.

The Solar System. The earth is one of a number of relatively small planets which revolve around the sun, accompanied by smaller bodies, the satellites, of which the moon is an example. They are dark bodies, shining only as they reflect the sunlight. The nine principal planets, including the earth, are somewhat flattened globes whose average distances from the sun range from four tenths to forty times the earth's distance. Thousands of smaller planets, the asteroids, describe their orbits in the middle distances. Comets and meteor swarms also revolve around the sun. Their orbits are, in general, more elongated than those of the planets, and they extend to greater distances from the sun.

These bodies together comprise the solar system, the only known system of this kind, although others may well exist. A similar planetary system surrounding the very nearest star could not be discerned with the largest telescope. Likewise, the telescopic view of our system from the nearest star would show only the sun, now having the appearance of a bright star.

The Stars. The sun is one of the multitude of stars, representing a fair average of the general run of stars. It is a globe of intensely hot gas 864,000 miles in diameter, and a third of a million times as massive as the earth. Some stars are much larger than the sun; others are smaller, and a few, at least, scarcely exceed the planets in size. Blue stars have higher surface temperatures than that of the sun, which is a yellow star. The red stars are cooler. But all are exceedingly hot, as compared with ordinary standards, and are radiating enormous quantities of energy. The stars are the power houses and the building blocks of the universe.

Vast spaces intervene between the stars. If the size of the sun is represented by one of the periods on this page, the sun's nearest neighbor among the stars, the double star Alpha Centauri, would be shown on this scale by two small dots ten miles away. The actual distance exceeds four light years; that is to say, a ray of light, whose speed is 186,000 miles a second, spends more than four years in its journey from that star to the sun. This is a fair sample of the spacing of the stars around us.

The interstellar spaces are not perfectly empty. They contain dust and gas perhaps equal in amount to the combined mass of all the stars. Patches of this material made luminous by neighboring stars constitute the bright nebulae. Other patches are practically dark, and can accordingly be detected only by their dimming and reddening of the stars behind them; these are responsible for the dark rifts which cause most of the variety in the Milky Way.

The Galactic System is the assemblage of stars whose most prominent feature, as we view it from inside, is the luminous girdle of the Milky Way. Most of the many thousand million stars in the system form a lenticular structure some 100,000 light years in diameter and 10,000 light years in thickness at its center. As might be inferred from its flattening, the system is rotating; the period of the rotation in the sun's neighborhood is of the order of 200 million years. The sun is near the principal plane of the system, but is 30,000 light years from the center which lies in the direction of the constellation Sagittarius. Analogy suggests that the galactic system may have the form of a double-armed spiral.

The Extragalactic Systems. The galactic system is a unit in a greater assemblage. Millions of other systems lie far beyond our own system. Their distances are expressed in millions of light years and their average separation is something like two million light years. The majority have the spiral form, and some of these "spiral nebulae" were recognized long ago. But it was not until the close of the first quarter of the present century that the spirals and associated objects were definitely established as extragalactic systems.

Many of the problems which confronted the astronomer two centuries ago, when he began to look beyond the solar system to study the stars systematically, now arise again in enormous enlargement as the explorations are extended beyond the galactic system. The characteristics of the different types of exterior systems and their relation to our own system, their motions, their clustering, and their arrangement in the vaster structure—these are prominent among the problems that claim the attention today.

Fremont Pass Station of Harvard Observatory. (*Photograph by L. Larmore*)

CHAPTER I

ASPECTS OF THE SKY

THE CELESTIAL SPHERE; ITS APPARENT DAILY ROTATION — DIURNAL
CIRCLES OF THE STARS — THE SUN'S APPARENT ANNUAL PATH —
THE CONSTELLATIONS

At the beginning of our study of astronomy it will be convenient
to suppose that the earth is a sphere situated at the center of a vast
spherical shell on which the stars are set. The stars may accordingly
be represented on the surface of a globe; their positions may be referred
to circles on the globe, just as the positions of towns and ships are denoted on the earth. It will be in order at first to recall the circles that
are employed on the earth's surface.

1·1. Circles on the Earth. The earth rotates daily from west to east
on the axis whose extremities are its *north and south poles*. Owing to
its rotation the earth is somewhat flattened at the poles and bulged at
the equator. For the present purpose we neglect the flattening and the
surface irregularities as well. If the earth is considered spherical, a
plane passed through its center in any direction cuts the surface in a
great circle. A plane which does not pass through the center cuts the
surface in a *small circle*.

The *equator* is the great circle of the terrestrial sphere halfway between the north and south poles and therefore 90° from each. *Meridians*
are halves of great circles extending from the north to the south pole,
and are therefore perpendicular to the equator. For certain purposes,
however, they are defined as complete circles; in this event, the *upper
branch* of the meridian is the half that includes the place considered, and
the *lower branch* is the opposite half. The *meridian of Greenwich,*
which passes through the Royal Observatory at Greenwich, England, is
taken as the *prime meridian* for reckoning longitude. *Parallels of latitude* are small circles parallel to the equator; they decrease in size with
increasing distance from the equator.

5

1·2. Longitude and Latitude. The position of a point on the earth's surface is denoted by the longitude and latitude of that point. The *longitude* of a point is its angular distance east or west of the prime meridian. Longitude is the arc intercepted on the equator between the prime meridian and the meridian of the point, or it is the angle at the pole between the two meridians; its value ranges from 0° to 180°. If the longitude of a point is 60° W., the point is somewhere on the meridian 60° west of the prime meridian.

The *latitude* of a point is its angular distance north or south of the equator. Latitude is measured along the meridian of the point, its value ranging from 0° at the equator to 90° at the poles. North latitude is sometimes denoted by the plus sign and south latitude by the minus sign, but more often they are distinguished by the abbreviations N and S. If the latitude of a point is 50° N., the point is somewhere on the parallel of latitude 50° north of the equator. If the longitude is also given, the position of the point is uniquely defined.

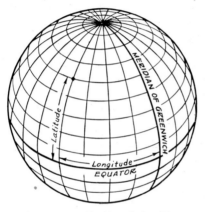

Fig. 1·2. Circles of the Terrestrial Sphere. The position of a point on the earth is denoted by its longitude and latitude.

In summary, the position of a point on the earth is referred to a system of circles in the following way: (1) The *primary circle* is the equator. (2) *Secondary circles,* the meridians, are drawn through the poles of the primary. (3) One of the secondary circles, the prime meridian, is selected as the *secondary circle of reference*. (4) The *first coordinate,* the longitude, is the angular distance of the point from the reference secondary measured along the primary circle. (5) The *second coordinate* of the point, the latitude, is the angular distance of the point from the primary circle.

Positions of stars in the sky are denoted in a similar way. While a single system of circles based on the equator suffices for the earth, four systems are required in the sky for the various purposes of astronomy. Three of these will be of immediate use to us; they are based on the horizon, the celestial equator, and the ecliptic.

THE CELESTIAL SPHERE; ITS APPARENT DAILY ROTATION

1·3. The Celestial Sphere is the conventional representation of the sky as a spherical shell on which the celestial bodies appear projected. Evidently of very great size, since the stars are far away, the celestial sphere has the properties of an infinite sphere. Its center may be anywhere at all, though it is usually taken as the observer's position. Parallel lines, regardless of their distance apart, are directed toward the same point on the sphere, just as the rails of a track seem to converge in the distance. The chief convenience of the celestial sphere is in representing the positions of the stars. Each star has its *apparent place* on the sphere, where it seems to be. It will be understood that we are describing nothing more than the direction of the star. Thus the *apparent distance* between two stars is their difference in direction, which will be regarded as angular distance on the celestial sphere.

Apparent places and distances are accordingly always expressed in angular measure, such as degrees, minutes, and seconds of arc, and never in linear measure, such as miles or feet. The statement that a star appears to be ten feet above the horizon has little meaning. If, however, its altitude is given as $10°$, we look for the star one ninth of the way from the horizon to the zenith. For estimating angular distances in the sky it is useful to remember that the apparent diameters of the sun and moon are about half a degree. The pointer stars of the Great Dipper are a little more than $5°$ apart.

1·4. Horizon and Celestial Meridian. The *zenith* is the point of the celestial sphere that is vertically overhead. The *nadir* is the opposite point of the sphere, vertically underfoot. These points are located by sighting along a plumb line, or vertical line. The *celestial horizon* is the great circle on the celestial sphere halfway between the zenith and nadir, and therefore $90°$ from each. This is the *horizon* of astronomy as distinguished from the visible horizon, the frequently irregular line where the earth and sky seem to meet. The horizon is an example of the circles that are imagined on the celestial sphere for the purpose of describing the places of the stars, just as circles such as the equator are imagined on the terrestrial sphere. The horizon is the primary circle of the horizon system of circles.

Vertical circles are great circles which pass through the zenith and nadir, and are therefore perpendicular to the horizon. There are as many of these secondary circles as may be required. The reference secondary is the observer's *celestial meridian,* the vertical circle that crosses the horizon at its north and south points. At right angles to the celestial meridian, the *prime vertical* is the vertical circle that crosses the horizon at its east and west points.

Celestial circles and coordinates may be somewhat confusing to the student at first, because they have unfamiliar names and especially because they are represented in two dimensions in the diagrams. The use of a blank globe on which the circles can be drawn is likely to contribute to the clearer understanding of many features described in this and subsequent chapters. It should preferably be a globe that can be rotated, and that has a movable meridian, so that the direction of the axis of rotation can be varied.

1·5. Azimuth and Altitude. The position of a star is denoted in the horizon system by its azimuth and altitude.

The *azimuth* of a star is the angular distance measured from the north point toward the east along the horizon to the vertical circle of

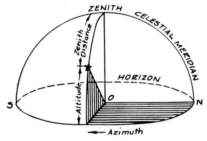

FIG. 1·5. Location of a Star by Azimuth and Altitude. Azimuth is measured from the north point eastward along the horizon. Altitude is the star's angular distance above (or below) the horizon. Zenith distance is the complement of altitude.

the star, or it is the corresponding angle at the zenith. It is measured completely around the horizon from 0° to 360°.

The *altitude* of a star is its angular distance above the horizon. Altitude is measured along the vertical circle through the star, its value ranging from 0° at the horizon to 90° at the zenith. Its complement, *zenith distance,* is measured downward from the zenith along the vertical circle. When the azimuth and altitude of a star are given, the star's place in the sky is known, as the following examples illustrate:

(1) Point to a star whose azimuth is 90° and altitude is 45°.
Answer: The star is directly in the east, halfway from the horizon to the zenith.

(2) Point to a star whose azimuth is 180° and altitude is 30°.

Answer: The star is directly in the south, one third of the way from horizon to zenith.

(3) State the azimuth and altitude of a star that is exactly in the south-west and two thirds of the way from horizon to zenith.

Answer: Azimuth 225°, altitude 60°.

The simplicity of the horizon system recommends it for various purposes in astronomy, navigation, and surveying. It is easy to visualize these circles and coordinates in the sky. The engineer's transit and the navigator's sextant or octant operate in this system. The lack of permanence of the coordinates, however, necessitates the use of other systems as well. Azimuths and altitudes of the celestial bodies are always changing, owing to the apparent daily rotation of the celestial sphere; and even at the same instant they vary with the observer's position on the earth.

1·6. Apparent Daily Rotation of the Celestial Sphere.

The westward movement of the sun across the sky, which causes it to rise and set, is an example of a motion in which all the celestial bodies share. It is as though the celestial sphere were rotating daily around the earth from east to west. This apparent daily rotation, or *diurnal motion,* of the heavens is an effect of the earth's rotation on its axis from west to east.

Every star describes its *diurnal circle* around the sky daily. All diurnal circles of the stars are parallel and are described in the same period; but those of the sun, moon, and planets, which change their places among the stars, are not quite parallel and have somewhat different periods. The rapidity with which a star proceeds along its diurnal circle depends on the size of the circle that it describes. The motion is fastest for stars that rise exactly in the east; it becomes progressively slower as the rising is farther from the east point, and vanishes altogether at the two opposite points in the sky around which the diurnal circles are described.

1·7. The Celestial Poles.

The two points on the celestial sphere having no diurnal motion are the *north and south celestial poles.* They are the points toward which the earth's axis is directed. For observers in the northern hemisphere the north celestial pole is situated vertically above the north point of the horizon; its place is marked approximately by Polaris, the *pole star,* or *north star,* at the end of the handle of the Little Dipper. Polaris is now about a degree from the pole, or twice the apparent diameter of the moon.

The south celestial pole is depressed below the southern horizon as much as the north pole is elevated in the northern sky. Its place is not marked closely by any bright star. This is the elevated pole for observers in the southern hemisphere.

It is possible to photograph the diurnal motions of the stars around the pole with an ordinary camera. Point the camera toward the pole star, and

FIG. 1·7. Circumpolar Star Trails. Photographed with a 2½-inch portrait lens and an exposure of one hour. The bright trail a little way below the center is that of Polaris. (*Photographed at Yerkes Observatory*)

expose a film for several hours on a clear evening, using the full aperture of the lens and having the focus adjusted for distance. The trails in the picture will be arcs of the diurnal circles whose common center is the celestial pole. Increasing the exposure makes the trails longer, but shows no more stars. With an ordinary camera the trails of only the brightest stars can be photographed.

1·8. Celestial Equator; Hour Circles. The *celestial equator* is the great circle of the celestial sphere halfway between the north and south celestial poles. It is in the same plane with the earth's equator and is the largest of the diurnal circles. For a particular place on the earth

the celestial equator occupies nearly the same position in the sky throughout the day and year; it is traced approximately by the sun's diurnal
motion on March 21, or September 23.

The *hour circles* are the secondary circles of the equator system; they
are great circles which pass through the celestial poles and therefore
at right angles to the equator. However, they are frequently regarded

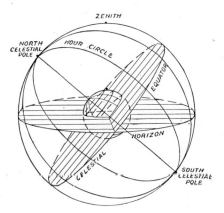

FIG. 1·8. The Celestial Equator in the Plane of the Earth's Equator. The
celestial equator is halfway between the celestial poles, the two points in the sky
toward which the earth's axis is directed. It crosses the horizon at the east and
west cardinal points at an inclination equal to the complement of the observer's
latitude.

as half circles from pole to pole, like meridians of the terrestrial
sphere (1·1).

1·9. Directions in the Equator System. North in this system is the
direction of any hour circle toward the north celestial pole. South is
the opposite way. *West is the direction of the diurnal motion,* which
is parallel to the celestial equator. With these definitions in mind there
will be no confusion about the directions, even in the vicinity of the pole.
As one faces north, the stars circle daily in the counterclockwise direction. From above the pole, north is downward and west is toward the
left; from under the pole, north is upward and west is toward the right.

1·10. Right Ascension and Declination. The hour circle that serves
the same purpose as the prime meridian on the earth is the one that
passes through the vernal equinox. This is the point where the sun's
center crosses the celestial equator at the beginning of spring. The *right*

ascension of a star is the angular distance measured in hours, or degrees, from the vernal equinox eastward along the celestial equator to the hour circle of the star.   Unlike terrestrial longitude, which is measured both east and west from the prime meridian, right ascension is always measured toward the east, from 0^h or $0°$ at the vernal equinox to 24^h or $360°$.

The *declination* of a star is its angular distance north or south of the celestial equator; declination is measured along the hour circle of the star, its value ranging from $0°$ at the equator to $90°$ at the poles.

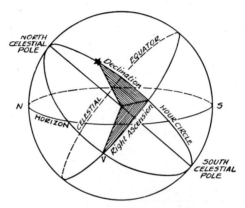

FIG. 1·10. Right Ascension and Declination. Right ascension is measured eastward from the vernal equinox along the celestial equator. Declination is measured north or south of the celestial equator along an hour circle.

If the star is north of the equator, the sign of the declination is plus; if the star is south, the sign is minus. The places of the celestial bodies are denoted by their right ascensions and declinations in most maps and catalogs.

As an example, the right ascension of the bright star Sirius is $6^h 43^m$, and the declination is $-16° 38'$; the star is therefore $6^h 43^m$, or $100° 45'$, east of the vernal equinox and $16° 38'$ south of the celestial equator.   In order to change from hours to degrees of right ascension, or conversely, since 24 hours equal $360°$, we can employ the following relations:

$$1^h = 15° \qquad\qquad 15° = 1^h$$
$$1^m = 15' \qquad\qquad 1° = 4^m$$
$$1^s = 15'' \qquad\qquad 1' = 4^s$$

1·11. Hour Angle. The place of a star is also denoted in the equator system by its hour angle and declination. In this case the reference secondary circle is the observer's celestial meridian, which is considered as having two branches. The *upper branch* of the celestial meridian is the half between the north and south celestial poles which includes the observer's zenith, and the *lower branch* is the opposite half which includes the nadir. A star is at *upper transit* when it crosses the upper branch of the celestial meridian, and at *lower transit* when it crosses the lower branch.

The *local hour angle* of a star is the angular distance measured along the celestial equator westward from the upper branch of the observer's celestial meridian to the hour circle of the star; or it is the corresponding angle at the celestial pole. The value of the hour angle accordingly ranges from 0° to 360°. Unlike the right ascension of a star, which remains nearly unchanged during the day, the hour angle of a star increases at the rate of about 15° an hour and at the same instant has different values in different longitudes. The *Greenwich hour angle* of a star is its local hour angle as observed at Greenwich. Greenwich hour angles of celestial bodies are tabulated in nautical and air almanacs at convenient intervals of the day throughout the year.

DIURNAL CIRCLES OF THE STARS

1·12. The Observer's Latitude Equals the Altitude of the North Celestial Pole. The *astronomical latitude* of any place on the earth is defined as the angle that a vertical line at that place makes with the plane of the earth's equator. It is easily seen from Fig. 1·12 that this angle equals the altitude of the north celestial pole and also the declination of the zenith. Here is the fundamental rule for determining the latitude by sights on the celestial bodies. If any irregularities of the earth's surface affect the direction of the vertical line, the astronomical latitude requires a slight correction to obtain the geographical latitude. The correction rarely exceeds 30″, and is usually very much smaller.

When the latitude of a place is given, the altitude of the celestial pole is an equal number of degrees, according to the rule. Thus the positions of the celestial poles and of the celestial equator midway between the poles become known relative to the horizon of the place. Since the diurnal circles are parallel to the celestial equator, we may inquire how these circles are related to the horizon for observers in different places on the earth.

1·13. At the Pole, Diurnal Circles Are Parallel to the Horizon. Viewed from the north pole, latitude 90° N., the north celestial pole is in the zenith and the celestial equator coincides with the horizon. Here the diurnal circles are parallel to the horizon. Stars north of the celestial equator never set, while those in the south celestial hemisphere are never seen. The sun, moon, and planets, which change their places

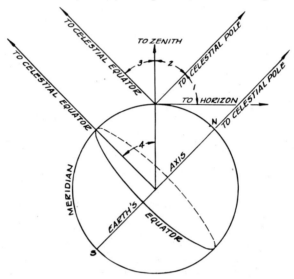

FIG. 1·12. The Observer's Latitude (4) Equals the Altitude of the North Celestial Pole (1), and also the Declination of the Observer's Zenith (3). Angles (1) and (3) are equal, because (1) + (2) and (2) + (3) are both equal to 90°, and (2) is common to both. Angles (3) and (4) are equal, because they are corresponding angles formed by the intersections of two parallel lines and a third line. Thus (4) = (1) = (3).

among the stars, come into view when they move northward across the equator, and set when they cross southward. At the south pole, of course, the south celestial pole is in the zenith and everything is reversed.

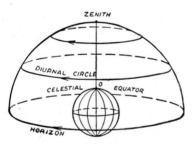

FIG. 1·13. Diurnal Circles Observed at the North (or South) Pole Are Parallel to the Horizon.

It will be seen later that some of the statements in this chapter require slight modification owing to the refraction of starlight in the earth's atmosphere.

1·14. At the Equator, Diurnal Circles Are Perpendicular to the Horizon. Viewed from the equator, latitude 0°, the celestial poles are on the horizon at its north and south points. The celestial equator is at right angles to the horizon at the east and west points, and passes directly overhead. All diurnal circles, since they are parallel to the equator, are also perpendicular to the horizon and are bisected by it. Thus every star is above the horizon 12 hours and below it 12 hours, while the duration of sunlight is 12 hours throughout the year.

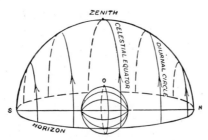

FIG. 1·14. Diurnal Circles Observed at the Equator Are Perpendicular to the Horizon.

It is to be noticed that places on the equator are the only ones from which the celestial sphere can be seen from pole to pole, so that all parts of the heavens are brought into view by the apparent daily rotation.

1·15. Elsewhere, Diurnal Circles Are Oblique.

From points of observation between the poles and the equator, the north celestial pole is elevated a number of degrees equal to the latitude of the place, while the south celestial pole is depressed the same amount. Although the celestial equator still cuts the horizon at the east and west points, it no longer passes through the zenith, but leans toward the south in the northern hemisphere by an angle equal to the latitude. Therefore, the diurnal circles of the stars cross the horizon obliquely.

The celestial equator is the only one of these circles bisected by the horizon. Northward, the visible portions of the diurnal circles become progressively greater, until the entire circles are in view; southward from the celestial equator they diminish, until they are wholly out of sight. The changing duration of sunlight from summer to winter serves as an illustration.

Owing to its oblique motion with respect to the horizon, the celestial sphere is conveniently divided into three parts: (1) a cap around the elevated celestial pole, whose radius equals the latitude of the place, contains the stars that are always above the horizon; (2) a cap of the same size around the depressed pole contains the stars that never come into view; (3) a band of the sky symmetrical with the celestial equator contains the stars that rise and set. In latitude 40°, for example, the two caps are 40° in radius, while all stars within 50° of the celestial equator rise and set.

As one travels south, the circumpolar caps grow smaller, and finally disappear when the equator is reached, where all stars rise and set. On the other hand, as one travels north, the circumpolar caps increase in

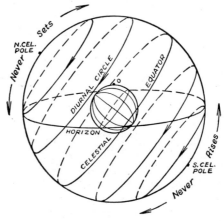

FIG. 1·15. Diurnal Circles Observed in Latitude 40° Are Oblique.

radius, until they join when the poles are reached. Here none of the stars rises or sets.

1·16. Circumpolar Stars.

If a star is nearer the celestial pole than the pole itself is to the horizon, the star does not cross the horizon; it is a *circumpolar star*. Consequently, for an observer in the northern hemisphere, *a star never sets if its north polar distance (90° minus its declination) is less than the observer's latitude; it never rises if its south polar distance is less than the latitude.* The following examples illustrate the rule:

(1) The Southern Cross, Decl. = −60°, never rises in latitude 40° N., because its south polar distance of 30° is less than the latitude. It becomes visible south of latitude 30° N., in Florida and southern Texas.

(2) The bowl of the Great Dipper, Decl. = +58°, never sets in latitude 40°, because its north polar distance of 32° is less than the latitude. Under the pole it is still 8° above the horizon. It rises and sets south of latitude 32° N.

(3) The sun on June 22, Decl. = +23½°, rises and sets in latitude 40°, because its north polar distance of 66½° is not less than the latitude; but north of latitude 66½° the sun is circumpolar on this date.

The *midnight sun* is an example of a circumpolar star.   The sun may be seen at midnight about June 22 as far south as the arctic circle.

FIG. 1·16.   The Midnight Sun at Etah, Greenland.   The exposures were made in July at intervals of twenty minutes while the sun was describing the lowest part of its diurnal circle above the north horizon.   (*Photographed by Donald B. MacMillan*)

Farther north it remains above the horizon for a long period, while at the north pole it shines continuously for six months.

THE SUN'S APPARENT ANNUAL PATH

1·17. Westward Advance of the Constellations With the Seasons. Almost everyone has noticed that different constellations appear in the evening sky at the different seasons.   From night to night at the same hour each star is found a little farther west.   For example, the familiar quadrilateral of Orion is seen rising in the east in the early evening in December.   With the arrival of March, Orion is seen in the south at the same hour.   As spring advances, it appears in the west and sets soon after the sun.

This steady westward march of the constellations during the year is caused by the sun's apparent eastward movement among the stars.   If the stars were visible in the daytime, as they are in the sky of the planetarium, we could watch the sun's progress.   We would observe that the sun is displaced toward the east about two of its diameters in a day, and completely around the heavens in a year. The sun's apparent annual movement around the celestial sphere is a consequence of the earth's annual revolution around the sun.

Not only does the sun move eastward with respect to the stars, but it moves north and south as well during the year, so that its path does not coincide with the celestial equator.

1·18. The Ecliptic; Equinoxes and Solstices. The *ecliptic* is the sun's apparent annual path on the celestial sphere. It is a great circle inclined 23½° to the celestial equator.

Four equidistant points on the ecliptic are the two *equinoxes*, where this circle intersects the celestial equator, and the two *solstices*, where

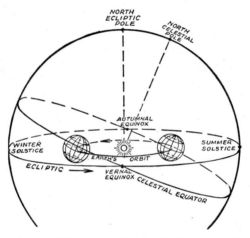

Fig. 1·18. Relation of Ecliptic and Celestial Equator. The inclination of the ecliptic to the celestial equator is the same (23½°) as the inclination of the earth's equator to its orbit.

it is farthest away from the equator. The *vernal equinox* is the sun's position on March 21, when it crosses the celestial equator going north; the *autumnal equinox* is its position on September 23, when it crosses on the way south. The *summer solstice* is the most northern point of the ecliptic, the sun's position on June 22; the *winter solstice* is the most southern point, the sun's position on December 22. Owing to the plan of leap years, these dates vary slightly. The north and south *ecliptic poles* are the two points 90° from the ecliptic; they are 23½° from the celestial poles.

The relation between the ecliptic and the celestial equator will be understood from Fig. 1·18, in which the earth's orbit is viewed nearly edgewise. Since parallel lines meet in the distant sky, the celestial poles, toward which the earth's axis is directed, are not displaced as the earth revolves around the sun; similarly the celestial equator is unaffected. Evidently the angle between the ecliptic and celestial equator is the same as the angle between the earth's orbit and equator. This inclination, or *obliquity*, of the ecliptic is 23° 27′; it is at the present time decreasing at the rate of 1′ in 128 years.

1·19. Relation Between Ecliptic and Horizon. The position of the celestial equator in the sky is not altered by the diurnal motion. The

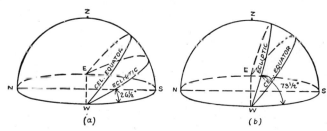

FIG. 1·19.   Relation Between the Ecliptic and Horizon. (*a*) The ecliptic is least inclined to the horizon in middle northern latitudes (26½° in latitude 40° N.) when the vernal equinox is rising and the autumnal equinox is setting. (*b*) It is most inclined (73½°) when the autumnal equinox is rising and the vernal equinox is setting.

angle at which it intersects the horizon remains the same; it is the complement of the observer's latitude. Thus in latitude 40° N. the celestial equator is inclined 50° to the horizon. The ecliptic, however, takes different positions in the sky.

Since the ecliptic is inclined 23½° to the celestial equator, its inclination to the horizon can differ as much as 23½°, either way, from that of the equator. One can easily see with the aid of a globe that the greatest and least angles between ecliptic and horizon in middle latitudes occur when the equinoxes are rising and setting.

In latitude 40° N., when the vernal equinox is rising and the autumnal equinox is setting, the angle between ecliptic and horizon is 50° − 23½° = 26½°. The visible half of the ecliptic lies below the celestial equator. When the autumnal equinox is rising and the vernal equinox is setting, the angle is 50° + 23½° = 73½°. The visible half of the ecliptic is now above the celestial equator.

We shall see that the variation in the angle between the ecliptic and the horizon is involved in the explanations of the harvest moon, the appearance of the planet Mercury as evening or morning star, and the favorable seasons for observing the zodiacal light.

1·20. Celestial Longitude and Latitude. The observations of early astronomers were confined for the most part to the sun, moon, and bright planets, which are never far from the ecliptic. It was accordingly the custom to denote the places of these objects with reference to the ecliptic by giving their celestial longitudes and latitudes. *Celestial longitude* is angular distance from the vernal equinox measured eastward along the ecliptic to the circle that passes through the celestial object at right angles to the ecliptic. *Celestial latitude* is the angular distance of the object from the ecliptic, measured northward or southward along the perpendicular circle.

These ancient coordinates still find use in problems of planetary motions. But they have been supplanted for many purposes by right ascension and declination, which are the counterparts of terrestrial longitude and latitude. The newer coordinates might well have been named celestial longitude and latitude, except that these names had already been appropriated.

Four different sets of coordinates for denoting the place of a celestial body have now been described. They are:

(1) *Azimuth and Altitude* (1·5). They are measured from the north point of the horizon, first eastward along the horizon and then perpendicular to that circle. They are much used in navigation.

(2) *Right Ascension and Declination* (1·10). They are measured from the vernal equinox, first eastward along the celestial equator and then perpendicular to that circle. They are employed in maps and catalogs.

(3) *Hour Angle and Declination* (1·11). They are measured from the upper branch of the celestial meridian, first westward along the celestial equator and then perpendicular to that circle. These coordinates are tabulated in nautical and air almanacs.

(4) *Celestial Longitude and Latitude* (1·20). They are measured from the vernal equinox, first eastward along the ecliptic and then perpendicular to that circle.

THE CONSTELLATIONS

1·21. The Primitive Constellations. In various parts of the celestial sphere the stars form interesting patterns which are well known to many people. There are dippers, crosses, and a variety of other figures easy to identify and to remember. *In the original sense,* the *constellations* are these configurations of stars.

Two thousand years ago, the Greeks recognized 48 constellations with which they associated the names and forms of heroes and animals of their mythology. The earliest nearly complete account of them that can be found in our libraries today is contained in the *Phenomena,* written about 270 B.C. by the poet Aratus. In the writings of Hesiod, more than five hundred years earlier, and in the Homeric epics the more

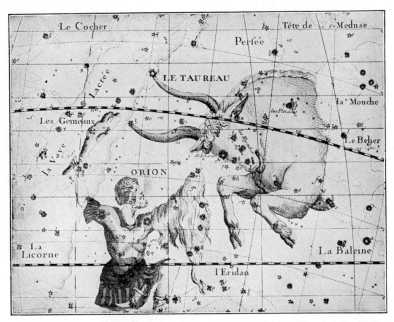

FIG. 1·21. Orion and Taurus. (From *Atlas Céleste de Flamsteed,* 1776)

conspicuous figures, such as Orion, the Pleiades, and the Great Bear, are mentioned familiarly. There are reasons for supposing that practically the whole scheme of the primitive constellations was transmitted to the Greeks, having originated thousands of years before among the peoples of the Euphrates valley.

The 48 original constellations are described in Ptolemy's *Almagest* (about 150 A.D.), which specifies the positions of the stars in the imagined creatures. Owing to the great authority of this book for many centuries afterward, these creatures and their names were perpetuated with only a few alterations. As examples of changes, the Ptolemaic constellations of the Horse, the Bird, and the Kneeler became respectively Pegasus, Cygnus, and Hercules; and the original Argo Navis, the ship of the Argonauts, is now divided into the separate constellations Puppis, Pyxis, Vela, and Carina.

The ancient star-creatures have nothing to do with the science of astronomy. But their names are still associated with striking groupings of stars which attract the attention now, just as they interested people long ago, and as they will doubtless interest people of the future.

1·22. Constellations as Regions of the Celestial Sphere. The original scheme of constellations did not cover the entire sky. Of the 1028 stars listed by Ptolemy, ten per cent were "unformed," that is, not included within the 48 figures. Moreover, a large area of the celestial sphere in the south, that never rose above the horizon of the Greeks, was uncharted. In the various star maps that appeared after the beginning of the seventeenth century new configurations were gradually added to fill the vacant places. At the present time 88 constellations (Table 1·I) are recognized, of which 70 are visible, at least in part, from the latitude of New York in the course of a year.

For the purposes of astronomy, the *constellations* are regions of the celestial sphere set off by arbitrary boundary lines. These divisions are useful for describing the approximate positions of the stars and other celestial bodies. The statement that Vega is in the constellation Lyra serves the same purpose as the information that a town is in Ohio. We know about where it can be found.

The boundaries of the majority of the constellations were originally very irregular. Revised by action of the International Astronomical Union, in 1928, the boundaries are now parts of circles parallel and perpendicular to the celestial equator. The boundary lines are not shown in the star maps in this book.

1·23. Names of Individual Stars. Fifty or more of the brighter stars are known to us by the names given them long ago by herdsmen, sailors, and nomads of the desert, as well as by the scholars. Some of the star names, such as Sirius and Capella, are of Greek and Latin origin; others are of Arabic derivation, for example, Vega, Rigel, Aldebaran. The influence of the Arabians in the development of astronomy is indicated by the frequent appearance of their definite article *al* in the names of the stars (Algol, Altair, etc.).

Many of the star names now regarded as personal were expressions giving the positions of the stars in the imaginary constellation figures. These descriptive terms, transcribed from Ptolemy's catalog into the Arabic, degenerated later into single words. Examples are Betelgeuse (armpit of the Central One), Fomalhaut (mouth of the Fish), Deneb (tail of the Bird), etc.

1·24. Designations of Stars by Letter and Number. The star maps of Bayer's *Uranometria* (1603) introduced the present plan of designating the brighter stars of each constellation by small letters of the Greek alphabet. In a general way, the stars are lettered in order of brightness, and the Roman alphabet is drawn upon for further letters. The full name of a star in the Bayer system is the letter followed by the genitive (possessive) of the Latin name of the constellation. Thus α Tauri is the brightest star in Taurus. When several stars in the constellation have nearly the same brightness, they are lettered in order of their positions in the figure, beginning at the head. Thus it happens that the stars of the Great Dipper, which are not much different in brightness, are lettered in order of position.

A different plan, adopted in Flamsteed's *Historia Coelestis* (1729), in which the stars are numbered consecutively from west to east across the constellation, permits the designation of a greater number of stars. The star 61 Cygni is an example. In modern maps of the lucid stars it is usual to employ the Bayer letters as far as they go, giving also the specific names of the brightest and most notable stars, and to designate other stars by the Flamsteed numbers.

These are the means of identifying the few thousands of stars visible to the unaided eye. Telescopic stars are referred to by their running numbers in the star catalogs. The position of the star HD 32416, for example, can be found by turning to that number in the *Henry Draper Catalogue*.

1·25. Magnitudes of the Stars. It is easier to identify a star when we know its brightness as well as its place in the sky. From Ptolemy's ancient catalog to the modern catalogs and maps of the stars, it has been the custom to express the relative brightness of a star by stating its *magnitude*. At first, the stars were divided arbitrarily into six classes, or magnitudes, in order of diminishing brightness. About 20 of the brightest stars were assigned to the first magnitude; Polaris and stars of the Great Dipper were representatives of the second magnitude; and so on, until stars barely visible to the naked eye remained for the sixth magnitude.

With the invention of the telescope, permitting the observation of still fainter stars, the number of magnitudes was increased, while greater precision in the measurements of brightness called for the use of decimals in denoting the magnitudes. Eventually, a factor slightly greater than 2.5 was adopted as the ratio in brightness corresponding to a difference of one magnitude. Thus a star of magnitude 3.0 is about 2½ times as bright as a star of magnitude 4.0.

The magnitudes assigned to the naked-eye stars by the early astronomers are not altered greatly by modern practice, except those of the brightest. The original first magnitude stars differ so much in brightness that the more brilliant ones have been promoted to brighter classes, and so to smaller numbers. The magnitude of the brightest star, Sirius, is −1.6; Canopus is −0.9; Vega, Capella, and Arcturus, the brightest stars of the north celestial hemisphere, are about 0.2. Altair (0.9) and Aldebaran (1.1) are nearly standard first magnitude stars.

In the maps that follow, the brightness of the stars is noted to whole magnitudes by the symbols whose meanings are explained in the key adjoining the circular maps. In the interest of simplicity, two stars of the minus first magnitude are designated as of zero magnitude, and a few fifth magnitude stars are designated as of the fourth magnitude. As a general thing, stars fainter than the fourth magnitude are not shown on these maps.

1·26. The North Circumpolar Map. Map 1 represents the appearance of the heavens to one facing north in middle northern latitudes. At the center is the north celestial pole, whose altitude equals the observer's latitude. Hour circles radiating from the center are numbered with the hours of their right ascensions. Parallels of declination appear as circles at intervals of ten degrees, from declination 90° at the center of the map to 50° at its circumference.

The names of the months around the circumference of the map facilitate its orientation to correspond with the sky at any time. If the map is turned so that the date of observation is uppermost, the vertical line through the center of the map represents the observer's celestial meridian at about 9 P.M., standard time. The constellations then have the same positions on the map as they have in the northern sky at that hour.

To orient the map for a later hour, turn it counterclockwise through as many hours of right ascension as the standard time is later than 9 P.M. For an earlier hour, turn the map clockwise. Thus the map may be made to represent the positions of the constellations in the northern sky at any time during the year.

1·27. The Constellations in the North. As an example of the use of Map 1 in middle northern latitudes, suppose that it is 9 o'clock in the evening, standard time, on the first of October. The map is accordingly held toward the north and turned so that this date is at the top. The constellations in the north may now be identified.

The Great Dipper is found nearly right side up somewhat to the left of the north cardinal point. The line joining the pointers, α and β Ursae Majoris, when it is extended upward about five times the distance between these stars, directs the eye to the pole star. Polaris marks the end of the handle of the Little Dipper.

A line from the middle of the Great Dipper's handle through the pole star and extended nearly an equal distance beyond leads to Cassiopeia, whose characteristic figure of a high-backed chair is outlined by seven stars. Westward from Cassiopeia, Cepheus resembles a church spire, as some people imagine. Like the chair-figure, it is inverted at this hour. Draco's head is a V of five stars. With the aid of the map it is easy to follow the winding body of the ancient Dragon around the ecliptic pole to the tip of the tail which lies between Polaris and the bowl of the Great Dipper.

Thus with the aid of Map 1 it is easy to identify the five conspicuous constellations in the north: Ursa Major, Ursa Minor, Cassiopeia, Cepheus, and Draco. It will be noticed that not all the constellations are represented on our maps. Some of the constellations, particularly the more modern ones, are simply regions of the sky in which no striking patterns of stars appear.

1·28. Star Maps for the Different Seasons. Maps 2, 3, 4, and 5 show the constellations which appear in the vicinity of the observer's celestial meridian in the evening during each of the four seasons. They extend from the north celestial pole, at the top, down to the south horizon of latitude 40° N. Hour circles radiating from the pole are marked in hours of right ascension near the bottom of the map. Circles of equal declination go around the pole; their declinations are indicated on the central hour circle.

Select the map for the present season and hold it toward the south. The hour circle above the date on which you are observing coincides with the celestial meridian at about 9 o'clock in the evening, standard time; the stars near this hour circle are at upper transit at about this time. If you are in a middle northern latitude and are facing south, the stars represented in the upper part of the map are behind you. But the northern constellations are arranged more conveniently in Map 1; they are repeated in the seasonal maps chiefly to show how they are related to constellations farther south.

Map 6 shows the region around the south celestial pole which is not visible from latitude 40° N.

1·29. Zenith Distance of a Star at Upper Transit. As we have seen, the maps are arranged to indicate on what date a star is crossing the upper branch of the observer's celestial meridian at a specified hour. It

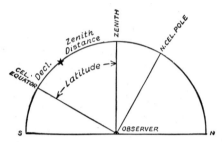

FIG. 1·29. The Zenith Distance of a Star at Upper Transit. It is equal to the observer's latitude minus the star's declination. This is evidently true because the observer's latitude equals the declination of his zenith (1·12).

is helpful to know how far from the zenith one must look at that time in order to find the star. The appropriate rule follows from the relation described in Section 1·12.

The zenith distance of a star at upper transit equals the observer's latitude minus the star's declination (Fig. 1·29). If the resulting zenith distance is positive, the star is south of the zenith; if it is negative, the star is north of the zenith. In the following examples the observer is in latitude 40° N.

(1) What is the sun's zenith distance at its upper transit on June 22?
Answer: The sun's declination on that date is +23½°. Its zenith distance is 40° − 23½° = + 16½°, south of the zenith.

(2) How close to the zenith does the bowl of the Great Dipper pass?
Answer: The declination is +58°. At upper transit the zenith distance is 40° − 58° = −18°, north of the zenith.

(3) What declination must a star have in order to pass through the zenith?
Answer: Since the zenith distance is zero, the star's declination must equal the observer's latitude (40°). Thus stars whose declinations are less than the latitude pass south of the zenith; those whose declinations are greater than the latitude pass north of the zenith. The sun is directly overhead at noon in the latitude which equals the sun's declination.

1·30. Use of the Seasonal Maps. Suppose that the constellation study is begun at 9 P.M., standard time, on September 15, or at 7 o'clock on

October 15. Along the hour circle above this date on Map 4 we find the constellations Cygnus (Northern Cross), Delphinus, often known as "Job's Coffin," and Capricornus. These constellations are accordingly along the celestial meridian. If our latitude is 40° N., then by the rule of Section 1·29 Cygnus (declination +40°) is in the zenith, Delphinus (declination +15°) is 25° south of the zenith, and Capricornus (declination −20°) is 60° south of the zenith. When these constellations have been recognized in the sky, rules for finding neighboring constellations can be made from the map.

Since the circles of the equator system are drawn on the maps, it is possible to read the right ascension and declination of any star shown. Thus the star Deneb in Cygnus is in right ascension 20^h 40^m and declination +45°. The sun, moon, and planets do not appear on the maps, of course, because they move among the stars. Their right ascensions and declinations can be found in an almanac for any date and their places among the stars can then be marked on the maps.

1·31. Examples of the Use of the Star Maps.
(1) On what date is the bowl of the Great Dipper (Map 1) directly above the celestial pole at 9 P.M., standard time?

Answer: May 1.

(2) Read from Map 1 the right ascension and declination of δ Ursae Majoris (where the handle and bowl of the Dipper join).

Answer: Right ascension 12^h 12^m, declination +57°.

(3) On what date is Antares (Map 3) at upper transit at 9 P.M., standard time? What is its zenith distance at that time in latitude 40° N.?

Answer: July 13. The star is 66° south of the zenith.

(4) Locate with respect to the constellations (Map 5) a planet in right ascension 5^h 30^m and declination +24°.

Answer: The planet is midway between β and ζ Tauri.

(5) At what time is Orion (Map 5) directly in the south on March 1?

Answer: Orion is at upper transit at 7 P.M., standard time, on March 1.

(6) Assuming that the constellation Orion can be recognized, make rules for pointing out the stars Sirius and Procyon.

Answer: The line of Orion's belt (δ, ε, and ζ Orionis) leads to Sirius. Procyon completes an equilateral triangle with Sirius and Betelgeuse in Orion.

(7) How far south must you be in order to view Canopus, Crux (Southern Cross), and the Large Magellanic Cloud (Map 6)?

Answer: At least as far south as latitudes 37°, 30°, and 21° N. respectively.

TABLE 1·I. NAMES OF THE CONSTELLATIONS

Latin Name	Possessive	English Equivalent	Map
*Androm′eda	Androm′edae	Andromeda	4, 5
Ant′lia	Ant′liae	Air Pump	
A′pus	A′podis	Bird of Paradise	
*Aqua′rius	Aqua′rii	Water Carrier	4
*Aq′uila	Aq′uilae	Eagle	3, 4
*A′ra	A′rae	Altar	6
*A′ries	Ari′etis	Ram	4, 5
*Auri′ga	Auri′gae	Charioteer	5
*Boö′tes	Boö′tis	Herdsman	2, 3
Cae′lum	Cae′li	Graving Tool	
Camelopar′dalis	Camelopar′dalis	Giraffe	
*Can′cer	Can′cri	Crab	2, 5
Ca′nes Vena′tici	Ca′num Venatico′rum	Hunting Dogs	2
*Ca′nis Ma′jor	Ca′nis Majo′ris	Larger Dog	5
*Ca′nis Mi′nor	Ca′nis Mino′ris	Smaller Dog	5
*Capricor′nus	Capricor′ni	Sea-Goat	4
†Cari′na	Cari′nae	Keel	6
*Cassiope′ia	Cassiope′iae	Cassiopeia	1, 4
*Centau′rus	Centau′ri	Centaur	2, 6
*Ce′pheus	Ce′phei	Cepheus	1, 4
*Ce′tus	Ce′ti	Whale	4, 5
Chamae′leon	Chamaeleon′tis	Chameleon	
Cir′cinus	Cir′cini	Compasses	
Colum′ba	Colum′bae	Dove	5
Co′ma Bereni′ces	Co′mae Bereni′ces	Berenice's Hair	2
*Coro′na Austra′lis	Coro′nae Austra′lis	Southern Crown	
*Coro′na Borea′lis	Coro′nae Borea′lis	Northern Crown	3
*Cor′vus	Cor′vi	Crow	2
*Cra′ter	Cra′teris	Cup	2
Crux	Cru′cis	Cross	6
*Cyg′nus	Cyg′ni	Swan	3, 4
*Delphi′nus	Delphi′ni	Dolphin	4
Dora′do	Dora′dus	Goldfish	6
*Dra′co	Draco′nis	Dragon	1, 3
*Equu′leus	Equu′lei	Little Horse	
*Erid′anus	Erid′ani	River	5, 6
For′nax	Forna′cis	Furnace	
*Gem′ini	Gemino′rum	Twins	5
Grus	Gru′is	Crane	4
*Her′cules	Her′culis	Hercules	3
Horolo′gium	Horolo′gii	Clock	
*Hy′dra	Hy′drae	Sea Serpent	2
Hy′drus	Hy′dri	Water Snake	6
In′dus	In′di	Indian	
Lacer′ta	Lacer′tae	Lizard	
*Le′o	Leo′nis	Lion	2

TABLE 1·1. NAMES OF THE CONSTELLATIONS—*Continued*

Latin Name	Possessive	English Equivalent	Map
Le'o Mi'nor	Leo'nis Mino'ris	Smaller Lion	
*Le'pus	Le'poris	Hare	5
*Li'bra	Li'brae	Scales	3
*Lu'pus	Lu'pi	Wolf	3
Lynx	Lyn'cis	Lynx	
*Ly'ra	Ly'rae	Lyre	3
Men'sa	Men'sae	Table Mountain	
Microsco'pium	Microsco'pii	Microscope	
Monoc'eros	Monocero'tis	Unicorn	
Mus'ca	Mus'cae	Fly	6
Nor'ma	Nor'mae	Level	
Oc'tans	Octan'tis	Octant	
*Ophiu'chus	Ophiu'chi	Serpent Holder	3
*Ori'on	Orio'nis	Orion	5
Pa'vo	Pavo'nis	Peacock	6
*Peg'asus	Peg'asi	Pegasus	4
*Per'seus	Per'sei	Perseus	4, 5
Phoe'nix	Phoeni'cis	Phoenix	4
Pic'tor	Picto'ris	Easel	
*Pis'ces	Pis'cium	Fishes	4
*Pis'cis Austri'nus	Pis'cis Austri'ni	Southern Fish	4
†Pup'pis	Pup'pis	Stern	6
†Pyx'is	Pyx'idis	Mariner's Compass	5, 6
Retic'ulum	Retic'uli	Net	
*Sagit'ta	Sagit'tae	Arrow	3, 4
*Sagitta'rius	Sagitta'rii	Archer	3
*Scor'pius	Scor'pii	Scorpion	3
Sculp'tor	Sculpto'ris	Sculptor's Apparatus	4
Scu'tum	Scu'ti	Shield	3
*Ser'pens	Serpen'tis	Serpent	3
Sex'tans	Sextan'tis	Sextant	
*Tau'rus	Tau'ri	Bull	5
Telesco'pium	Telesco'pii	Telescope	
*Trian'gulum	Trian'guli	Triangle	4, 5
Trian'gulum Austra'le	Trian'guli Austra'lis	Southern Triangle	6
Tuca'na	Tuca'nae	Toucan	6
*Ur'sa Ma'jor	Ur'sae Majo'ris	Larger Bear	1, 2
*Ur'sa Mi'nor	Ur'sae Mino'ris	Smaller Bear	1, 3
†Ve'la	Velo'rum	Sails	2, 6
*Vir'go	Vir'ginis	Virgin	2
Vo'lans	Volan'tis	Flying Fish	
Vulpec'ula	Vulpec'ulae	Fox	

* One of the 48 constellations recognized by Ptolemy.

† Carina, Puppis, Pyxis, and Vela once formed the single Ptolemaic constellation Argo Navis.

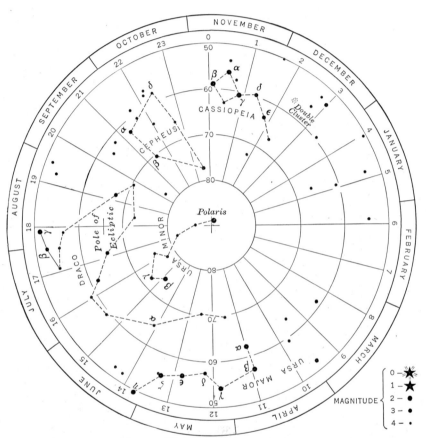

Map 1. The Northern Constellations.

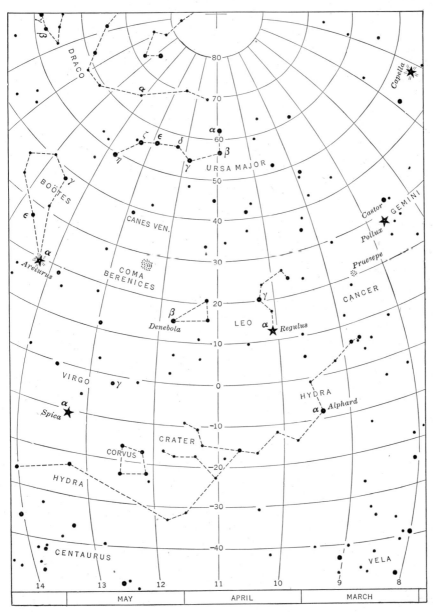

Map 2. The Spring Constellations.

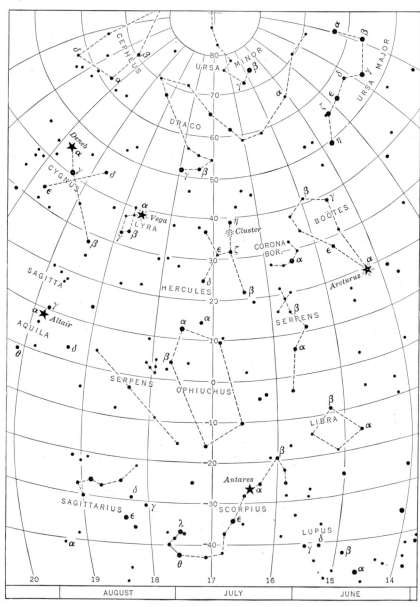

Map 3. The Summer Constellations.

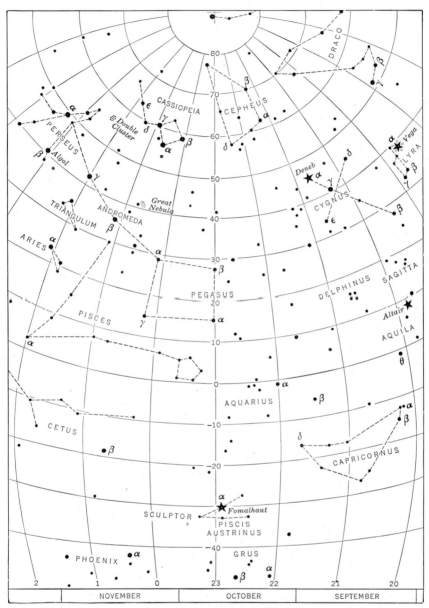

Map 4. The Autumn Constellations.

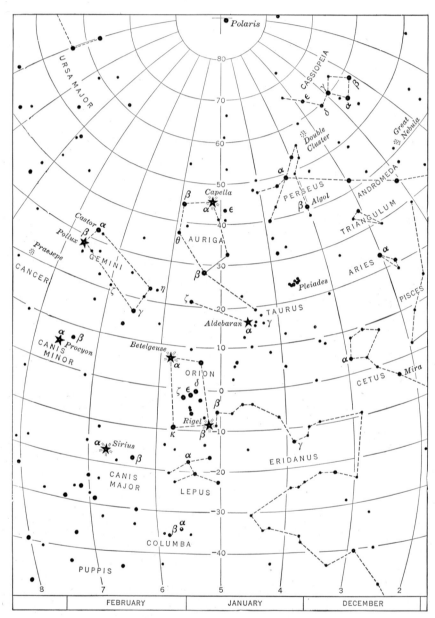

Map 5. The Winter Constellations.

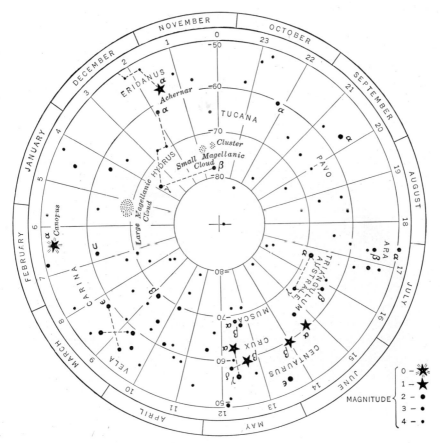

Map 6. The Southern Constellations.

TABLE I·II GREEK ALPHABET (SMALL LETTERS)

α	alpha	ι	iota	ρ	rho
β	beta	κ	kappa	σ	sigma
γ	gamma	λ	lambda	τ	tau
δ	delta	μ	mu	υ	upsilon
ε	epsilon	ν	nu	φ	phi
ζ	zeta	ξ	xi	χ	chi
η	eta	ο	omicron	ψ	psi
θ	theta	π	pi	ω	omega

1·32. The Planetarium is a remarkably successful device for bringing the heavens indoors where their conspicuous features can be demonstrated to many people. The sky of the planetarium is the interior of a large dome which forms the ceiling of the chamber in which the audience is seated. The planetarium instrument, shaped like a dumbbell 12 feet long, rests on a carriage in the center of the room. It is a composite stereopticon containing many projectors for displaying the sun,

FIG. 1·32. Interior of a Planetarium. The appearance of the sky is faithfully reproduced on the interior of the dome by the projection apparatus in the center. The lecturer is calling the attention of the audience to the Hyades in Taurus. (*By courtesy of Carl Zeiss, Inc.*)

moon and bright planets, the stars, and the Milky Way on the surface of the dome.

It is a moving picture of the heavens that is shown. The dumbbell and its various parts are turned by motors controlled by switches at the lecturer's desk. The celestial bodies rise and set. The sun moves along the ecliptic. The moon in its changing phases describes its monthly circuit of the heavens. The planets steer looped courses among the stars. All these movements are faster in the planetarium than in the real sky, so that they are more readily observed and understood.

The Adler Planetarium in Chicago, opened to the public in 1930, is the pioneer in America. The others of this type in this country are the Fels Planetarium in Philadelphia, the Hayden Planetarium in New

York, the Griffith Observatory in Los Angeles, and the Buhl Planetarium in Pittsburgh.   There are about twenty planetariums in Europe.

REVIEW QUESTIONS

1. State the azimuths and altitudes of stars in the following places: (a)
Directly in the east and a third of the way from horizon to zenith; (b)
Directly overhead; (c) At the west point of the horizon.

2. What coordinates of the celestial sphere most nearly resemble longitude and latitude on the earth?   In what respect does longitude differ from
its counterpart in the sky?

3. Name the celestial circle or coordinate corresponding to each of the
following definitions:

(a) The vertical circle passing through the celestial poles.
(b) The sun's annual path.
(c) The circle halfway between the celestial poles.
(d) The angle at the pole between the celestial meridian and the hour
circle of a star.
(e) Angular distance measured eastward from the vernal equinox along
the celestial equator.

4. State the right ascension and declination of the vernal equinox; summer solstice; autumnal equinox; winter solstice.

5. Tabulate the circles, points, and coordinates in each of the three celestial systems corresponding to the general terms (1·2) at the left.

General	Horizon System	Equator System	Ecliptic System
Primary circle			
Secondary circles			
Reference secondary			
Origin			
Coordinate 1			
Coordinate 2			

6. From what places on the earth are the following situations true?

(a) Celestial equator coincides with horizon.
(b) Celestial equator passes through zenith.
(c) South celestial pole has altitude 30°.
(d) Interval from sunrise to sunset is 12 hours throughout the year.

7. Which of the following stars never set, never rise, or rise and set from
where you are: γ Draconis (Map 1), Arcturus (Map 3), Capella (Map
5), Canopus and Achernar (Map 6)?

8. Name six bright stars not mentioned in Question 7, and the constellation containing each.

9. Describe the characteristic geometrical figures formed by the prominent stars of the constellations Ursa Major, Leo, Boötes, Cygnus, Pegasus, and Orion.

10. Name a constellation that is near your zenith in the evening at each of the four seasons. During what month is each one nearly overhead at 9 P.M. standard time?

11. Find from Maps 4, 5, 2, and 3 the positions of the vernal equinox, summer solstice, autumnal equinox, and winter solstice among the stars.

12. Find in an astronomical almanac the right ascensions and declinations of the sun, moon, and bright planets for a particular date, and locate these objects on the Maps with reference to the constellations.

The Adler Planetarium and Astronomical Museum, Chicago.

CHAPTER II

THE EARTH IN MOTION

THE EARTH'S ROTATION — THE EARTH'S REVOLUTION — THE EARTH'S PRECESSIONAL MOTION — THE SEASONS AND THE CALENDAR

The earth has a variety of motions which might seem confusing if we should try to think of them all together. It is fortunately convenient to consider them separately. We are concerned in this chapter with three of the motions: (1) The earth's daily rotation on its axis; (2) The earth's annual revolution around the sun; (3) The earth's precessional motion which resembles the gyration of a spinning top. Before these motions and some of their consequences are described, it will be useful to have some data on the form and dimensions of the earth itself.

2·1. The Earth's Globular Form. Scholars of ancient Greece were convinced that the earth is globular. They cited as evidence of its curvature the gradual appearance of an incoming ship over the sea horizon, and the rising of unfamiliar constellations when they traveled south; they noticed the circular shadow of the earth on the moon during lunar eclipses, a shadow such as a globe would cast. This and other evidence suggests that the earth is globular. More refined observations are needed to show what regular solid the earth most nearly resembles.

If the earth were a perfect sphere, after mountains and depressions are smoothed, all meridians would be circles, so that a degree of latitude would have the same length in statute miles wherever the degree is measured. Since the latitude equals the altitude of the north celestial pole (1·12), the length of one degree of latitude is the distance one must go along the meridian in order to have the pole rise or drop one degree; this distance can be measured by the appropriate method of surveying. Many such measurements, usually over longer arcs, show that a degree of latitude is everywhere nearly equal to 69 statute miles. The conclusions are:

At the equator, latitude 0°, 1° of latitude = 68.7 miles
$$20° \qquad = 68.8$$
$$40° \qquad = 69.0$$
$$60° \qquad = 69.2$$
At the poles, latitude 90°, 1° of latitude = 69.4 miles.

The *statute mile,* which is commonly used for measuring land distances, is the unit in which distances are expressed in astronomy. It is equal to 5280 feet. The *nautical mile,* which is used in marine navigation, is very nearly the length of one minute of arc of a great circle on the terrestrial sphere. It is equal to about 6080 feet.

2·2. The Earth Is an Oblate Spheroid.
Although the length of a degree of latitude is nowhere far from 69 miles, the steady increase in

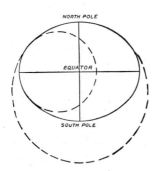

its value from the equator to the poles is significant. The greater value at the poles shows that the meridians curve less rapidly there than at the equator. The meridians are not circles, but ellipses; and the earth is therefore not a sphere, but an *oblate spheroid*—flattened at the poles and bulging at the equator. This figure is also an *ellipsoid of revolution,* generated by the rotation of an ellipse around its minor axis, or in this case by the rotation of a meridian around the earth's axis.

FIG. 2·2. Curvature of a Meridian at the Pole and Equator. The greater length of a degree of latitude at the pole shows that the meridian is there part of a larger circle.

2·3. Dimensions of the Earth; Its Oblateness.
The *dimensions of the earth* are the dimensions of the regular spheroid whose surface most nearly fits the irregular surface of the earth. The dimensions which follow were calculated from measurements of the United States Coast and Geodetic Survey:

$$\text{Equatorial diameter} = 7926.68 \text{ miles}$$
$$\text{Polar diameter} = 7899.98$$
$$\text{Difference} = 26.70$$

$$\text{Oblateness of the earth} = \frac{26.70}{7926.68} = \frac{1}{297}.$$

The *oblateness,* or *ellipticity,* of the spheroid is found by dividing the difference between the equatorial and polar diameters by the equa-

torial diameter. It is the conventional way of denoting the degree of
flattening at the poles. The small value of this fraction for the earth
shows that the flattening is slight. If the earth is represented by a globe
18 inches in diameter, the radius at the poles is only about a thirty-
second of an inch less than the equatorial radius, and the highest mountain is less than an eightieth of an inch above sea level. It has been
said that the earth is rounder and smoother than most of the balls in a
bowling alley.

2·4. The Interior of the Earth. The earth's mass is 6.6×10^{21} tons,
or 5.98×10^{27} grams. Dividing the second figure by the volume of the
earth, which is 1.083×10^{27} cm³, we find that the density is 5.52 times
that of water. In other words, the earth has 5.5 times the mass of an
equal volume of water.

The earth's interior is denser than the surface layers. This is certain because the earth as a whole is 5.5 times as dense as water, while
the surface rocks average only 2.7. High compression in the interior is
responsible for some of the increasing density with increasing depth;
near the center of the earth the pressure of the overlying rocks is of the
order of 50 million pounds to the square inch. But compression alone
is not a sufficient explanation.

The interior is composed of heavier materials. The earth is made
up of three concentric parts, like a baseball. The relatively thin outer
layer, or "crust," corresponds to the horsehide cover of the ball; it consists mainly of granite underlain with basalt. Next, in position comparable with the baseball's string winding, is the intermediate layer composed mostly of magnesium silicate. The nucleus, some 3000 miles in
diameter, corresponds to the rubber core of the baseball; its density is
such that it could be composed of iron and nickel.

Measurements in borings show that the temperature of the rocks
rises about 1° C for every 100 feet increase in depth. If the rule holds
for greater depths, the temperature 60 miles below the surface must
exceed the ordinary melting points of the rocks. But the accompanying
increase in pressure may well maintain the solid state all the way to
the center.

THE EARTH'S ROTATION

In astronomy it is the custom to distinguish sharply between the
terms rotation and revolution. It is well to keep this in mind because
the terms are often used interchangeably in other sciences. *Rotation is
motion around an axis within the body.* Thus the earth rotates daily.

Revolution is motion in an orbit. The earth revolves around the sun annually.

2·5. Absence of Proof of the Earth's Rotation in Early Times.

While the early Greek scholars cited evidence that the earth is globular, they believed with few exceptions that the earth was motionless. Even as late as the time of Copernicus and in fact beyond it, no convincing proof was available that the earth had any motion at all. The alternation of day and night and the rising and setting of the stars could mean either that the heavens are turning daily from east to west or that the earth is rotating from west to east; but the second interpretation was generally dismissed as unreasonable.

Copernicus favored the earth's rotation because it seemed to him more probable that the tiny earth should turn around daily rather than the vast celestial sphere. He was convinced that the earth revolves around the sun as well. Yet he could offer no rigorous proof of either of these motions. Meanwhile, many effects of the earth's rotation have become known, which are so conspicuous that anyone can observe them.

FIG. 2·6. The Foucault Pendulum. (*From a drawing by Russell W. Porter*)

2·6. The Foucault Pendulum.

A freely swinging pendulum affords a simple and effective demonstration of the earth's rotation. The experiment was first performed for the public by the French physicist Foucault in 1851 under the dome of the Panthéon in Paris. It was widely acclaimed as convincing proof of the earth's rotation, a fact that was not universally accepted even at that late date. The original Foucault pendulum consisted of a large iron ball suspended from the center of the dome by a steel wire some 200 feet long and with the least possible friction at the point of support.

When the pendulum was set in motion, it was soon noticed that the plane of the oscillation was slowly turning relative to marks on the floor. The pendulum was, in fact, not changing direction. What the audience saw was the gradual change in direction of the dome; the south side was being carried eastward by the earth's rotation faster than the north side.

The apparent deviation of the Foucault pendulum is zero at the equator, where the direction of a meridian is unaltered during the day, and is fastest at the pole, where the direction of the meridian is changed most rapidly by the earth's rotation. In general, the deviation in an hour is about $15°$ times the sine of the latitude. It is clockwise in the northern hemisphere and counterclockwise in the southern. It is left to the reader to notice that the behavior of the pendulum may also be considered as an example of the deflection effect which will now be described.

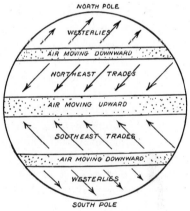

FIG. 2·7. Directions of Prevailing Winds. As a consequence of the earth's rotation the moving air is deflected to the right in the northern hemisphere, and to the left in the southern hemisphere.

2·7. Deflection of Objects Moving Horizontally.
Since all parts of the earth rotate in the same period, the linear speed of the rotation varies with the latitude; it is greatest at the equator and diminishes toward the poles.

In its flight toward the target, a projectile retains the speed of the eastward rotation at the place from which it started, aside from air resistance. Fired northward in the northern hemisphere, the projectile moves toward a place of slower rotation; it is therefore deflected ahead of, or to the east of, the target. If it is fired southward instead, the projectile moves toward a place of faster rotation; it now falls behind, or to the west of, the target. In either event the deflection is to the right when the observer faces in the direction of the flight. If the projectile is fired in the southern hemisphere, it will be evident that the deflection is to the left.

In general, *objects moving along the earth's surface are deflected to the right in the northern hemisphere and to the left in the southern hemisphere.* The deflection is relative to a meridian which is skewed by the earth's rotation while the projectile continues to move in the same plane. While this consequence of the earth's rotation is not conspicuous in the case of ordinary projectiles, convincing deflections are found in the directions of prevailing winds and of ocean currents, such as the Gulf Stream. Another example is seen in the spiral motions of cyclones.

2·8. Cyclones Illustrate the Deflection Effect. The *cyclones,* or depressions, of the temperate zones are great vortices in the atmosphere averaging 1500 miles in diameter, which migrate eastward and are likely to bring stormy weather. Marked "low" on the weather map, they are areas of low barometric pressure into which the surface air moves from various directions. The inflowing currents are deflected like projectiles, so that they spiral inward *in the counterclockwise direction in the northern hemisphere and clockwise in the southern hemisphere.*

Anticyclones, marked "high" on the weather map, are areas from which the surface air moves. These outflowing currents are deflected by the earth's rotation so that they spiral outward, clockwise in the northern hemisphere and counterclockwise in the southern hemisphere. Thus the vortex motions of cyclones and anticyclones are consequences of the earth's rotation.

2·9. Cause of the Earth's Oblateness. The effort of a stone to escape when it is whirled around at the end of a string is an example of the centrifugal tendency of whirling bodies. Similarly, all parts of the earth, owing to its rotation, tend to move away from the earth's axis; this apparent outward acceleration is greatest at the equator and diminishes to nothing at the poles. This effect at any place may be regarded as the resultant of two effects operating at right angles to each other:

(1) *The lifting effect* is opposed to the earth's attraction and therefore diminishes the weight of an object at that place. This would cause an object weighed on a spring balance to weigh less at the equator than at the poles by 1 pound in 289 if the earth were a sphere. The actual

reduction in weight is 1 pound in 190. An object at the equator also weighs less than at the poles because it is farther from the center of the earth. Here we have additional evidence of the earth's oblateness.

(2) *The sliding effect* of the earth's rotation is directed along the surface toward the equator. But things that are free to move, the water of the oceans for example, have not assembled around the equator, as they would if the earth were a sphere. The centrifugal effect of the earth's rotation has produced enough oblateness of the earth itself to compensate this sliding effect.

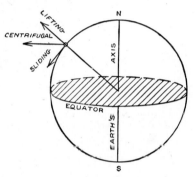

2·10. Gravity at the Earth's Surface.

Gravity is the result of the earth's attraction (gravitation), which is directed nearly toward its center, diminished by the lifting effect of the earth's rotation. The acceleration of gravity, g, is the rate at which a falling body picks up speed; its value at sea level increases from 32.09 feet/sec^2 at the equator to 32.26 feet/sec^2 at

FIG. 2·9. Effect of the Earth's Rotation on a Body at Its Surface. The centrifugal effect directed away from the earth's axis is resolved into two effects at right angles. One diminishes the weight of the body; the other urges it toward the equator.

the poles. The weight of an object, which equals its mass multiplied by g, is therefore less at the equator than at the poles by 0.17/32.26, or 1 pound in 190.

One of the best methods for determining the acceleration of gravity at different places, and therefore the amount of the earth's oblateness, is by swinging a pendulum. For the simple pendulum $g = 4\pi l/t^2$, where l is the length of the pendulum and t is the time in seconds of a complete oscillation.

2·11. Wandering of the Terrestrial Poles.

This effect is also known as the *variation of latitude* from the data by which it is studied. The latitude of any place on the earth is found to be varying if the measurements are sufficiently accurate. Since latitude is reckoned from the equator, which is midway between the poles, it follows that the north and south poles are not stationary points. Repeated measurements of latitudes at different places have determined the character of the wandering of the poles.

These motions are irregular, but are roughly resolvable into two separate effects.   One is a motion in an ellipse 30 feet long in a period of 12 months, whose cause may well be meteorological.   The other is a circular motion of slightly less amplitude in a period of 14 months. Neither pole can withdraw from its average position much more than 40 feet, so that the extreme variation in the latitude of any place is less

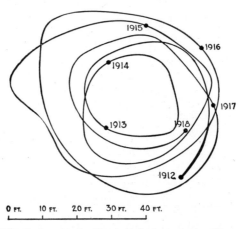

FIG. 2·11.   Wandering of the North Pole 1912-1918.   The complex path of the pole on the earth's surface is shown, with its position at the beginning of each year.

than a second of arc.   The wandering of each pole is confined within an area smaller than that of a baseball diamond.

2·12. Variations in the Speed of the Rotation.   The earth's rotation provides the master clock by which all terrestrial and celestial occurrences are timed.   It is accordingly important to check the reliability of this clock—whether it ever runs fast or slow, or both.   The situation is something like that of a person who relies entirely on the accuracy of his own watch and presently finds that he is always late in keeping appointments.

Reviews of the records of periodic events which are independent of the earth's rotation, such as meridian transits of the moon, transits of the planet Mercury across the sun's disk, and revolutions of Jupiter's satellites have revealed unmistakable departures from the times predicted by theories of the motions of these bodies.   Such discrepancies are ascribed to variations in the period of the earth's rotation.   The variations are resolvable into two effects:

(1) *A steady retardation of the rotation,* so that the length of the day is increasing at the rate of at least 0.001 second a century. This effect is caused chiefly by the friction of the tides.

(2) *Irregular changes in the rotation period,* so that it has been at times longer and at other times shorter than average. The greatest observed error of the earth clock with respect to the average was 30 seconds. Such fluctuations could be caused by expansions and contractions of the earth, which need not alter the radius by more than a few feet.

THE EARTH'S REVOLUTION

2·13. Evidence of the Earth's Revolution. The sun's annual motion among the constellations is a consequence but not a proof of the earth's

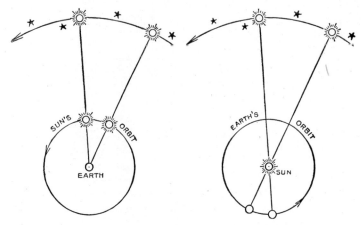

FIG. 2·13. The Sun's Apparent Motion Among the Constellations Is Not a Conclusive Proof of the Earth's Revolution. The same effect is obtained whether the earth revolves around the sun or the sun around the earth.

revolution around the sun; for by itself it leaves doubt as to whether the sun or the earth is really moving. With the aid of the telescope other annually periodic phenomena are observed which may be regarded not only as consequences but also as proofs of the earth's revolution, since they arise from this cause much more plausibly than from any other that can be assigned. Among the effects of this kind are the following:

(1) *The annual parallaxes of the stars* are the periodic changes in the alignments of the nearer stars relative to the more distant ones. This effect, which is described later (Chapter XI) in connection with

the distances of the stars, is so minute that it was not detected until 1838. The failure to observe it had contributed greatly to the persistence of the idea that the earth was stationary, until another effect became known which serves just as well as a proof of the earth's revolution and is much easier to observe.

(2) *The aberration of starlight* was discovered by the English astronomer Bradley in 1727. It is an annually periodic change in the directions of the stars.

2·14. Aberration of Starlight. Raindrops descending vertically on a calm day strike the face of the pedestrian. Whatever direction he takes,

FIG. 2·14. Aberration of Raindrops. The source of the raindrops is apparently displaced in the direction of the observer's motion. (*From a drawing by W. H. Steavenson*)

the source of the raindrops seems to be displaced from overhead in that direction. If he runs instead, the apparent slanting direction of the rain becomes more noticeable; and if he drives rapidly, the direction may seem to be almost horizontal. This is a familiar example of aberration.

Aberration of starlight is the apparent displacement of a star in the direction the earth is moving. The amount of the displacement depends on three factors: (1) It is directly proportional to the speed of the observer. (2) It is inversely proportional to the speed of light. While the moderate speed of the pedestrian in the rain causes a considerable displacement of the source of the raindrop, very swift movement such as that of the revolving earth is required to produce the appreciable displacement of a star.   (3) The displacement is greatest when the earth moves at right angles to the direction of the star, and becomes zero if the earth moves directly toward or away from the star.

If the earth were motionless, there would be no aberration of star-light.   If it had only uniform motion in a straight line, the displace-ment of the star would be always the same and would therefore be un-noticed.   If the earth revolves, the changing direction of its motion would cause the star's displacement to change direction as well, always keeping ahead of us, so that the star seems to describe a little orbit. This is precisely what the telescope shows.   The aberration of starlight is a convincing proof of the earth's revolution around the sun.

2·15. Aberration Orbits of the Stars; the Constant of Aberration.

A star at either pole of the ecliptic has a circular apparent orbit, because

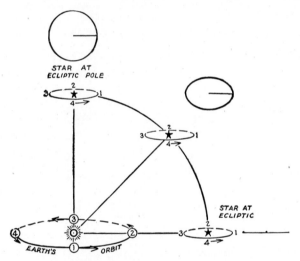

FIG. 2·15.   Aberration Orbits of the Stars.   The numbers mark correspond-ing positions of the earth in its orbit and of the stars in their apparent aber-ration orbits.   The outer figures show the observed forms of the aberration orbits.

the earth's motion is always perpendicular to its direction.   A star on the ecliptic oscillates in a straight line.   Between the ecliptic and its poles the aberration orbit is an ellipse.   In other words, we view the little orbits of Fig. 2·15 flatwise at the ecliptic pole, edgewise on the ecliptic, and at various angles in between.

The *constant of aberration* is the apparent displacement of a star if the earth is moving at average speed at right angles to the star's direction. It is the same for all stars regardless of their distance or direction; it is the radius of the circle at the ecliptic pole, half the major axis of the ellipse, and half the length of the straight line on the ecliptic. The value of the constant of aberration is about 20″.5. It is nearly thirty times as great for all stars as the parallax effect for even the nearest star, and was accordingly the earlier of the two to be detected.

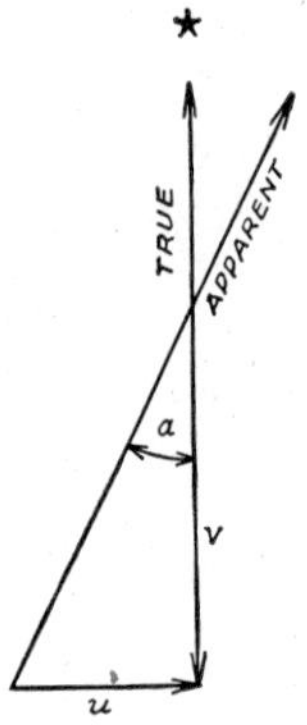

The situation is represented by the right triangle of Fig. 2·15A. The side u is the earth's average speed in its orbit, the side V is the speed of light, and the angle a is the aberration constant. By trigonometry the relation is:

$$\tan a = u/V.$$

If the earth did not revolve, so that u would be zero, a would be zero. If light were propagated instantly, so that V would be infinite, a would again be zero. The observed aberration of starlight demonstrates both the earth's revolution and the finite speed of light.

FIG. 2·15A.

Aberration of Starlight. The amount of the aberration, a, depends on the velocity of the observer, u, and the velocity of light, V.

2·16. The Earth's Orbit Is an Ellipse of small eccentricity with the sun at one focus. It is the path the earth follows in its revolution around the sun and it must not be confused with the ecliptic, the great circle which the sun seems to describe annually on the celestial sphere. The plane of the earth's orbit is also the plane of the ecliptic. Since the orbits of the celestial bodies are generally ellipses, the following definitions will be useful here and elsewhere.

The ellipse is a plane curve such that the sum of the distances from any point on its circumference to two points within, the foci, is always constant and equal to the major axis of the ellipse (Fig. 2·16).

The eccentricity of the ellipse, e, is half the distance between the foci divided by the semi-major axis. It is the conventional way of denoting the degree of flattening of the ellipse. The eccentricity may have any value between $e = 0$, when the figure is a circle, and $e = 1$, when it becomes

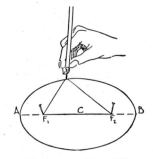

FIG. 2·16. The Ellipse. An easy way to draw an ellipse is shown. The sum of the distances from any point on the circumference to two points within, *the foci, F₁, F₂,* is always the same, and equal to the major axis, *AB.* The eccentricity of the ellipse is the fraction: F_1F_2/AB.

a parabola.   The eccentricity of the earth's orbit is about 0.017 or
1/60.

2·17. The Earth's Distance from the Sun.   *The earth's mean dis-*
tance from the sun is about 92,900,000 miles; it is half the length of
the major axis of the orbit, or the average between the least and
greatest distances from the sun.   This mean distance is known as the
astronomical unit, because it is frequently taken as the unit in stating
celestial distances.

Perihelion and *aphelion* are the two points on the earth's orbit respectively nearest and farthest from the sun; they are at the extremities
of the major axis.   The earth is at perihelion early in January, when its
distance from the sun is 1.7 per cent, or about 1.5 million miles, less
than the mean.   It is at aphelion early in July, when its distance is the
same amount greater than the mean.   At the extremities of the minor
axis of its orbit, the earth is at its mean distance from the sun early in
April and October.

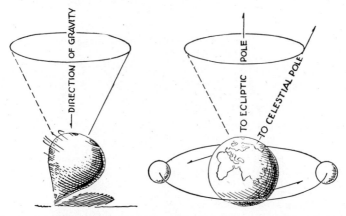

FIG. 2·18.   The Earth Resembles a Spinning Top.   The effort of the moon
to bring the earth's equator into the plane of the moon's orbit (on the average
the ecliptic plane) combined with the earth's rotation gives the earth's axis a
slow conical motion around the line joining the ecliptic poles.

THE EARTH'S PRECESSIONAL MOTION

2·18. Conical Motion of the Earth's Axis.   The axis of a spinning
top describes a cone around a line perpendicular to the floor.   When it
stops spinning, the top falls over.   But while it is spinning, the action

of gravity, instead of tipping the axis, causes the conical motion that we observe. This is the precession of the top.

Just as the axis of the top leans away from the vertical, so the earth's axis is inclined $23\frac{1}{2}°$ from the perpendicular to the plane of its orbit. If the earth did not rotate, the attractions of the moon and sun, both nearly in the plane of the ecliptic, on the earth's equatorial bulge would bring the equator into the ecliptic plane. Owing to the earth's rotation, however, the inclination is not much affected. Again, as in the case of the top, these attractions produce a conical motion of the axis, but in the opposite direction with respect to the rotation.

The earth's precessional motion is the slow conical movement of the earth's axis westward around a line joining the ecliptic poles, having a period of about 26,000 years.

The effect we are considering is a change in the direction of the earth's axis relative to the stars. It is not to be confused with the wandering of the terrestrial poles (2·11) which is caused by a shifting of the earth upon its axis.

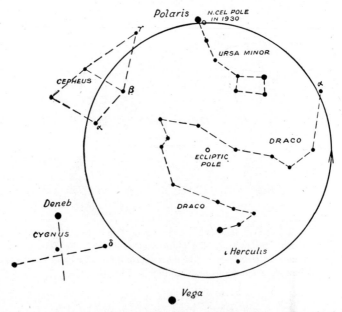

FIG. 2·19. Precessional Path of the North Celestial Pole. The celestial pole describes a circle among the constellations, having a radius of $23\frac{1}{2}°$ and the ecliptic pole at its center. Alpha Draconis was the pole star about 3000 B.C. In the year 7500 Alpha Cephei will be the pole star, and in 14,000 Vega (Alpha Lyrae) will have this distinction.

2·19. Precessional Paths of the Celestial Poles. The conical movement of the earth's axis causes the celestial poles, toward which the axis is directed, to slowly describe circles around the ecliptic poles; the radii of the two circles are the same and equal to $23\frac{1}{2}°$. This is the movement of the poles with reference to the constellations.

As one faces north, the precessional motion of the celestial pole is counterclockwise. This pole is now about one degree from the star Polaris, which it will continue to approach until the minimum distance of slightly less than half a degree is reached, about the year 2100. Thereafter, the diurnal circle of Polaris will grow larger. For those who live in the year 7500, Alpha Cephei will be the nearly invariable pole star and Polaris will circle daily around it 28° away.

Since the celestial poles are the centers of the regions where the stars never set or never rise, the precessional motion slowly shifts the constellations relative to these regions—out of them or into them. The Southern Cross, which rose and set 6000 years ago throughout the United States, is now visible only from the extreme southern part of this country.

2·20. Variations in Precession. It is really the *luni-solar precession* that has been described. The sun's attraction contributes to this effect as well as the moon's, but in smaller amount. A complete account of precession involves additional factors. Owing to the variation of the inclination of the moon's orbit to the plane of the earth's equator, the celestial pole completes a little ellipse around its mean position on the circular precessional path. The semi-major axis of the ellipse in the direction of the ecliptic pole is $9''.2$. This is the chief term in *nutation,* the nodding of the pole.

Nor is the ecliptic pole stationary. *Planetary precession* is the effect of the planets on the plane of the earth's orbit, so that the ecliptic swings away very slowly toward the east relative to the celestial equator. The result of the two precessions is *general precession.* For these and other reasons the movement of the celestial pole is complex; it is not exactly circular and is not the same with reference to the constellations from one cycle to the next.

2·21. Precession of the Equinoxes. Precession has been defined as the conical movement of the earth's axis. It can also be considered as the motion of the equator. The equator slides slowly westward, maintaining very nearly the same inclination with reference to the plane of the earth's orbit. The celestial equator, of course, performs the same gyration relative to the ecliptic, so that the points of their intersection, the equinoxes, slide westward along the ecliptic. This is *precession of the equinoxes*. It proceeds at the rate of 50″.26 a year.

Since the vernal equinox is a fundamental point of reference on the celestial sphere, the westward precession of this equinox introduces a number of important effects. Three of these are as follows:

(1) *The right ascensions and declinations of the celestial bodies are changing.* The motion of the equinox in celestial longitude is 50″.26

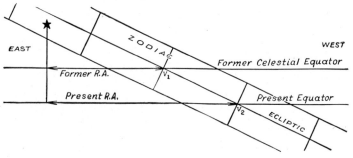

FIG. 2·21. Precession of the Equinoxes. The westward motion of the vernal equinox from V_1 to V_2 causes the signs of the zodiac (the twelve equal divisions of the zodiac marked off from the vernal equinox) to slide westward away from the corresponding constellations of the zodiac. The right ascensions and declinations of the stars are altered by precession.

a year. The annual displacement in right ascension is 46″.09, or 3ˢ.07, and in declination is 20″.04. Thus the equatorial coordinates of a star, whose origin is the vernal equinox, change continually. Accurate catalogs give these positions of stars at a stated time and their annual variations so that the positions at any other time may be calculated.

(2) *The tropical year (year of the seasons) is shorter than the true period of the earth's revolution,* because the vernal equinox moves westward to meet the sun before it has gone completely around the ecliptic. The year of the seasons is shortened 50″.26/360° of 365.25 days, a little more than 20 minutes.

(3) *The signs of the zodiac no longer agree with the constellations of the same name* (2·22).

2·22. Signs and Constellations of the Zodiac. The *zodiac* is the band of the celestial sphere, 16° in width, through which the ecliptic runs centrally.   It contains at all times the sun and moon, and the principal planets, with the exceptions of Venus and Pluto; these two and many asteroids are not confined within its limits.

The *signs of the zodiac* are twelve equal divisions, each 30° long, which are marked off eastward from the vernal equinox.   The signs are

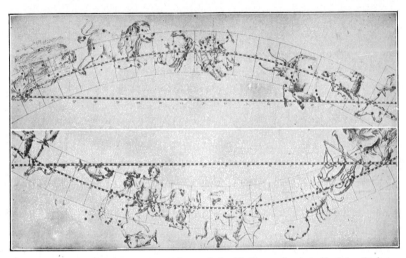

FIG. 2·22.   The Twelve Constellations of the Zodiac.   As described by Ptolemy about 150 A.D.

named from the twelve *constellations of the zodiac* as they were situated in these divisions some two thousand years ago.   The names of the signs and the seasons in which the sun is passing through them are as follows:

Aries		Libra	
Taurus	Spring	Scorpius	Autumn
Gemini		Sagittarius	
Cancer		Capricornus	
Leo	Summer	Aquarius	Winter
Virgo		Pisces	

Owing to the precession of the equinoxes, the vernal equinox has moved westward about 30°, and the signs have moved with it, away from the constellations after which they were named.   Thus the signs and constellations of the zodiac of the same names no longer have the same positions.   When the sun, on March 21, arrives at the vernal equinox, and therefore enters the sign of Aries, it is in the constellation

Pisces. The sun does not enter the constellation Aries until the latter part of April.

THE SEASONS AND THE CALENDAR

2·23. The Year of the Seasons. The year is the period of the earth's revolution, or of the sun's apparent motion in the ecliptic. The kind of year depends on the point of reference to which the motion is referred, whether it is fixed or is itself in motion. Just as the day in common use is not the true period of the earth's rotation, so the ordinary year is not the true period of its revolution. Two kinds of year have the greatest use.

The *sidereal year* is the interval of time in which the sun apparently performs a complete revolution with reference to the stars. Its length is $365^d\ 6^h\ 9^m\ 9^s.5$ ($365^d.25636$) of mean solar time, which is now increasing at the rate of $0^s.01$ a century, in addition to any change caused by variations of the earth's rotation. The sidereal year is the true period of the earth's revolution.

The *tropical year* is the interval between two successive returns of the sun to the vernal equinox. Its length is $365^d\ 5^h\ 48^m\ 46^s.0$ ($365^d.24220$) of mean solar time, and it is now diminishing at the rate of $0^s.53$ a century. It is the year of the seasons, the ordinary year to which the calendar must conform. Owing to the westward precession of the equinox, the tropical year is twenty minutes shorter than the sidereal year ($2·21$).

2·24. Cause of the Seasons. Since the earth's equator is inclined to the plane of its orbit, and since it maintains nearly the same direction in space during a complete revolution, each pole is presented to the sun for part of the year, and turned away from it for the remainder. This is the cause of the changing seasons. The amount of the inclination determines the boundaries of the climatic zones. The *frigid zones* are the regions within $23\frac{1}{2}°$ from the poles, in which the sun becomes circumpolar, and where the seasons are accordingly extreme. The *torrid zone* has as its boundaries the tropics of Cancer and Capricorn, $23\frac{1}{2}°$ from the equator. Here the sun may be overhead at noon; the durations of sunlight and darkness never differ greatly, and temperature changes during the year are not marked. In the *temperate zones* the sun never appears in the zenith, nor does it become circumpolar.

The inclination of the earth's equator to its orbit causes the sun's annual migration in declination. When the sun is farthest north, at the summer solstice, its average altitude in the daytime is the greatest for our region of the world, and the duration of sunlight is the longest. At the winter solstice we have the other extreme, namely, the lowest sun and the shortest duration of sunlight.

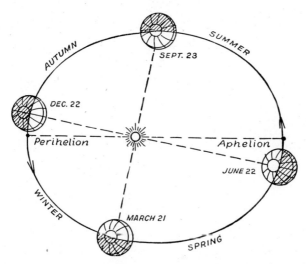

FIG. 2·24. The Seasons in the Northern Hemisphere. This hemisphere is tipped farthest toward the sun at the summer solstice (June 22), and farthest away at the winter solstice (December 22). Soon after the time of the winter solstice the earth arrives at perihelion, about the first of January.

2·25. Seasonal Changes in Temperature arise from progressive variations in the *insolation,* or exposure to sunshine, of a region of the earth's surface. The daily amount of the insolation depends on its intensity and duration. The intensity of the sunshine depends on the sun's altitude, aside from the effects of the sun's varying distance, which will be discussed later, and of variations in the output of its radiation and in the state of the intervening atmosphere.

When the sun's rays strike the ground obliquely, a given amount of radiation spreads over more territory than when the sun is at the zenith, and is therefore less effective in heating any part of it. Moreover, when the sun is low, its rays have to penetrate a greater thickness of air before they reach the ground; they are subject to more absorption and scattering. Summer is a warmer season than winter because the two factors conspire together to produce higher temperatures; the sun's altitude is greater and the daily duration of sunlight is longer.

At the time of the summer solstice the sun is higher at noon in the latitude of New York than it is at the equator, and it is visible for a longer time, so that the amount of heat delivered is fully 25 per cent greater. Even at the north pole at that time the daily insolation at the surface is nearly the same as that at the equator. The uninterrupted radiation from the midnight sun compensates its lower altitude; but the temperature is lower there because much of the heat is taken up in the melting of the ice.

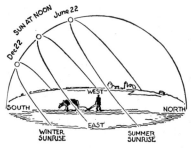

FIG. 2·25. Diurnal Circles of the Sun in Different Seasons. The daily duration of sunlight is longer in the summer, and the sun is higher at noon.

2·26. Lag of the Seasons. If the temperature depended on insolation alone, the warmest days in the northern hemisphere should come around June 22, and the coldest part of the winter about December 22. But the records show that the highest temperatures, on the average, are delayed until early August, and the lowest until early February. Thus the seasons lag. The reason is found in the conservation of heat by the atmosphere.

The air serves as a great blanket around the earth preventing the rapid dissipation of its heat. It is the balance of heat on hand at any time that determines the temperature. As with one's bank balance, the quantity increases as long as the deposits exceed the withdrawals. On June 22 we receive the maximum amount of radiation. Afterwards, as the sun moves south again, the quantity received grows less, but until early August it exceeds the amount the earth returns into space. After this date, the temperature falls.

In the winter, although the sun's altitude and the duration of sunshine increase after December 22, it is not until early February that the rate of heating overtakes the rate of cooling. A diurnal lag of the same kind is noticeable; the warmest part of the day is likely to come in the afternoon.

2·27. The Seasons in the Southern Hemisphere differ from those in the northern hemisphere, of course, in that the same season occurs at the opposite time of the year. Another difference is introduced by the eccentricity of the earth's orbit. Summer in the southern hemisphere begins at the date of the winter solstice, which is only a little while before the earth arrives at perihelion, nearest the sun. It might be supposed that the southern summer would be hotter than the northern summer, which occurs when the earth is near aphelion, and similarly that the southern winter would be colder than the northern winter.

But the earth's distance from the sun at perihelion is only about three per cent less than the distance at aphelion; and the slightly greater extremes of temperature that might otherwise be experienced in the southern hemisphere are modified by the greater extent of the oceans in that hemisphere. It will be interesting to notice later that the conditions which might produce more extreme temperatures in the southern hemisphere are nearly repeated in the case of the planet Mars. There they actually cause greater extremes owing to the greater eccentricity of that planet's orbit.

2·28. The Calendar. The difficulty in the construction of calendars arises from the incommensurability of the natural divisions of time. The periods of the earth's rotation, the moon's revolution, and the earth's revolution cannot be compromised into a convenient chronological scheme that will keep step with these astronomical occurrences without frequent arbitrary adjustment. Leap year is an example.

Our calendar is inherited, much modified, from the Romans, who first divided the year into ten months beginning with March. Four of their number months, September to December, survive, but without the original significance. January and February were added later to make 12 months in all, each one equal as nearly as possible to the period of the moon's phases, about 29½ days. Since the calendar year contained only 355 days, an extra month was occasionally intercalated.

At the time of Julius Caesar the calendar had been managed so unwisely that the vernal equinox was coming in December. With the advice of an astronomer, Caesar instituted a drastic reform. He increased the lengths of the months, disregarding the moon, and thus abolished the intercalary month. The "last year of confusion," 46 B.C., was made 445 days in length; the vernal equinox was thereby brought forward to March 25.

2·29. The Julian Calendar. The chief feature of the Julian reform was the adoption of 365¼ days as the length of the calendar year, beginning January 1, 45 B.C. Here leap year entered. Three common years of 365 days were followed by a fourth containing 366 days—the bissextile year, so called because the extra day was then introduced by repeating the sixth day before March 1. Leap year in the Julian calendar occurred whenever the number of the year was evenly divisible by 4; the years ending in 00, 04, 08, 12, and so on were leap years.

This calendar year of $365^d 6^h$ was $11^m 14^s$ longer than the tropical year ($365^d 5^h 48^m 46^s$), the year of the seasons. The difference accumulated to 3 days in about 400 years. At this rate the date of the vernal equinox fell back in the calendar.

When the Council of Nice convened in A.D. 325, the vernal equinox came the evening before March 21, the leap year scheme accounting for the extra day. At this important meeting of churchmen the rule was adopted for fixing the date of Easter—the first Sunday after the 14th day of the moon (nearly full moon) which occurs on or immediately after March 21.

As the date of the vernal equinox fell back in the calendar, March 21 and anniversaries such as Easter, which are reckoned from it, advanced in relation to the seasons. At the end of the sixteenth century the vernal equinox had fallen back to March 11. Another reform was demanded.

2·30. The Gregorian Calendar. In 1582 Pope Gregory XIII, with the advice of the astronomer Clavius, advocated the suppression of 10 days in the calendar of that year, in order to bring the vernal equinox back to March 21. On this plan the day following October 4, 1582, became the 15th of that month.

To make the average calendar year more nearly equal to the tropical year it was necessary to omit three days in 400 years, by which the Julian calendar was too long. This was accomplished by making the century years common years, unless the number is evenly divisible by 400. Thus the years 1700, 1800, and 1900 became common years of 365 days, while 2000 is a leap year as before.

The Gregorian calendar was adopted by Italy, France, Spain, Portugal, and Poland in 1582, and by Holland, Flanders, and most of the German Roman Catholic states in 1583. Other countries conformed in the following order: the German and Dutch Protestant states and Denmark, in 1700; the British dominions, in 1752 (the day following Sept. 2 was Sept. 14); Sweden, in 1753; Japan, in 1873; China, in 1912; Bulgaria, in 1915; Russia, in 1917; Yugoslavia and Rumania, in 1919; Greece, in 1923; Turkey, in 1927, when the difference between the two calendars had increased to 13 days.

The average length of the year in the Gregorian calendar is $365^d 5^h 49^m 12^s$ of mean solar time, which exceeds the tropical year by only 26 seconds. In its close accordance with the year of the seasons the present calendar is satisfactory. Agitation for further reform is owing to the inequality in the lengths of the months, and the absence of fixed relations between the days of the month and of the week.

A proposed revision of the present calendar, known as the "world calendar," rearranges the lengths of the 12 months so that the quarters are identical. Each quarter begins on Sunday and ends on Saturday; its first month has 31 days and its second and third months 30 days, making a total of 364 days for the year. It is suggested that the 365th day of the common year, which has been called "Year-End Day," follow December 30 and be considered an extra Saturday, and that the added day of the leap year follow June 30 as an extra Saturday as well.

REVIEW QUESTIONS

1. Associate each of the following effects with the earth's rotation or revolution:

 (a) Ellipticity of the earth.
 (b) Aberration of starlight.
 (c) Sun's motion along the ecliptic.
 (d) Diurnal motions of the stars.
 (e) Vortex motions of cyclones.

2. Which of the effects in Question 1 constitute convincing proofs of the earth's motions?

3. Account for the behavior of the Foucault pendulum as an example of the deflection effect (2·7).

4. If the earth should stop rotating and should maintain its ellipticity (which is unlikely), what would be the distribution of land and water?

5. Show that the aberration of starlight proves both the earth's revolution and the finite speed of light.

6. Draw ellipses having (a) zero eccentricity, (b) small eccentricity, and (c) high eccentricity, showing in each case the positions of the foci.

7. The precessional motion of an ordinary top is in the direction of its rotation, while that of the earth is in the opposite direction. Account for the difference.

8. Explain the effect of the earth's precessional motion on the positions of the celestial poles and of the equinoxes.

9. Account for the difference in length between the tropical and sidereal years. With which should the calendar year agree?

10. Give two reasons why the weather is warmer in summer than in winter.

11. (a) State the chief feature of the Julian reform of the calendar. (b) State the two changes made in the Gregorian reform and the reason for each change.

12. Name the term which is defined by each of the following:

 (a) The earth's daily turning around its axis.
 (b) The displacement of a star in the direction of the earth's motion.
 (c) The point in its orbit where the earth is nearest the sun.
 (d) The average distance of the earth from the sun.
 (e) The motion of the vernal equinox among the stars.
 (f) The twelve equal divisions of the zodiac.

CHAPTER III

TIME AND PLACE

The celestial bodies have always served as timekeepers and as guides to voyagers on land and sea. With the recent rapid development of marine and air transportation the determinations of time and positions on the earth by observation of the stars become increasingly important. We now consider some features of time and celestial navigation as applications of astronomical principles which were treated in the preceding chapters.

TIME AND ITS USES

For practical purposes we are concerned with intervals of time. Time of day is the interval that has elapsed since the beginning of the day. To measure such intervals we require a timekeeper whose motion is perfectly uniform. Clocks and other artificial devices do not entirely fulfill this requirement; even the best clocks have variable rates. The earth's rotation, or the consequent daily rotation of the heavens, provides a natural timekeeper that is not far from meeting the requirement of uniformity. The day and its arbitrary subdivisions, the hour, minute, and second, are units for measuring intervals of time.

3·1. Time Reckoning. Two features on the face of a clock are essential for telling time: first, a time reckoner, the pointer of the hour hand; second, a reference line, the line from the noon mark to the center of the dial. The angle between the hour hand and the reference line, when it is converted from degrees to hours and minutes, denotes the time of day. Divisions and numerals around the dial are added for convenience, and interpolating devices, the minute and second hands, add accuracy to the reading of the time.

To observe the time from the master clock in the sky, a point on the celestial sphere is chosen as the *time reckoner*. The part of the hour circle which joins this point to the celestial pole may be regarded as the hour hand circling westward once in a day around the pole. The *reference line* is the observer's celestial meridian.

It is *noon* when the time reckoner is at upper transit (1·11), and *midnight* when it is at lower transit. A *day* is the interval between two successive upper or lower transits of the time reckoner. *Time of day* is either the hour angle of the time reckoner if the day begins at noon, which is true of the sidereal day, or it is the hour angle of the time reckoner plus 12 hours if the day begins at midnight. These definitions apply to any kind of local time.

The three time reckoners in use are the vernal equinox, the apparent sun, and the mean sun. The corresponding kinds of time are respectively sidereal time, apparent solar time, and mean solar (or civil) time.

3·2. The Sidereal Day Is Shorter than the Solar Day. In the upper position of the earth, in Fig. 3·2, it is both sidereal and solar

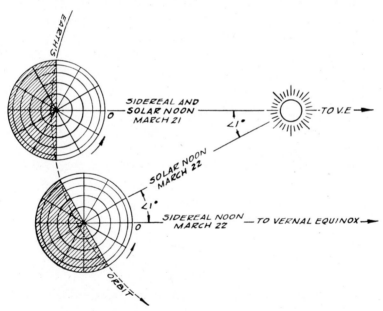

FIG. 3·2. The Sidereal Day Is Shorter Than the Solar Day. Owing to the earth's revolution, the meridian of the observer at *O* must be rotated once around to complete the sidereal day, and nearly one degree more to complete the solar day.

noon on March 21 for the observer at *O*. The sun and the vernal equinox are both at upper transit over his meridian. By the time the earth has made a complete rotation, so that this meridian is parallel to its original direction, the earth in its revolution around the sun has moved to its lower position in the diagram. In the new position it is sidereal noon of the following day. The vernal equinox on the remote celestial sphere is again at upper transit, so that the sidereal day is completed. Owing to its revolution, however, the earth must rotate still farther before the solar day is completed. Thus the sidereal day is shorter than the solar day.

Now the angle through which the earth revolves in one day is $360°/365.25$, or a little less than $1°$. It is evident from the Figure that this is also the angle through which the earth must rotate after completing the sidereal day before the ending of the solar day. Since the earth's rotation proceeds at the rate of $15°$ an hour, or $1°$ in 4 minutes, *the sidereal day is about 4 minutes shorter than the solar day.*

More exactly, the difference is $3^m 55^s.909$, so that the length of the sidereal day is $23^h 56^m 4^s.091$ of mean solar time. Owing to the precession of the equinox ($2·21$), the sidereal day is slightly shorter than the true period of the earth's rotation, which is $23^h 56^m 4^s.099$ of mean solar time.

3·3. Sidereal Time is the local hour angle of the vernal equinox. The sidereal day begins at the upper transit of the vernal equinox, and is reckoned through 24 hours to the next upper transit. Sidereal time agrees with ordinary time about September 21. Thereafter, it gains $3^m 56^s$ a day, which accumulates to two hours in a month, and to a whole day in the course of a year. Evidently the earth rotates once more in a year than there are days in the calendar.

The specific convenience of sidereal time is that it is star time. At any place, a star rises or transits always at the same sidereal time. On ordinary time a star rises or crosses the celestial meridian four minutes earlier from night to night, or two hours earlier from month to month. Thus a star which rises at 10 o'clock in the evening on November 1 will rise at 8 o'clock on the first of December. The westward march of the constellations with the advancing seasons ($1·17$) is caused by the difference in length between the sidereal and the solar day.

3·4. Determining the Sidereal Time. The correct civil time is brought to us by wire and radio from clocks in certain observatories. Those clocks are corrected by comparison with the master clock in the sky, which is a sidereal clock. The determination of sidereal time is made most often by observing the transits of stars across the celestial

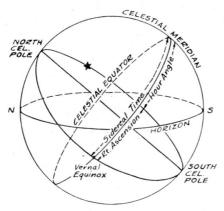

FIG. 3·4. Relation Between Sidereal Time, Right Ascension, and Hour Angle. Sidereal time equals the right ascension of a star plus its hour angle. If the star is at upper transit (hour angle zero), the sidereal time equals the star's right ascension.

FIG. 3·4A. A Transit Instrument of the Naval Observatory, Washington. Formerly employed for correcting the clocks of the Naval Observatory, it is now replaced for this purpose by the 8-inch photographic zenith tube.

meridian. The simple rule employed, which can be verified by reference to Figure 3·4, is as follows: *The sidereal time at any instant equals the right ascension of the star that is at upper transit at that instant.* In order to apply the rule it is necessary to know precisely when a star is at upper transit. This can be done by use of the transit instrument.

The *transit instrument* is a rather small telescope mounted on a single horizontal axis which is set east and west. The telescope may be pointed only along the observer's celestial meridian. Having directed the telescope toward a star that will soon transit, the observer looks into the eyepiece and watches the star move toward the middle of the field of view. A vertical wire in the middle of the field marks the celestial meridian. At the instant that the star is bisected by the wire, the reading of the sidereal clock is recorded.

Suppose that the clock reading is $6^h\,40^m\,17^s.2$ and that the star's right ascension is given in the almanac as $6^h\,40^m\,15^s.7$. The clock is accordingly $1^s.5$ fast, because at the instant of the upper transit the star's right ascension is the correct sidereal time. The correct standard time can then be easily calculated.

3·5. Apparent Solar Time.

Although sidereal time is suited to many activities of the observatory, it is not useful for civil purposes, because our daily affairs are governed by the sun's position in the sky, and not by the vernal equinox. Sidereal noon, for example, comes at night during a part of the year.

The *apparent sun* is the sun we see. The hour angle of its center plus 12 hours is *apparent solar time,* or simply apparent time. The apparent solar day begins at midnight and is reckoned through 24 hours continuously. Unfortunately the sun itself is not a reliable time keeper. It runs fast or slow, at times nearly half a minute in a day. The sundial is the only timepiece adapted to its erratic behavior. The lengths of apparent solar days at different times in the year, measured in mean solar time, are:

1945, January 1	24^h	0^m	$28^s.3$
April 1	23	59	41 .9
July 1	24	0	11 .6
October 1	23	59	40 .8

Two causes contribute chiefly to the irregularity in the lengths of apparent solar days: (1) The variable revolution of the earth, owing to the eccentricity of its orbit. (2) The obliquity of the ecliptic.

3·6. Effect of the Earth's Variable Revolution. Because of the eccentricity of the earth's orbit, the speed of the earth around the sun is not uniform. The closer it is to the sun, the faster the earth revolves. This relation is expressed precisely as a particular case of Kepler's law of areas: *The line joining the earth to the sun sweeps over equal areas in equal intervals of time.*

When the earth is near perihelion, early in January, it revolves farthest in a day. Since the difference in length between the solar day and the constant sidereal day depends on the amount of the earth's orbital motion (3·2), apparent solar days would then have the maximum length. When the earth is near aphelion, early in July, it makes the smallest advance in its orbit in a day; apparent solar days would then have minimum length if this were the only cause of their variation.

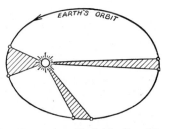

FIG. 3·6. Variable Revolution of the Earth. Since, by Kepler's law, the line joining the earth and the sun sweeps over the same area every day, the earth travels farther in a day when it is nearer the sun.

This effect can also be understood by shifting the attention from the earth's eastward revolution around the sun to the consequent apparent eastward motion of the sun along the ecliptic. It is this motion that delays the sun's return to the meridian. The farther the earth revolves in a day, the greater is the sun's eastward displacement along the ecliptic and the longer the apparent solar day. Thus, as the sun's daily progress along the ecliptic varies through the year, the lengths of apparent solar days are not the same.

3·7. Effect of the Obliquity of the Ecliptic. Even if the sun's motion in the ecliptic were uniform, the length of the apparent solar day would remain variable, because the ecliptic is inclined to the celestial equator. It is the projection of the sun's eastward motion upon the celestial equator that determines the delay in completing the apparent solar day.

Near the equinoxes, a considerable part of the sun's motion in the ecliptic is north or south, which does not delay the sun's return. Near the solstices, where the ecliptic is parallel to the equator, the entire motion is eastward; moreover, the hour circles are closer together here. Therefore, so far as the obliquity of the ecliptic is concerned, apparent solar days would be longest at the solstices and shortest at the equinoxes.

It will be noticed that both causes conspire to make the apparent day longest in winter.

3·8. Mean Solar Day; Civil Time. The *mean solar day,* as the term implies, is the *average* apparent solar day. It is therefore of the same length throughout the year and remains practically constant over a long period of time. It is the basis of all ordinary measurements of time. The *mean sun* is an imaginary point which moves uniformly eastward in the celestial equator, completing its circuit in the same period as that of the apparent sun in the ecliptic. The interval between two successive upper or lower transits of the mean sun is the mean solar day.

Local civil time is the specific reckoning of mean solar time from the beginning of the day at local midnight through 24 hours to the following midnight. *Greenwich civil time* is accordingly the local civil time at the Greenwich meridian; it has frequent use in astronomy and navigation, and is sometimes called *universal time.* Civil time is still quite commonly reckoned in two 12-hour divisions of the day with the designations A.M. and P.M. But the preference for its continuous reckoning through the 24 hours is found in various places. In astronomical practice 6:30 P.M. is recorded as $18^h 30^m$, while in the operations of ships and planes it is written as 1830.

3·9. The Equation of Time is the difference at any instant between apparent solar and civil time; it is the difference between the hour angles of the apparent and mean sun. Four times a year, as Table 3·I shows, the two agree. At other times the apparent sun is either fast or slow in the westward diurnal motion; early in November the sundial is more than a quarter of an hour ahead of local civil time. The Table gives the value of the equation of time at Greenwich civil midnight on the first of each month in 1945 or, very nearly, in any other year.

TABLE 3·I. EQUATION OF TIME

(Apparent time faster or slower than local civil time)

Jan. 1	$3^m 21^s$	slow		July 1	$3^m 31^s$	slow
Feb. 1	13 36	slow		Aug. 1	6 14	slow
Mar. 1	12 35	slow		Sept. 1	0 11	slow
Apr. 1	4 8	slow		Oct. 1	10 5	fast
May 1	2 53	fast		Nov. 1	16 19	fast
June 1	2 27	fast		Dec. 1	11 9	fast

The rapid change in the equation of time near the winter solstice noticeably affects the times of sunrise and sunset; at this time of year apparent solar time is becoming slower *fastest.* As the sun begins to move north after passing the solstice, it might be expected to rise earlier and set later. But the change in the equation of time delays both rising and setting as expressed in civil time. For this reason the sun does not begin to rise earlier until about two weeks after the date of the winter solstice, though it begins to set later some two weeks before that date.

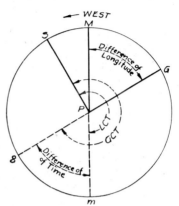

FIG. 3·10. Difference of Local Time Between Two Places (*M* and *G*) Equals Their Difference of Longitude.

3·10. Difference of Local Time Equals Difference of Longitude.

In any one of the three kinds of local time, a day of 24 hours is completed when the earth has made a complete rotation, through 360°, relative to the point in the sky that serves as the time reckoner. Thus 24 hours of that kind of time equal 360° or 24 hours of longitude on the earth; and there is a difference of one hour between the local times of two places whose longitudes differ by 15° or one hour.

When the local time at one place is given and the corresponding local time at another place is required, *add the difference of their longitudes if the second place is east of the first; subtract if it is west.*

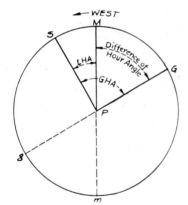

FIG. 3·11. Difference of Hour Angle of a Celestial Body (*S*) Between Two Places Equals Their Difference of Longitude.

3·11. The Time Diagram.

Relations between time and longitude are often visualized by means of the *time diagram* (Fig. 3·10). This is a projection of the earth as viewed from above the south pole. The pole appears at the center and the earth's equator is the circle around it. Meridians are represented by radii of the circle and are labeled around the outside. Thus G is the Greenwich meridian and g is its lower branch; M is the observer's local meridian, usually placed at the top, and m is its lower branch. S is the meridian at which the particular celestial body is at upper transit (here it is supposed to be the mean sun). West is the counterclockwise direction.

Fig. 3·10 is intended to demonstrate the rule (3·10) that difference of time equals difference of longitude. The observer is in longitude 60° W., or 4^h W. The Greenwich civil time (GCT) is 18^h and the local civil time (LCT) is 14^h, so that the difference, 4^h, equals the difference between the observer's longitude and that of Greenwich.

Fig. 3·11 is similar to the preceding one, but is intended to show that *difference between the hour angles of a celestial body at two places at any instant equals the difference of longitude between the two places.* The celestial body is again taken as the mean sun. This relation, for which we shall have later use, follows immediately from the previous one. Since local civil time equals 12 hours plus the hour angle of the mean sun, the difference of time between two places is evidently the same as the difference of hour angle of the mean sun.

Fig. 3·12. Time Zone Diagram. The numbers outside the circle are the longitudes of the standard meridians. The numbers inside are zone descriptions.

3·12. Zone Time. Since difference of local time equals difference of longitude, local civil time is later at places east of us and earlier at places west of us. The inconvenience of continually resetting our watches as we travel east or west is avoided by the use of zone time at sea and standard time on land. These are conventionalized forms of civil time.

Standard meridians are marked on the earth at intervals of 15° or one hour east and west of the meridian of Greenwich. The local civil time of each standard meridian is the time to be kept by timepieces in the entire zone within 7° 30′ east and west of that meridian. *Zone time* for any place is accordingly the local civil time of the standard meridian nearest the place. Thus the earth is divided into 24 zones whose times differ by whole hours from Greenwich civil time. There are, however, some exceptions to the rule. Near land, a time zone may be modified to correspond with the time kept ashore.

The time zones employed in the operations of ships at sea and of many aircraft over the sea are represented in the time diagram of Fig. 3·12. The numbers outside the circle are the longitudes of the standard meridians, while those inside the circle are the zone descriptions. The *zone description* is the correction in whole hours from a particular zone time to Greenwich civil time. For example, the zone description is +6 for the zone around the standard meridian whose longitude is 90° W. When the time in this zone is 0950, or 9:50 A.M., the Greenwich civil time is 1550, or 3:50 P.M.

3·13. Standard Time belts on land are less uniform than time zones at sea. Their boundaries are determined by local preferences and may be altered by legislative action. Moreover, the adoption of standard time is not universal; in some areas the legal time differs from adjacent belts by a fraction of an hour. The time zones and belts are shown in the Hydrographic Office *Time Zone Chart of the World* (H.O. No. 5192).

Four standard times are used in continental United States and the greater part of Canada, namely, Eastern, Central, Mountain, and Pacific. They are respectively the local civil times of the meridians 75°, 90°, 105°, and 120° west of Greenwich, and are therefore 5, 6, 7, and 8 hours slow as compared with Greenwich civil time. The confusion in the keeping of time on land is increased by the practice of setting clocks ahead an hour so that they show "daylight saving time," or "summer time."

3·14. The International Date Line. Referring again to Fig. 3·12, we notice that the zone description is +12 for the eastern half of the zone whose standard meridian is 180°, while it is −12 for the western half. The eastern half is a whole day behind the western half. The rule on shipboard is to change the date at the 180° meridian. At the westward crossing of this meridian the date is advanced a day, and at the eastward crossing it is set back a day. Thus, if the eastward cross-

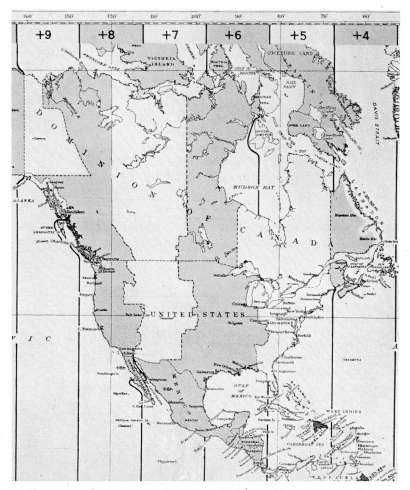

FIG. 3·13. Time Zone Chart of North America. The large numbers at the top are zone descriptions. (*Adapted from H.O. 5192 by permission of U. S. Navy Hydrographic Office*)

ing is made on Tuesday, June 7, the date becomes Monday, June 6, and *vice versa*.

For the land areas in this vicinity the boundary between the earlier and later dates is the *international date line*. This line departs in places from the 180° meridian so as not to divide politically associated areas. For example, the line bends to the east of the 180° meridian around Siberia and to the west around the Aleutian Islands.

3·15. Conversion to Greenwich Civil Time. The most frequent conversion of time is from zone or standard time to Greenwich civil time (GCT). This is true because almanacs which have the greatest use tabulate their data for intervals of GCT.

In passing from zone time to GCT the correction is a whole number of hours which is added if the longitude of the place is west of Greenwich and subtracted if it is east. This correction is the zone description (3·12) whose value is found by dividing the longitude by 15 and taking the nearest whole number. It is important to notice whether or not the date is the same in both places. In passing from standard time to GCT the correction is not always a whole hour and it may not otherwise be the same as the zone description for a specified longitude, owing to irregularities in the boundaries of the standard time belt. The following examples illustrate the conversion:

(1) Required the zone description at a place whose longitude is 70° 20′ W. Answer: +5 hours.

(2) The zone time is 22^h 15^m, July 21, at a place whose longitude is 66° 10′ W. Required the corresponding GCT and date.

Answer: The GCT is 2^h 15^m, July 22.

(3) The zone time is 4^h 17^m, April 20, at a place whose longitude is 130° 40′ E. Required the corresponding GCT and date.

Answer: The GCT is 19^h 17^m, April 19.

(4) The central standard time is 3^h 55^m, May 17. Required the GCT and date.

Answer: The GCT is 9^h 55^m, May 17.

CELESTIAL NAVIGATION

3·16. Navigation, in general, is the art of conducting a plane or ship from the point of departure to the destination in the best possible way. The charted *course line* between the two places represents the desired track of the craft; its direction is the *course* which is measured, like azimuth (1·5), from the north clockwise up to 360°. The speed of the craft is also marked on this line either in statute miles per hour or in knots. The *knot* is one nautical mile per hour. Thus the *dead reckoning position,* deduced from course and speed, may be noted on the chart at intervals during the voyage.

The true position of the craft is likely to differ from the dead reckoning position, owing to steering errors, air currents, and other factors. It is accordingly the navigator's duty to determine his position from time to time by whatever means are available. Two ways of accomplishing this are the following:

(1) *By use of terrestrial landmarks* whose places are shown on the chart. These may be prominent features of the landscape, whose directions are sighted, or else radio beacons whose directions are determined by radio compass. These methods of *geo-navigation* are treated in books on navigation under the headings: piloting and radio direction finding.

(2) *By use of celestial objects* whose places in the heavens are found in the almanacs. *Celestial navigation* has to do with the determination of the position of a craft by sextant sights of celestial objects. It is this astronomical feature of navigation with which we are here concerned. This brief account begins with the line of position and fix, which are the end products of the process, and then takes up the separate steps leading to these results.

3·17. The Circle of Position. The *geographical point* of a celestial object is the point on the earth's surface at which the object is in the

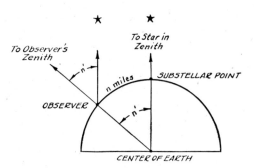

FIG. 3·17. The Observer's Distance in Nautical Miles from the Geographical Point of a Celestial Object Equals the Distance of That Object in Minutes of Arc from the Observer's Zenith.

zenith at a particular instant. This point is also known specifically as the *subsolar point,* the *sublunar point,* or the *substellar point.* Its position can be quickly taken from an almanac. The latitude of the point is the same as the declination of the object in the zenith (1·12). The longitude equals the Greenwich hour angle of the object if the hour angle is less than 180°, or it is 360° minus the hour angle if that angle exceeds 180°; in the first case the longitude is west, while in the second case it is east of Greenwich.

It will be seen, in Fig. 3·17, that *the observer's distance in minutes of arc, or in nautical miles, from the geographical point of a celestial object equals the distance of that object in minutes of arc from the observer's zenith.* This equality, as will presently be seen, is the basis of celestial navigation.

Suppose that the navigator of a plane sights a certain star and finds that its altitude is 60°, so that its zenith distance is 30°, or 1800′. According to the rule he then knows that he is somewhere on the *circle of position* 1800 nautical miles in radius around the star's geographical point. Suppose that the navigator calculates that the star would have had the altitude 59° (zenith distance 31°, or 1860′), if the plane had been in the expected (dead reckoning) position at the time of the sight; he would then have been on the circle 1860 miles in radius around the geographical point of the star.

3·18. The Line of Position. In practice it is unnecessary to plot the circle of position. The expected position of the plane is established on

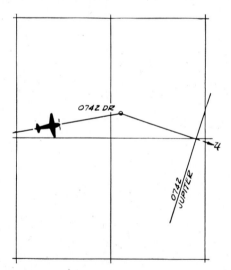

FIG. 3·18. A Line of Position. Determined by a sight on Jupiter.

the navigator's chart, and the azimuth of the star can be calculated for that position, or can be observed from the plane. Thus the possible positions of the plane are restricted to a small arc of the circle, which may be well enough represented by a short line tangent to that arc. This is the *line of position;* it is also known as the *Sumner line,* after the name of the American shipmaster who first employed the method about a century ago.

In order to determine a line of position by means of a star or other celestial object, the navigator observes the altitude of the star and then calculates the altitude and azimuth that the star would have if the plane were in the dead reckoning position. The difference between the observed and calculated altitudes in minutes of arc equals the *altitude intercept,* the distance in miles of the plane from the DR position in the direction of the star. Fig. 3·18 shows how the line of position is plotted as the solution of the following problem.

Problem: A plane is proceeding on course 080° and with speed 200 knots over the ground. At 7:42 A.M., Greenwich civil time, the navigator sights the planet Jupiter and finds the observed altitude 39′ greater than the altitude calculated for the dead reckoning position. The planet's azimuth is 108°. Required the line of position at that time.

Procedure: From the DR position draw the azimuth line in the direction 108° from the north. Lay off the distance of 39 nautical miles on this line in the direction of the planet; this altitude intercept is *toward* because the observed altitude is greater than the calculated value. At the extremity of the altitude intercept construct a line perpendicular to the azimuth line. This is the line of position, the locus of possible positions of the plane at the time.

Evidently the plane is not in the 0742 DR position, but we cannot say precisely where it is, unless a sight is made on an object in another part of the sky; this would provide a second line of position intersecting the first one.

3·19. The Fix and Running Fix. The *fix* is the true position of the plane, aside from errors of observation, as distinguished from the dead reckoning position which is the intended position. The fix is the intersection of two (or more) lines of position determined from sights that are made simultaneously or so nearly so that the progress of the plane between them may be neglected. The fix is considered most reliable when the two lines of position are not far from perpendicular to each other.

The *running fix* is determined when the two sights are not taken simultaneously, as is most likely to be the case. The procedure is to advance the earlier line of position parallel to itself along the course line the distance the plane has moved between the sights. The intersection of the advanced line and the second line of position is the running fix, whose reliability is likely to decrease as the interval between the sights becomes greater.

The fix represented in Fig. 3·19 is the intersection of the line of position from the sight on the planet Jupiter (Fig. 3·18) and the second

line from the sight at the same time on the star Betelgeuse. The calculated azimuth of the star was 220° and the altitude intercept was 22

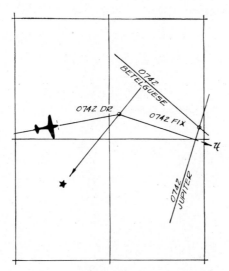

FIG. 3·19. A Fix. The intersection of two lines of position determined by
simultaneous sights on Jupiter and Betelgeuse.

miles *away* from the DR position. It is now in order to consider how
the observed and calculated altitudes of a celestial object are determined.

3·20. The Sextant is an instrument used for measuring the angular
distance between two objects; the objects are usually a celestial body
and the sea horizon or else a bubble in the instrument itself which represents the horizontal. It contains a small telescope system and two
glasses set at right angles to the plane of the instrument. These are:
(1) the fixed *horizon glass,* one half clear and the other half silvered,
toward which the telescope is directed, and (2) the *index glass,* a mirror
set on a moving arm. The extremity of the arm moves along an arc
which is graduated in degrees and fractions.

The instrument is strictly a sextant if the arc is about one sixth of
a circle, and an octant if it is about one eighth of a circle, but the word
"sextant" is often applied to both. Sextants are of two general types:
the marine sextant and the bubble sextant, which is usually an octant.

The *marine sextant* is used to measure the altitude of a star or other
celestial object above the sea horizon. By manipulating the arm the
observer brings the star to coincidence with the horizon and reads on
the arc the actual angle between the two.

The *bubble octant* is employed chiefly in air navigation. The sight consists in bringing the star to the center of the reflected image of a bubble which represents the celestial horizon and then reading the alti-

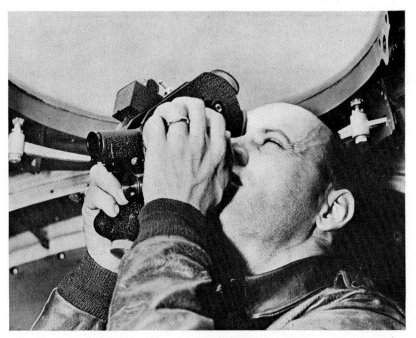

FIG. 3·20. "Shooting the Sun." The navigator in the top turret of a U. S. bomber sights the sun with a Bausch and Lomb bubble octant. (*Official photograph, U. S. Army Air Forces*)

tude as before. Less accurate than the marine sextant, the octant is indispensible to the navigator when the sea horizon is not available.

3·21. The Air Almanac. Two astronomical almanacs are published by the United States Government especially for the use of the navigator. They are *The American Nautical Almanac* and *The American Air Almanac*. The former lists the required data to the tenth of a minute of arc, while the latter provides them to the whole minute, which is sufficient for air navigation and for most purposes of marine navigation as well.

The almanac data required for determining the line of position are: (1) Corrections to be applied to the sextant reading of the sight in order to obtain the true, known as the observed, altitude of the celestial object. Examples are: corrections for instrumental errors, atmospheric refraction, and the moon's parallax; (2) The Greenwich hour angle and declination of the object. These, together with the assumed latitude and longitude of the plane, are needed for deducing the calculated altitude of the object, as we shall presently see.

Table 3·II contains three extracts from the *Air Almanac*. The first is part of a daily sheet; it lists for ten-minute intervals of Greenwich civil time the hour angles of the sun, the vernal equinox, three suitably placed planets, and also the declinations of these objects. The second extract is a table for the interpolation of the Greenwich hour angle. The third is a selected list of bright stars; a complete list of the 55 principal navigational stars appears on the inside back cover of the *Almanac*.

3·22. Greenwich Hour Angle and Declination. An inspection of Table 3·II will show at once how to take the data from the *Almanac*

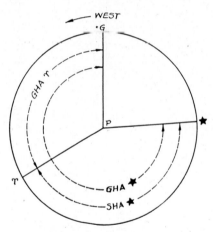

FIG. 3·22. The Greenwich Hour Angle of a Star. It equals the sum of the Greenwich hour angle of the vernal equinox and the sidereal hour angle of the star.

for a specified Greenwich civil time. If, for example, the time is 6^h $14^m 20^s$, take the GHA from the daily sheet for $6^h 10^m$ and add the value for $4^m 20^s$ from the interpolation table. The desired declination is the tabulated value nearest the time. An additional step is required in the case of a star.

The Greenwich hour angle of a star is the sum of the Greenwich hour angle of the vernal equinox (Greenwich sidereal time) and the sidereal hour angle of the star (Fig. 3·22):

$$GHA* = GHA\Upsilon + SHA*.$$

TABLE 3·II. EXTRACT FROM "THE AMERICAN AIR ALMANAC"

INTERPOLATION OF GHA

SUN, PLANETS, ♈

Int. (m s)	Corr. (° ')	Int. (m s)	Corr (° ')	Int. (m s)	Corr. (° ')
00 00	0 00	03 17	0 50	06 37	1 40
01	0 01	21	0 51	41	1 41
05	0 02	25	0 52	45	1 42
09	0 03	29	0 53	49	1 43
13	0 04	33	0 54	53	1 44
17	0 05	37	0 55	57	1 45
21	0 06	41	0 56	07 01	1 46
25	0 07	45	0 57	05	1 47
29	0 08	49	0 58	09	1 48
33	0 09	53	0 59	13	1 49
37	0 10	57	1 00	17	1 50
41	0 11	04 01	1 01	21	1 51
45	0 12	05	1 02	25	1 52
49	0 13	09	1 03	29	1 53
53	0 14	13	1 04	33	1 54
57	0 15	17	1 05	37	1 55
01 01	0 16	21	1 06	41	1 56
05	0 17	25	1 07	45	1 57
09	0 18	29	1 08	49	1 58
13	0 19	33	1 09	53	1 59
17	0 20	37	1 10	57	2 00
21	0 21	41	1 11	08 01	2 01
25	0 22	45	1 12	05	2 02
29	0 23	49	1 13	09	2 03
33	0 24	53	1 14	13	2 04
37	0 25	57	1 15	17	2 05
41	0 26	05 01	1 16	21	2 06
45	0 27	05	1 17	25	2 07
49	0 28	09	1 18	29	2 08
53	0 29	13	1 19	37	2 09
57	0 30	17	1 20	41	2 11
02 01	0 31	21	1 21	45	2 12
05	0 32	25	1 22	49	2 13
09	0 33	29	1 23	53	2 14
13	0 34	33	1 24	57	2 15
17	0 35	37	1 25	09 01	2 16
21	0 36	41	1 26	05	2 17
25	0 37	45	1 27	09	2 18
29	0 38	49	1 28	13	2 19
33	0 39	53	1 29	17	2 20
37	0 40	57	1 30	21	2 21
41	0 41	06 01	1 31	25	2 22
45	0 42	05	1 32	29	2 23
49	0 43	09	1 33	33	2 24
53	0 44	13	1 34	37	2 25
57	0 45	17	1 35	41	2 26
03 01	0 46	21	1 36	45	2 27
05	0 47	25	1 37	49	2 28
09	0 48	29	1 38	53	2 29
13	0 49	33	1 39	57	2 30
17	0 50	37	1 40	10 00	
21		41			

MOON

Int. (m s)	Corr. (° ')	Int. (m s)	Corr. (° ')	Int. (m s)	Corr. (° ')
00 00	0 00	03 20	0 49	06 39	1 37
02	0 01	24	0 50	43	1 38
06	0 02	29	0 51	47	1 39
10	0 03	33	0 52	52	1 40
14	0 04	37	0 53	56	1 41
18	0 05	41	0 54	07 00	1 42
22	0 06	45	0 55	04	1 43
26	0 07	49	0 56	08	1 44
31	0 08	53	0 57	12	1 45
35	0 09	58	0 58	16	1 46
39	0 10	04 02	0 59	20	1 47
43	0 11	06	1 00	25	1 48
47	0 12	10	1 01	29	1 49
51	0 13	14	1 02	33	1 50
55	0 14	18	1 03	37	1 51
01 00	0 15	22	1 04	41	1 52
04	0 16	27	1 05	45	1 53
08	0 17	31	1 06	49	1 54
12	0 18	35	1 07	54	1 55
16	0 19	39	1 08	58	1 56
20	0 20	43	1 09	08 02	1 57
24	0 21	47	1 10	06	1 58
29	0 22	51	1 11	10	1 59
33	0 23	56	1 12	14	2 00
37	0 24	05 00	1 13	18	2 01
41	0 25	04	1 14	23	2 02
45	0 26	08	1 15	27	2 03
49	0 27	12	1 16	31	2 04
53	0 28	16	1 17	35	2 05
58	0 29	20	1 18	39	2 06
02 02	0 30	25	1 19	43	2 07
06	0 31	29	1 20	47	2 08
10	0 32	33	1 21	52	2 09
14	0 33	37	1 22	56	2 10
18	0 34	41	1 23	09 00	2 11
22	0 35	45	1 24	04	2 12
26	0 36	49	1 25	08	2 13
31	0 37	54	1 26	12	2 14
35	0 38	58	1 27	16	2 15
39	0 39	06 02	1 28	21	2 16
43	0 40	06	1 29	25	2 17
47	0 41	10	1 30	29	2 18
51	0 42	14	1 31	33	2 19
55	0 43	18	1 32	37	2 20
03 00	0 44	23	1 33	41	2 21
04	0 45	27	1 34	45	2 22
08	0 46	31	1 35	50	2 23
12	0 47	35	1 36	54	2 24
16	0 48	39	1 37	58	2 25
20	0 49	43		10 00	
24					

Correction to be added to GHA for interval of GCT

STARS

No.	Name	Mag.	SHA	Dec.	No.	Name	Mag.	SHA	Dec.
1	Achernar . .	0. 6	336 05	S57 31	12	Dubhe . . .	2. 0	194 56	N62 03
2	Acrux . . .	1. 1	174 08	S62 47	13	Fomalhaut .	1. 3	16 21	S29 55
3	Aldebaran .	1. 1	291 49	N16 24	14	Peacock . .	2. 1	54 41	S56 55
4	Alpheratz .	2. 2	358 37	N28 47	15	Pollux . .	1. 2	244 31	N28 10
5	Altair . . .	0. 9	62 59	N 8 43	16	Procyon . .	0. 5	245 54	N 5 22
6	Antares . .	1. 2	113 30	S26 19	17	Regulus . .	1. 3	208 39	N12 14
7	Arcturus . .	0. 2	146 43	N19 28	18	Rigel . . .	0. 3	282 02	S 8 16
8	Betelgeux .	0. 1–1. 2	271 57	N 7 24	19	Rigil Kent. .	0. 3	141 03	S60 36
9	Canopus . .	−0. 9	264 19	S52 40	20	Sirius . . .	−1 6	259 19	S16 38
10	Capella . .	0. 2	281 51	N45 56	21	Spica . . .	1. 2	159 26	S10 52
11	Deneb . . .	1. 3	50 07	N45 05	22	Vega	0. 1	81 14	N38 44

TABLE 3·II. EXTRACT FROM "THE AMERICAN AIR ALMANAC" (Cont.)

GREENWICH A. M. 1944 OCTOBER 28 (SATURDAY)

GCT (h m)	☉ SUN GHA	☉ SUN Dec	♈ GHA	VENUS −3.4 GHA	VENUS Dec	JUPITER −1.3 GHA	JUPITER Dec	SATURN 0.2 GHA	SATURN Dec	☾ MOON GHA	☾ MOON Dec
0 00	184 02	S13 00	36 13	151 48	S22 29	225 23	N 5 04	294 34	N22 12	48 49	S 9 45
10	186 32		38 43	154 18		227 53		297 05		51 14	43
20	189 02		41 14	156 48		230 23		299 35		53 39	41
30	191 32 · ·		43 44	159 18 · ·		232 54 · ·		302 06 · ·		56 03 ·	39
40	194 02		46 14	161 48		235 24		304 36		58 28	37
50	196 32		48 45	164 18		237 54		307 07		60 52	35
1 00	199 02	S13 01	51 15	166 48	S22 29	240 25	N 5 04	309 37	N22 12	63 17	S 9 33
10	201 32		53 46	169 18		242 55		312 07		65 41	31
20	204 02		56 16	171 47		245 25		314 38		68 06	28
30	206 32 · ·		58 46	174 17 · ·		247 56 · ·		317 08 · ·		70 31 ·	26
40	209 02		61 17	176 47		250 26		319 39		72 55	24
50	211 32		63 47	179 17		252 56		322 09		75 20	22
2 00	214 02	S13 02	66 18	181 47	S22 30	255 27	N 5 04	324 39	N22 12	77 44	S 9 20
10	216 32		68 48	184 17		257 57		327 10		80 09	18
20	219 02		71 18	186 47		260 28		329 40		82 33	16
30	221 32 ·		73 49	189 17 · ·		262 58 · ·		332 11 · ·		84 58 ·	14
40	224 02		76 19	191 46		265 28		334 41		87 23	12
50	226 32		78 50	194 16		267 59		337 12		89 47	10
3 00	229 02	S13 03	81 20	196 46	S22 30	270 29	N 5 04	339 42	N22 12	92 12	S 9 07
10	231 32		83 51	199 16		272 59		342 12		94 36	05
20	234 02		86 21	201 46		275 30		344 43		97 01	03
30	236 32 ·		88 51	204 16 · ·		278 00 · ·		347 13 · ·		99 25 ·	9 01
40	239 02		91 22	206 46		280 30		349 44		101 50	8 59
50	241 02		93 52	209 16		283 01		352 14		104 15	57
4 00	244 02	S13 04	96 23	211 45	S22 31	285 31	N 5 04	354 44	N22 12	106 39	S 8 55
10	246 32		98 53	214 15		288 01		357 15		109 04	53
20	249 02		101 23	216 45		290 32		359 45		111 28	50
30	251 32 · ·		103 54	219 15 · ·		293 02 · ·		2 16 · ·		113 33 ·	48
40	254 02		106 24	221 45		295 32		4 46		116 18	46
50	256 32		108 55	224 15		298 03		7 16		118 42	44
5 00	259 02	S13 05	111 25	226 45	S22 32	300 33	N 5 04	9 47	N22 12	121 07	S 8 42
10	261 32		113 55	229 14		303 03		12 17		123 31	40
20	264 02		116 26	231 44 ·		305 34		14 48		125 56 ·	38
30	266 32 · ·		118 56	234 14 · ·		308 04 · ·		17 18 · ·		128 20 ·	36
40	269 02		121 27	236 44		310 34		19 49		130 45	33
50	271 32		123 57	239 14		313 05		22 19		133 10	31
6 00	274 02	S13 05	126 28	241 44	S22 32	315 35	N 5 03	24 49	N22 12	135 34	S 8 29
10	276 32		128 58	244 14		318 05		27 20		137 59	27
20	279 02		131 28	246 44		320 36		29 50		140 23	25
30	281 32 · ·		133 59	249 13 · ·		323 06 · ·		32 21 · ·		142 48 ·	23
40	284 02		136 29	251 43		325 36		34 51		145 13	·21
50	286 32		139 00	254 13		328 07		37 21		147 37	18
7 00	289 02	S13 06	141 30	256 43	S22 33	330 37	N 5 03	39 52	N22 12	150 02	S 8 16
10	291 32		144 00	259 13		333 07		42 22		152 26	14
20	294 02		146 31	261 43		335 38		44 53		154 51	12
30	296 32 · ·		149 01	264 13 · ·		338 08 · ·		47 23 · ·		157 16 ·	10
40	299 02		151 32	266 43		340 38		49 54		159 40	08
50	301 32		154 02	269 12		343 09		52 24		162 05	05
8 00	304 02	S13 07	156 32	271 42	S22 34	345 39	N 5 03	54 54	N22 12	164 29	S 8 03
10	306 32		159 03	274 12		348 09		57 25		166 54	8 01
20	309 02		161 33	276 42		350 40		59 55		169 19	7 59
30	311 32 · ·		164 04	279 12 · ·		353 10 · ·		62 26 · ·		171 43 ·	57
40	314 02		166 34	281 42		355 40		64 56		174 08	55
50	316 32		169 04	284 12		358 11		67 26		176 32	52
9 00	319 02	S13 08	171 35	286 41	S22 34	0 41	N 5 03	69 57	N22 12	178 57	S 7 50
10	321 32		174 05	289 11		3 11		72 27		181 21	48
20	324 02		176 36	291 41		5 42		74 58		183 46	46
30	326 32 · ·		179 06	294 11 · ·		8 12 · ·		77 28 · ·		186 11 ·	44
40	329 02		181 37	296 41		10 43		79 59		188 35	42
50	331 32		184 07	299 11		13 13		82 29		191 00	39
10 00	334 02	S13 09	186 37	301 41	S22 35	15 43	N 5 03	84 59	N22 12	193 24	S 7 37
10	336 32		189 08	304 11		18 14		87 30		195 49	35
20	339 02		191 38	306 40		20 44		90 00		198 14	33
30	341 32 · ·		194 09	309 10 · ·		23 14 · ·		92 31 · ·		200 38 ·	31
40	344 02		196 39	311 40		25 45		95 01		203 03	29
50	346 32		199 09	314 10		28 15		97 31		205 27	26
11 00	349 02	S13 10	201 40	316 40	S22 35	30 45	N 5 03	100 02	N22 12	207 52	S 7 24
10	351 32		204 10	319 10		33 16		102 32		210 17	22
20	354 02		206 41	321 40		35 46		105 03		212 41	20
30	356 32 · ·		209 11	324 10 · ·		38 16 · ·		107 33 · ·		215 06 ·	17
40	359 02		211 41	326 39		40 47		110 03		217 30	15
50	1 32		214 12	329 09		43 17		112 34		219 55	13
12 00	4 02	S13 10	216 42	331 39	S22 36	45 47	N 5 02	115 04	N22 12	222 20	S 7 11

Marginal correction table (☾s Par. / Alt. +Corr.):

Alt.	+Corr.
0°	0
1	61
10	60
14	59
18	58
21	57
23	56
25	55
27	54
29	53
31	52
33	51
35	50
36	49
38	48
39	47
41	46
42	45
44	44
45	43
46	42
48	41
49	40
50	39
31	38
52	37
54	36
55	35
56	34
57	33
58	32
59	31
60	30
61	29
62	28
64	27
65	26
66	25
67	24
68	23
69	22
70	21
71	20
72	19
73	18
74	17
75	16
76	15
77	14
78	13
79	12
80	11
80	10

SD ☉ 16   SD ☾ 16   Corr. HA ☾   Int. Corr. m 0 ° 0   10 0

Diagram labels (sky chart): East — West; Antares, VENUS, MARS, MERCURY, Spica, JUPITER, Regulus, SATURN, Aldebaran

The *sidereal hour angle* of a star is the angular distance measured west-ward along the celestial equator from the vernal equinox to the hour circle of the star. It is 360° minus the star's right ascension. The GHA of the vernal equinox is taken from the *Almanac* in the same way as that of the sun; the star's SHA and declination are found in the star table. The following examples employ the data of Table 3·II. All are for October 28, 1944.

(1) Required the GHA and declination of the sun at GCT 4^h 27^m 30^s.

Answer: GHA at 4^h 20^m	249° 02'
Add for 7^m 30^s	1 53
GHA	250° 55'
Dec.	13° 04' S.

(2) Required the GHA and Dec. of the moon at GCT 5^h 24^m 17^s.

Answer: GHA at 5^h 20^m	125° 56'
Add for 4^m 17^s	1 02
GHA	126° 58'
Dec.	8° 37' S.

(3) Required the GHA and Dec. of Jupiter at GCT 7^h 42^m 20^s.

Answer: GHA at 7^h 40^m	340° 38'
Add for 2^m 20^s	0 35
GHA	341° 13'
Dec.	5° 03' N.

(4) Required the GHA and Dec. of the star Betelgeuse (also spelled Betelgeux) at GCT 7^h 42^m 20^s.

Answer: GHAϓ at 7^h 40^m	151° 32'
Add for 2^m 20^s	0 35
GHAϓ	152° 07'
SHA*	271 57
GHA*	64° 04'
Dec.*	7° 24' N.

3·23. The Meridian Angle.

The three data specifically required for the calculation of the altitude of the celestial object are the assumed latitude of the plane, the declination of the object, and its meridian angle at the time of the sight. The *meridian angle* is the angle at the celestial pole between the upper branch of the local celestial meridian and the hour circle of the object; it is measured either east or west from the meridian from 0° to 180°, unlike hour angle which is reckoned toward the west from 0° to 360°. The following examples show how to pass from Greenwich hour angle to local hour angle (3·11) and then to meridian angle, *t:*

(1) The GHA of Jupiter is 341° 13'. Required its meridian angle in assumed longitude 39° 13' W.

Answer: GHA   341° 13'
Long. −39 13
LHA   302° 00'
t 58° 00' E.

(2) The GHA of Betelgeuse is 64° 04'. Required its meridian angle in assumed longitude 39° 04' W.

Answer: GHA   64° 04'
Long. −39 04
LHA   25° 00'
t 25° 00' W.

3·24. The Astronomical Triangle is a triangle on the celestial sphere whose vertices are the celestial pole, the observer's zenith, and a celestial object. The sides of the triangle (Fig. 3·24) are complements of the

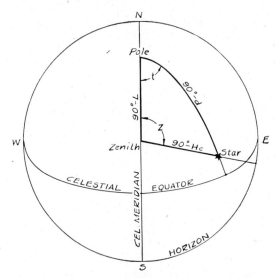

FIG. 3·24. The Astronomical Triangle. It is a triangle on the celestial sphere whose vertices are the celestial pole, the observer's zenith, and a celestial object.

observer's latitude, L, and of the declination, d, and altitude, H, of the object. The angle at the pole is the meridian angle, t; the angle at the zenith, Z, is either the azimuth, Z_n, if the object is east of the meridian, or it is 360° minus the azimuth if the object is west.

Given the latitude and the meridian angle and declination of the object from the almanac data for the time of the sight, the navigator knows the values of two sides and the included angle of the triangle. He could then calculate by appropriate trigonometric formulae the azimuth of the object and altitude, H_c, that would have been measured if the plane had been in its assumed position at the time. Instead, he arrives at the solution by one of the many devices that are intended to save time and effort. We now examine one of the tabular solutions and by this means reach the final step in the process developed in the Examples of the preceding Sections.

3·25. Tables of Computed Altitude and Azimuth.

These tables (*Hydrographic Office Publication* No. 214) are in nine volumes, each one covering a 10° interval of latitude either north or south. With the exception of a single correction they provide immediately the calculated altitude and azimuth of any celestial body, whose Greenwich hour angle and declination are known, for an assumed position of the plane.

The *assumed latitude* is the whole number of degrees nearest the DR latitude. The *assumed longitude* is the value nearest the DR longitude which, when combined with the Greenwich hour angle, results in a local hour angle, and therefore meridian angle, having a whole number of degrees. The navigator may proceed from his DR position, if he prefers, though it is slightly less rapid. Either way results in the same line of position.

Our Table 3·III contains extracts from H.O. 214. It will be noticed that the declination is tabulated at half-degree intervals. We accordingly enter the column for the declination nearest the actual value, and then correct the tabular altitude to the desired altitude. The correction is found by use of the factor Δd; divide this factor by 100 and multiply by the difference between the tabular and actual values of the declination. In practice the correction is read from a convenient multiplying table in H.O. 214.

We are now ready for the complete solution of the problem begun in the preceding Sections.

3·26. Determining a Fix.

Problem: At GCT 0742, October 28, 1944, the dead reckoning position of a plane was: latitude 41° 12′ N., longitude 38° 54′ W. By simultaneous sights at this time the true altitude, H_o, of Jupiter was 27° 57′, and of Betelgeuse 49° 07′. From the *Almanac* (3·21) the planet's GHA was 341° 13′, and its declination

TABLE 3·III. EXTRACT FROM TABLES OF COMPUTED ALTITUDE AND AZIMUTH. H.O.214

DECLINATION SAME NAME AS LATITUDE

Lat. 41° H.A.	5° 00′ Alt. (Δd Δt)	Az.	5° 30′ Alt. (Δd Δt)	Az.	6° 00′ Alt. (Δd Δt)	Az.	6° 30′ Alt. (Δd Δt)	Az.	7° 00′ Alt. (Δd Δt)	Az.	7° 30′ Alt. (Δd Δt)	Az.	H.A.
00	54 00.0 1.0 01	180.0	54 30.0 1.0 01	180.0	55 00.0 1.0 01	180.0	55 30.0 1.0 01	180.0	56 00.0 1.0 01	180.0	56 30.0 1.0 01	180.0	00
1	53 59.3 1.0 03	178.3	54 29.3 1.0 03	178.3	54 59.3 1.0 03	178.3	55 29.3 1.0 03	178.2	55 59.3 1.0 04	178.2	56 29.3 1.0 04	178.2	1
2	53 57.3 1.0 06	176.6	54 27.3 1.0 06	176.6	54 57.3 1.0 06	176.5	55 27.2 1.0 06	176.5	55 57.2 1.0 06	176.5	56 27.2 1.0 06	176.4	2
3	53 54.0 1.0 08	174.9	54 23.9 1.0 08	174.9	54 53.8 1.0 08	174.8	55 23.8 1.0 08	174.7	55 53.7 1.0 08	174.7	56 23.6 1.0 08	174.6	3
4	53 49.3 1.0 10	173.2	54 19.2 1.0 10	173.2	54 49.1 1.0 10	173.1	55 18.9 1.0 10	173.0	55 48.8 1.0 10	172.9	56 18.7 1.0 11	172.8	4
05	53 43.3 99 12	171.6	54 13.1 99 12	171.5	54 42.9 99 12	171.4	55 12.7 99 13	171.3	55 42.5 99 13	171.2	56 12.3 99 13	171.1	05
6	53 36.0 99 14	169.9	54 05.8 99 14	169.8	54 35.5 99 15	169.7	55 05.2 99 15	169.5	55 34.9 99 15	169.4	56 04.6 99 15	169.3	6
7	53 27.4 99 16	168.2	53 57.1 99 17	168.1	54 26.7 99 17	168.0	54 56.3 99 17	167.8	55 25.9 99 17	167.7	55 55.5 99 17	167.5	7
8	53 17.6 98 19	166.6	53 47.1 98 19	166.4	54 16.6 08 19	166.3	54 46.1 98 19	166.1	55 15.6 98 19	166.0	55 45.1 08 20	165.8	8
9	53 06.4 98 21	165.0	53 35.8 98 21	164.8	54 05.2 98 21	164.6	54 34.6 98 21	164.4	55 04.0 98 22	164.3	55 33.3 08 22	164.1	9
10	52 54.1 98 23	163.3	53 23.3 98 23	163.2	53 52.6 97 23	163.0	54 21.8 97 23	162.8	54 51.1 97 24	162.6	55 20.3 97 24	162.4	10
1	52 40.5 97 25	161.7	53 09.6 97 25	161.5	53 38.7 97 25	161.3	54 07.8 97 25	161.1	54 36.9 97 26	160.9	55 05.9 97 26	160.7	1
2	52 25.7 97 27	160.1	52 54.7 97 27	159.9	53 23.6 96 27	159.7	53 52.5 96 27	159.5	54 21.4 96 28	159.3	54 50.3 96 28	159.0	2
3	52 09.7 96 29	158.6	52 38.5 96 29	158.3	53 07.3 96 29	158.1	53 36.1 96 29	157.9	54 04.8 96 30	157.6	54 33.5 96 30	157.4	3
4	51 52.6 96 30	157.0	52 21.2 95 31	156.8	52 49.9 95 31	156.5	53 18.4 95 31	156.3	53 47.0 95 32	156.0	54 15.5 95 32	155.8	4
15	51 34.4 95 32	155.5	52 02.8 95 33	155.2	52 31.3 95 33	155.0	52 59.7 95 33	154.7	53 28.0 94 34	154.4	53 56.3 94 34	154.2	15
6	51 15.0 94 34	154.0	51 43.3 94 34	153.7	52 11.6 94 35	153.4	52 39.8 94 35	153.2	53 07.9 94 35	152.9	53 36.0 94 36	152.6	6
7	50 54.6 94 36	152.5	51 22.7 94 36	152.2	51 50.8 93 36	151.9	52 18.8 93 37	151.6	52 46.7 93 37	151.3	53 14.6 93 37	151.0	7
8	50 33.2 93 37	151.0	51 01.1 93 38	150.7	51 28.9 93 38	150.4	51 56.7 93 38	150.1	52 24.5 92 39	149.8	52 52.2 92 39	149.5	8
9	50 10.8 92 39	149.6	50 38.5 92 39	149.3	51 06.1 92 40	149.0	51 33.7 92 40	148.6	52 01.2 92 40	148.3	52 28.7 91 41	148.0	9
20	49 47.4 92 41	148.1	50 14.8 91 41	147.8	50 42.3 91 41	147.5	51 09.6 91 42	147.2	51 36.9 91 42	146.9	52 04.2 91 42	146.5	20
1	49 23.0 91 42	146.7	49 50.3 91 42	146.4	50 17.5 91 43	146.1	50 44.6 60 43	145.8	51 11.7 90 44	145.4	51 38.7 90 44	145.1	1
2	48 57.7 90 44	145.4	49 24.8 90 44	145.0	49 51.7 90 44	144.7	50 18.7 90 45	144.4	50 45.5 89 45	144.0	51 12.3 89 46	143.6	2
3	48 31.5 90 45	144.0	48 58.4 89 45	143.7	49 25.1 89 46	143.3	49 51.8 89 46	143.0	50 18.5 89 47	142.6	50 45.1 88 47	142.2	3
4	48 04.5 89 46	142.7	48 31.1 89 47	142.3	48 57.7 88 47	142.0	49 24.1 88 48	141.6	49 50.6 88 48	141.2	50 16.9 88 48	140.9	4
25	47 36.6 88 48	141.4	48 02.9 88 48	141.0	48 29.2 88 49	110.6	48 55.6 87 49	140.3	49 21.8 87 49	139.9	49 47.9 87 50	139.5	25
6	47 07.9 87 49	140.1	47 34.1 87 49	139.7	48 00.2 87 50	139.3	48 26.3 87 50	139.0	48 52.2 86 51	138.6	49 18.1 86 51	138.2	6
7	46 38.5 87 50	138.8	47 04.4 86 51	138.4	47 30.3 86 51	138.1	47 56.2 86 51	137.7	48 21.9 86 52	137.3	48 47.6 85 52	136.9	7
8	46 08.3 86 52	137.5	46 34.0 86 52	137.2	46 59.7 85 52	136.8	47 25.3 85 53	136.4	47 50.8 85 53	136.0	48 16.3 85 53	135.6	8
9	45 37.4 85 53	136.3	46 02.9 85 53	135.9	46 28.4 85 53	135.6	46 53.7 84 54	135.2	47 19.0 84 54	134.8	47 44.2 84 55	134.4	9
30	45 05.8 85 54	135.1	45 31.1 84 54	134.7	45 56.3 84 55	134.4	46 21.5 84 55	134.0	46 46.5 83 55	133.6	47 11.5 83 56	133.2	30
1	44 33.5 84 55	133.9	44 58.6 84 55	133.6	45 23.6 83 56	133.2	45 48.5 83 56	132.8	46 13.4 83 56	132.4	46 38.2 82 57	132.0	1
2	44 00.6 83 56	132.8	44 25.4 83 56	132.4	44 50.3 83 57	132.0	45 15.0 82 57	131.6	45 39.6 82 57	131.2	46 04.2 82 58	130.8	2
3	43 27.0 82 57	131.6	43 51.7 82 57	131.2	44 16.3 82 58	130.8	44 40.8 82 58	130.4	45 05.3 81 58	130.0	45 29.6 81 59	129.6	3
4	42 52.9 82 58	130.5	43 17.4 81 58	130.1	43 41.8 81 59	129.7	44 06.1 81 59	129.3	44 30.3 81 59	128.9	44 54.4 80 60	128.5	4
35	42 18.2 81 59	129.4	42 42.5 81 59	129.0	43 06.7 81 59	128.6	43 30.8 80 60	128.2	43 54.8 80 60	127.8	44 18.7 80 60	127.4	35
6	41 42.9 80 60	128.3	42 07.0 80 60	127.9	42 31.0 80 60	127.5	42 54.9 80 61	127.1	43 18.7 79 61	126.7	43 42.5 79 61	126.3	6
7	41 07.1 80 60	127.3	41 31.0 79 61	126.9	41 54.8 79 61	126.5	42 18.6 79 61	126.0	42 42.2 79 62	125.6	43 05.7 78 62	125.2	7
8	40 30.8 79 61	126.2	40 54.6 79 62	125.8	41 18.3 78 62	125.4	41 41.7 78 62	125.0	42 05.1 78 63	124.6	42 28.5 78 63	124.2	8
9	39 54.1 79 62	125.2	40 17.6 78 62	124.8	40 41.0 78 63	124.4	41 04.4 78 63	124.0	41 27.6 77 63	123.5	41 50.8 77 64	123.1	9
40	39 16.8 78 63	124.2	39 40.2 78 63	123.8	40 03.4 77 63	123.4	40 26.6 77 64	122.9	40 49.7 77 64	122.5	41 12.6 76 64	122.1	40
1	38 39.2 77 64	123.2	39 02.3 77 64	122.8	39 25.4 77 64	122.4	39 48.4 76 64	121.9	40 11.3 76 65	121.5	40 34.1 76 65	121.1	1
2	38 01.1 77 64	122.2	38 24.0 76 64	121.8	38 46.9 76 65	121.4	39 09.7 76 65	121.0	39 32.5 76 65	120.5	39 55.1 75 66	120.1	2
3	37 22.5 76 65	121.2	37 45.4 76 65	120.8	38 08.1 76 65	120.4	38 30.7 75 66	120.0	38 53.3 75 66	119.6	39 15.7 75 66	119.2	3
4	36 43.6 76 65	120.3	37 06.3 75 66	119.9	37 28.8 75 66	119.5	37 51.3 75 66	119.1	38 13.7 74 67	118.6	38 36.0 74 67	118.2	4
45	36 04.4 75 66	119.4	36 26.8 75 66	119.0	36 49.2 75 67	118.5	37 11.6 74 67	118.1	37 33.8 74 67	117.7	37 55.9 74 67	117.3	45
6	35 24.7 75 67	118.4	35 47.0 74 67	118.0	36 09.3 74 67	117.6	36 31.5 74 67	117.2	36 53.5 73 68	116.8	37 15.5 73 68	116.4	6
7	34 44.7 74 67	117.5	35 06.9 74 67	117.1	35 29.0 74 68	116.7	35 51.0 73 68	116.3	36 12.9 73 68	115.9	36 34.8 73 68	115.5	7
8	34 04.4 74 68	116.7	34 26.4 73 68	116.2	34 48.4 73 68	115.8	35 10.3 73 68	115.4	35 32.1 72 69	115.0	35 53.7 72 69	114.6	8
9	33 23.8 73 68	115.8	33 45.7 73 68	115.4	34 07.5 73 69	114.9	34 29.2 72 69	114.5	34 50.9 72 69	114.1	35 12.4 72 69	113.7	9
50	32 42.9 73 69	114.9	33 04.6 72 69	114.5	33 26.3 72 69	114.1	33 47.9 71 70	113.7	34 09.3 71 70	113.3	34 30.8 71 70	112.8	50
1	32 01.6 72 69	114.1	32 23.3 72 69	113.6	32 44.8 72 70	113.2	33 06.3 71 70	112.8	33 27.7 71 70	112.4	33 48.9 71 70	112.0	1
2	31 20.2 72 70	113.2	31 41.7 72 70	112.8	32 03.1 71 70	112.4	32 24.4 71 70	112.0	32 45.7 71 70	111.6	33 06.8 70 71	111.1	2
3	30 38.4 71 70	112.4	30 59.8 71 70	112.0	31 21.1 71 70	111.6	31 42.3 71 71	111.1	32 03.4 70 71	110.7	32 24.5 70 71	110.3	3
4	29 56.4 71 70	111.6	30 17.7 71 71	111.1	30 38.8 70 71	110.7	30 59.9 70 71	110.3	31 21.0 70 71	109.9	31 41.9 70 71	109.5	4
55	29 14.2 71 71	110.7	29 35.3 70 71	110.3	29 56.4 70 71	109.9	30 17.4 70 71	109.5	30 38.3 70 71	109.1	30 59.1 69 72	108.7	55
6	28 31.7 70 71	109.9	28 52.8 70 71	109.5	29 13.7 70 71	109.1	29 34.6 69 72	108.7	29 55.4 69 72	108.3	30 16.1 69 72	107.9	6
7	27 49.1 70 71	109.2	28 10.0 70 72	108.7	28 30.8 69 72	108.3	28 51.6 69 72	107.9	29 12.3 69 72	107.5	29 32.9 69 72	107.1	7
8	27 06.2 70 72	108.4	27 27.0 69 72	108.0	27 47.7 69 72	107.6	28 08.4 69 72	107.1	28 29.0 69 72	106.7	28 49.5 68 73	106.3	8
9	26 23.1 69 72	107.6	26 43.8 69 72	107.2	27 04.5 69 72	106.8	27 25.1 68 73	106.4	27 45.6 68 73	106.0	28 06.1 68 73	105.6	9
60	25 39.9 69 72	106.8	26 00.5 69 73	106.4	26 21.0 68 73	106.0	26 41.5 68 73	105.6	27 01.9 68 73	105.2	27 22.3 68 73	104.8	60
1	24 56.4 69 73	106.1	25 17.0 68 73	105.7	25 37.4 68 73	105.3	25 57.8 68 73	104.9	26 18.1 68 74	104.5	26 38.4 67 74	104.0	1
2	24 12.8 68 73	105.3	24 33.3 68 73	104.9	24 53.7 68 73	104.5	25 14.0 68 74	104.1	25 34.3 67 74	103.7	25 54.4 67 74	103.3	2
3	23 29.1 68 73	104.6	23 49.5 68 73	104.2	24 09.8 68 73	103.8	24 30.0 67 74	103.4	24 50.2 67 74	103.0	25 10.3 67 74	102.6	3
4	22 45.2 68 73	103.8	23 05.5 68 74	103.4	23 25.7 67 74	103.0	23 45.9 67 74	102.6	24 06.0 67 74	102.2	24 26.0 67 74	101.8	4
65	22 01.2 67 74	103.1	22 21.4 67 74	102.7	22 41.5 67 74	102.3	23 01.6 67 74	101.9	23 21.7 67 74	101.5	23 41.7 66 74	101.1	65
6	21 17.0 67 74	102.4	21 37.1 67 74	102.0	21 57.2 67 74	101.6	22 17.3 67 74	101.2	22 37.3 67 74	100.8	22 57.2 66 74	100.4	6
7	20 32.7 67 74	101.7	20 52.8 67 74	101.3	21 12.8 67 74	100.9	21 32.8 67 74	100.5	21 52.7 66 74	100.1	22 12.6 66 75	99.7	7
8	19 48.3 67 74	101.0	20 08.3 67 74	100.6	20 28.3 66 74	100.2	20 48.2 66 74	99.8	21 08.1 66 75	99.4	21 27.9 66 75	99.0	8
9	19 03.8 67 74	100.3	19 23.8 66 74	99.9	19 43.7 66 75	99.5	20 03.6 66 75	99.1	20 23.4 66 75	98.7	20 43.1 66 75	98.3	9
70	18 19.2 66 74	99.6	18 39.1 66 75	99.2	18 59.0 66 75	98.8	19 18.8 66 75	98.4	19 38.6 66 75	98.0	19 58.3 66 75	97.6	70

5° 03′ N.; the star's GHA was 64° 04′, and its declination 7° 24′ N. Required the two lines of position and the 0742 fix.

Solution, made with *Air Almanac* and H.O. 214:

	Jupiter	Betelgeuse
GHA	341° 13′	64° 04′
Assumed long.	39 13	39 04
LHA	302° 00′	25° 00′
t	58 00 E.	25 00 W.
d	5 03 N.	7 24 N.
d (H.O. 214)	5 00 N.	7 30 N.
Assumed lat.	41 00 N.	41 00 N.
Altitude	27° 06′	49° 48′
Correction for Δd	+02	−05
H_c	27° 08′	49° 43′
H_o	27 57	49 07
a	Toward 49 miles	Away 36 miles
Z	108°.4	139°.5
Azimuth	108 .4	220 .5

Thus the line of position from the sight on Jupiter runs 49 nautical miles from the assumed position (1 degree of latitude equals 60 nautical

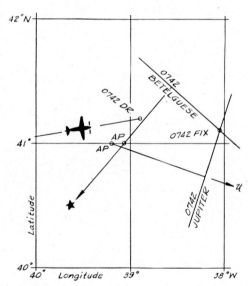

FIG. 3·26. The Fix Determined from Sights on Two Celestial Objects. This is the solution of the problem of Sec. 3·26.

miles) measured perpendicularly in the direction of the planet. The line of position from the sight on Betelgeuse runs 36 miles away. The intersection of the two lines (Fig. 3·26) is the fix, or actual position, of the plane at 0742. By comparison with Fig. 3·19, it is seen that the lines of position and fix are the same whether the calculation is made with reference to the assumed or dead reckoning position.

REVIEW QUESTIONS

1. Name the terms associated with time, which are defined by each of the following:

(a) Hour angle of the vernal equinox.
(b) Hour angle of the mean sun plus 12 hours.
(c) Right ascension of a star that is at upper transit.
(d) Difference between apparent and mean solar time.
(e) Meridians spaced 15° apart beginning with the meridian of Greenwich.

2. Notice in Map 1 that the star β Cassiopeiae is nearly on the hour circle of the vernal equinox. (a) Show that the line from Polaris to this star of Cassiopeia can serve roughly as the hour hand for denoting the sidereal time. (b) What is the sidereal time when this hour hand points to the zenith?

3. Explain why different groups of constellations are visible at the same hour of the evening at the different seasons.

4. Show that days by the sundial are longer in winter than in summer owing to the eccentricity of the earth's orbit.

5. Explain the difference between the standard time belts and the time zones used at sea, and the reason for the difference.

6. When it is noon by Greenwich civil time, what are the standard times in each of the time belts of the United States?

7. When the standard time is $21^h 00^m$ on April 14 at a place whose longitude is 74° W., the Greenwich civil time is $2^h 00^m$ on April 15. Show by means of a time diagram that this is true.

8. Why is the actual position of a plane at a particular time likely to differ from the dead reckoning position? In what conditions must the navigator depend entirely on the celestial bodies for the line of position?

9. Name the term employed in navigation that is associated with each of the following definitions:

(a) Speed of a plane in nautical miles an hour.
(b) Point on the earth where the sun is in the zenith.
(c) Locus of possible positions of a plane at a particular time.
(d) True position of plane as determined by sights.
(e) Angular distance of a star measured *westward* from the vernal equinox.

10. Explain how the navigator proceeds from the recorded time of his sight on a star to the calculated altitude and azimuth of the star.

11. Explain the following steps in the process of plotting a line of position after a sextant sight on a star:

(a) Dead reckoning or assumed position of plane.
(b) Azimuth line of star.
(c) Altitude intercept.
(d) Line of position.

12. Distinguish between a fix and a running fix.

PROBLEMS

1. The constellation Orion rises at about $23^h 30^m$ sidereal time on September 21. State the local civil time of its rising on that date; the sidereal and local civil times of its rising on November 21. Explain the answers.

Answers: About $23^h 30^m$; $23^h 30^m$; $19^h 30^m$.

2. When the hour angle of Arcturus (right ascension $14^h 13^m$) is $30° 0'$ on July 21, what are the sidereal and approximate local civil times?

Answers: $16^h 13^m$; $20^h 13^m$.

3. When it is Greenwich civil midnight on November 1, what are the local civil time and date at a place whose longitude is $9^h 22^m 40^s$ W.? What is the local apparent time (Table $3 \cdot I$)?

Answers: $14^h 37^m 20^s$ October 31; $14^h 53^m 39^s$.

4. A plane on course 260° is about to cross the international date line at zone time 0840 May 22. Required zone time and date ten minutes later, after the crossing; the GCT and date.

Answers: 0850 May 23; 2050 May 22.

5. A plane is in DR latitude $41° 15'$ N., longitude $41° 45'$ W. At zone time $5^h 37^m 26^s$ October 28, 1944, a sextant sight is taken on the planet Jupiter with the result: $H_o = 34° 51'$. Required: (a) calculated altitude, H_c, altitude intercept, a, and azimuth, Z_n, for assumed position of plane. Use extracts from *Air Almanac* (Table $3 \cdot II$) and H.O. 214 (Table $3 \cdot III$); (b) latitude and longitude of assumed position.

Answers: (a) $H_c = 34° 47'$; $a = 4$ miles toward; $Z_n = 117°.5$; (b) $aL = 41°$; $a\lambda = 42° 02'$.

6. A second sight on the star Procyon is made simultaneously from the same plane with the result: $H_o = 58° 05'$. Required the data similar to those in Problem 5.

Answers: (a) $H_c = 58° 15'$; $a = 10$ miles away; $Z_n = 196°.8$; (b) $aL = 41°$; $a\lambda = 41° 50'$.

7. Draw astronomical triangles (3·24) to represent the hour angles, declinations, and latitudes in the solutions of Problems 5 and 6 in order to check the resulting azimuths.

8. On a Mercator chart similar to that of Fig. 3·26 represent the two lines of position and the fix resulting from the sights of Problems 5 and 6. How is the fix related to the DR position of the plane?

Answer: The fix is 6 miles in the direction 223° from the DR position.

CHAPTER IV

LIGHT AND THE TELESCOPE

REFRACTION OF LIGHT — THE REFRACTING TELESCOPE — THE RE-
FLECTING TELESCOPE — SPECTRUM ANALYSIS

REFRACTION OF LIGHT

4·1. Light as Wave Motion. The wave theory of light supposes that
the energy which causes it radiates in waves from a source such as a
lamp or the sun in something like the way that ripples spread over the
surface of a pond when a stone is dropped into the water. When these
waves of different lengths enter the eye, they produce the group of sen-
sations we designate as the different colors of light. It is more often
convenient to define light as the wave motion itself.

The *wave length* of the light is the distance between the same phase
of successive waves, as from crest to crest; it ranges from somewhat less
than 4×10^{-5} cm, or about $1/70,000$ inch, for violet light to nearly
twice that length for the reddest light we can see.

The *velocity of light* is 186,300 miles a second, or about 3×10^{10}
cm/sec. This is its speed in a vacuum. The speed is reduced in a
medium such as air or glass, depending on the density of the medium;
and in the same medium the reduction is greater for shorter wave
lengths than for longer ones.

The *frequency* of the light is the number of waves emitted by the
source in a second; it equals the velocity of light divided by the wave
length. Thus the frequency of violet light having the wave length
4×10^{-5} cm is 7.5×10^{14} cycles.

The sensation of light is produced by only a small part of the total
radiation that emerges from a source. Radiation goes on in a far wider
range of wave lengths than the eye can detect. All radiation has the
constant "velocity of light" in empty space.

4·2. Refraction of Light. A *"ray of light"* denotes the direction in
which any portion of the wave system is moving. It is often convenient

to picture rays of light as radiating in all directions from the source and continuing always in straight lines as long as they remain in the same homogeneous medium. Thus light is said to travel in straight lines.

When a ray of light passes from a rarer to a denser medium, as from air into glass, it proceeds through the denser medium with reduced speed. If the ray falls obliquely on the surface of the glass, the part of each wave crest on one side of the "ray" enters the glass and has its speed reduced before the other side enters. The crest is therefore swung around and the ray changes direction (Fig. 4·2). The parallel lines in the Figure represent the progress of a wave crest in equal intervals of time.

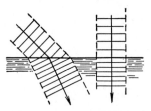

FIG. 4·2. Refraction of Light. A ray of light passing from a rarer into a denser medium is refracted toward the perpendicular.

Refraction of light is the change in the direction of a ray of light when it passes from one medium into another of different density. The change is generally *toward the perpendicular to the boundary if the second medium is the denser, and away from the perpendicular if it is the less dense.*
When the ray enters the second medium at right angles to its surface, there is no refraction; for all parts of the wave crest enter and are retarded together.

We now consider some effects of refraction by the earth's atmosphere and the lenses of telescopes.

4·3. Refraction Increases the Altitude of a Star. As a ray of starlight enters the atmosphere, it is refracted downward according to the rule just given; and the bending continues until the earth's surface is reached, because the density of the air increases downward. The point in the sky from which the light appears to come is therefore above the star's true direction. Atmospheric refraction elevates the celestial bodies by amounts which depend on the distance from the zenith.

Zenith Distance	Refraction	Zenith Distance	Refraction
0°	0′ 00″	85°	9′ 45″
20	0 21	86	11 37
40	0 48	87	14 13
60	1 40	88	18 06
70	2 37	89	24 22
80	5 16	90	34 50

These values for average conditions are somewhat altered by variations in the temperature and pressure of the air.

A star directly overhead is not displaced by refraction, because its rays are perpendicular to the atmospheric layers. The amount of the refraction increases as the distance from the zenith increases, but so slowly at first that for considerably more than half way to the horizon the effect on a star's direction is appreciable only with the telescope. As

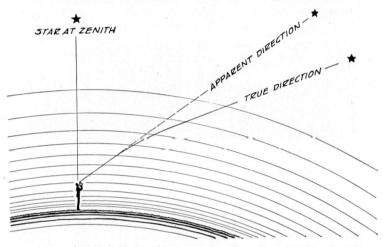

STAR AT ZENITH

APPARENT DIRECTION

TRUE DIRECTION

FIG. 4·3. Atmospheric Refraction Increases the Star's Altitude. Since the starlight is bent down in passing through the air, the star is apparently elevated. A star in the zenith is not displaced by refraction.

the horizon is approached, the effect becomes rapidly more noticeable. A star at the horizon is raised by refraction more than half a degree, or slightly more than the apparent diameter of the sun, or moon.

4·4. Refraction Effects Near the Horizon. Owing to atmospheric refraction the sun comes fully into view in the morning before any part of it would otherwise appear above the horizon, and it remains visible in the evening after it would otherwise have passed below the horizon. Thus refraction lengthens the daily duration of sunshine. Similarly, the risings of the moon and stars are hastened and their settings are delayed. Refraction also increases by more than half a degree the radius of the region around the north celestial pole whose stars never set, and diminishes by the same amount the opposite region whose stars never rise (1·15).

Since atmospheric refraction increases with increasing distance from the zenith, the lower edge of the sun's disk is raised more than the upper edge. This apparent vertical contraction of the sun becomes noticeable near the horizon, because it is there that the amount of the refraction increases most rapidly with increasing zenith distance (4·3). Sometimes the sun appears so conspicuously oval when it is near the

FIG. 4·4. Flattening of Setting Sun by Refraction. (*Photographed at Yerkes Observatory*)

horizon that even the casual observer remarks on its resemblance to a football.

Another effect near the horizon has no connection with refraction. It is the well-known illusion that the sun, moon, and constellation figures seem magnified when they are near the horizon.

4·5. Twinkling of the Stars. The *twinkling,* or scintillation, of the stars, that is to say, their very rapid fluctuations in apparent brightness, results from the continual turmoil in the atmosphere near the earth's surface. Vertical currents and horizontal movements of layers differing in temperature and water content produce varying irregularities in the density of the air through which the rays of starlight pass. Two factors contribute to the twinkling: first, the *variable refraction* of the rays; at any point they may be focused at one instant and spread out at the next. The second factor is *interference* of the light, which may result either in the reinforcement or else in the destruction of the rays so focused. Thus starlight comes to us non-uniformly, just as sunlight gathers in dancing patches at the bottom of a brook. Stars near the horizon are likely to twinkle most noticeably.

Ordinarily the large planets do not twinkle; their steady light distinguishes them from neighboring stars. Similarly, the moon does not twinkle, nor does a street light that is close at hand. The planets, like the moon, are luminous disks, although a telescope is required to show them as such. While each point of the disk may twinkle, the effects are not synchronized; for the rays from different points of the disk take slightly different paths through the air and do not encounter the same irregularities. Thus the planet's light maintains a fairly steady average brightness.

THE REFRACTING TELESCOPE

4·6. Refraction by Simple Lenses. Lenses are generally of two kinds: converging lenses, which are thicker at the center than at the edge, and

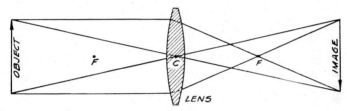

FIG. 4·6. The Simple Lens as an Objective. The lens produces an inverted real image of the object.

diverging lenses, which are thinner at the center. An example of the former is the double convex lens, two of whose important uses are to form a real image of an object and to serve as a magnifying glass.

The *focal length* of the lens is the distance from the center, *C*, to the *principal focus, F* (Fig. 4·6), where parallel rays of light are focused by the lens. When the object is farther from the lens than the prin-

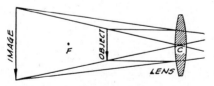

FIG. 4·6A. The Simple Lens as an Eyepiece. It produces an erect and enlarged virtual image.

cipal focus, the lens produces an inverted real image of the object, which may be shown on a screen or photographic plate. As will be noticed in the Figure, rays passing through the center of a thin lens are unchanged in direction.

When the object is nearer the lens than the principal focus, the eye behind the lens sees an erect and enlarged virtual image of the object

(Fig. 4·6A). This is the use of the lens as a magnifying glass. In combination, two double convex lenses can form a refracting telescope. The first lens is the *objective* of the telescope, which forms an inverted image of the object. The second lens, *the eyepiece,* placed at the proper distance behind that image, permits the eye to view the object, which now appears magnified and still inverted. Two other lenses can be added at the eye end to reinvert the image.

4·7. The Refracting Telescope.
The discovery of the principle of the telescope is generally credited to a Dutch spectacle maker. Galileo, in 1609, was one of the first to apply this principle in the observation of

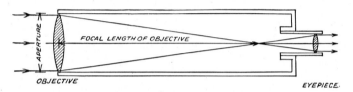

FIG. 4·7. The Simple Refracting Telescope. In its simplest form the refracting telescope consists of two convex lenses whose separation equals the sum of their focal lengths. In modern refracting telescopes both objective and eyepiece are compound lenses.

the celestial bodies. Two of his telescopes are preserved intact in the Galileo Museum in Florence, Italy; the larger one, having a paper tube about four feet long and less than two inches in diameter, magnifies 32 times. The Galilean telescope has a double concave eyepiece; it has the merit of giving an erect image of the object observed, but its field of view is small.

The simple astronomical telescope, which is the basis of modern refracting telescopes, contains two double convex lenses whose distance apart equals the sum of their focal lengths (Fig. 4·7). The objective has the greater *aperture,* or clear diameter, and the longer focal length; it receives the parallel rays from each point of the remote celestial object and forms an inverted image of the object at the principal focus. The eyepiece, set in a sliding tube, serves as a magnifying glass for viewing the image produced by the objective. As he looks through it, the observer sees an inverted and enlarged image of the celestial object.

The early refracting telescopes proved disappointing, especially as larger telescopes were constructed. The view of the celestial bodies was blurred. An important cause of the poor definition and the means by which it is partly eliminated in modern telescopes will now be considered.

4·8. Dispersion of Light; Chromatic Aberration. Whenever light is refracted, it is also separated into its constituent colors. An example is seen in the rainbow that is formed when sunlight is refracted by drops of water. Refraction, as we have seen, is caused by the change in speed of the light when it passes from one medium to another of different density. But the reduction in speed in the denser medium becomes greater with diminishing wave length of the light. Thus the amount of the refraction varies with the wave length; violet light is changed in direction the most and red the least. Refraction of light is accompanied by its *dispersion* in order of wave length, or color.

When light is focused by a single lens, the different colors are accordingly brought to focus at different distances from the lens, violet light at the least distance and red light farthest away. The image of a star formed in any particular color is confused by out-of-focus images in the other colors. This is *chromatic aberration*. As long as the telescope contained only single lenses, the only known way to improve the view was to lengthen the telescope. Toward the end of the seventeenth century, refracting telescopes as long as 150 and 200 feet were attempted; but they were so unwieldy that not much could be done with them.

4·9. The Achromatic Telescope. The new era of the refracting telescope began in 1758 with the introduction of the achromatic objective.

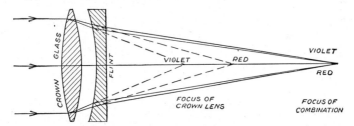

FIG. 4·9. Principle of the Achromatic Objective. The crown lens focuses the different colors at different distances, so that a clear image of the star is not obtained anywhere. The addition of the flint lens increases the focal length, and, since it affects the violet more than the red light, brings the different colors to focus at more nearly the same point.

By an appropriate combination of lenses of different curvatures and compositions it is possible to unite a limited range of colors, but not all of them, at the same focus. The majority of present telescope objectives are combinations of two lenses. The upper lens is double convex and of crown glass; the lower lens, either cemented to the upper one or separated by an air space, is likely to be plano-concave and is of heavier, flint glass. By the use of two lenses other difficulties inherent in the use of single spherical lenses may be compensated as well.

The average modern refracting telescope brings together the yellow and adjacent colors, to which the eye is specially sensitive. But it cannot focus with them the deep red, or the blue and violet light which most strongly affects the ordinary photographic plate. Evidence of this is seen in the purple fringe around the image of the moon, especially when it is viewed with a large telescope. Thus a refracting telescope giving fine definition visually does not produce clear photographs.

The aperture, or clear diameter of the objective, is usually stated in denoting the size of a telescope. Thus a 12-inch telescope has an objective with an aperture of 12 inches. In ordinary refracting telescopes the ratio of aperture to focal length is about 1 to 15, so that a 12-inch telescope is likely to be about 15 feet long.

When the refracting telescope is used as a camera, the photographic plate is exposed at or near the focal point of the objective. If the telescope was intended for visual purposes, a correcting lens is introduced a short distance before the plate, or else a yellow filter to transmit only the light that can be sharply focused. Some refracting telescopes, such as the 30-inch refractor of the Allegheny Observatory, are intended for photography; the objectives are designed to give clear images in blue and violet light.

For photography of large areas of the sky, the ratio of aperture to focal length must be as great as possible. Special telescopes are designed for this purpose, whose objectives have more than two lenses.

THE REFLECTING TELESCOPE

4·10. Reflection from Curved Mirrors. When a ray of light encounters a polished surface that prevents its further progress in the

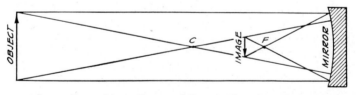

FIG. 4·10. Image Formed by a Concave Mirror. The mirror forms an inverted real image of an object beyond its center of curvature.

original direction, the ray bounds back from, or is *reflected* by, the surface. If the mirror is appropriately curved, it forms an image of an object, taking the place of a lens. Consider, for example, a concave spherical mirror (Fig. 4·10), having its center of curvature at *C* and its principal focus at *F*. Of any object beyond *C* the mirror forms an inverted real image which may be viewed on a screen or with an eyepiece. Thus the mirror can serve as the objective of a telescope.

The mirror has the advantage over the lens of being perfectly achromatic; there is no dispersion when light is reflected. But the spherical mirror, in greater degree than the spherical lens, introduces *spherical aberration;* the focal point is not the same for different parts of the mirror. This effect is seen in the caustic curve formed on the surface of the cup of coffee by light reflected from the sides of the cup. The perfect remedy for spherical aberration is to make the mirror paraboloidal instead of spherical.

There are several other reasons why the objectives of very large telescopes are mirrors rather than lenses. (1) It is easier to make a disk of glass for a mirror, because the light does not go through the glass. Striae and other defects in the disk, which would render it useless as a lens, do not make it unfit for use as a mirror. (2) The optician has to figure only one surface instead of four. (3) The entire back of the mirror can be supported, while the lens can be supported only at its edge; a large lens may bend slightly under its own weight, affecting its figure and therefore its performance. (4) The focal length of the mirror can conveniently be made less than that of the lens (the ratio of aperture to focal length of the mirror is often about 1 to 5), so that mounting and dome may be smaller, with reduction in the cost of construction.

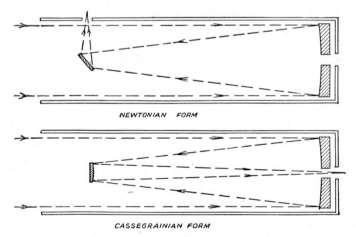

NEWTONIAN FORM

CASSEGRAINIAN FORM

FIG. 4·11. The Reflecting Telescope in Two Forms. The objective is a concave mirror which reflects the light to focus. In the Newtonian form the converging beam is diverted to the side of the tube by a small diagonal plane mirror. In the Cassegrainian form it is reflected by a small convex mirror through the central aperture in the large mirror to focus below it.

4·11. The Reflecting Telescope. The objective of the reflecting telescope is a concave mirror at the lower end of the tube, which receives
the light of the star and reflects it to the focus near the top of the tube.
The objective is a circular block of glass having its front surface ground
to a parabolic curvature and coated with metal such as silver or alumi-

FIG. 4·11A. The Mirror of the 100-inch Telescope of the Mount Wilson Observatory, After Aluminizing.

num. The light does not pass through the glass, which serves simply to
support and to give the required shape to the metal surface. But the
image formed by the large mirror is in the middle of the tube, where
it cannot be viewed without obstructing the incoming light. The two
types of reflecting telescope in common use employ different devices for
diverting the focus to a convenient place.

In the *Newtonian* form a small plane mirror at an angle of 45° near
the top of the telescope receives the converging beam before it comes
to focus, and reflects it to an eyepiece outside the tube, at right angles
to the direction of the star.

In the *Cassegrainian* form a small *secondary* convex mirror receives the converging beam from the large mirror, and reflects it back again through an opening in the large mirror to the eyepiece below it. In this form the observer looks in the direction of the star, as with the refracting telescope. In the great telescopes of the Mount Wilson Observatory the large mirrors have no openings. The returning light is reflected to the side by a third mirror set diagonally in front of the large mirror. Most reflecting telescopes can be used in either the Newtonian or Cassegrainian form.

4·12. The Schmidt Telescope. The type of reflecting telescope described in the preceding Section is not suitable for the photography of

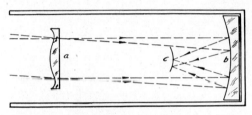

FIG. 4·12. Optical System of the Schmidt Telescope. The starlight passes through the correcting lens, *a,* before it is reflected by the spherical mirror, *b,* to focus on the curved photographic plate, *c.*

large areas of the sky. Aside from a small area of good definition the images deteriorate rapidly with increasing distance from the optical axis. The design of a wide-angle type, devised by an optical worker at the Hamburg Observatory in Germany, was made available in 1936. The objective is a spherical mirror which by itself cannot bring parallel rays to focus; the rays reflected by the middle of the mirror are focused farther from the mirror than the rays reflected from its outer zones. The correction is effected by a thin lens placed at the center of curvature of the mirror. This lens, which may have several different forms, slightly diverges the outer part of the beam of light with respect to the middle, so that all parts are brought to the same focus by the mirror.

With this type of telescope a considerable area of the sky can be brought to focus on a slightly curved photographic plate. The lens is so thin that it introduces no appreciable chromatic aberration. The focal ratio can be made so small that the instrument is photographically "fast."

An example is the 24-inch telescope of the Warner and Swasey Observatory, Cleveland. The lens is 0.3 inch in thickness. The mirror is 36 inches in diameter. This telescope can photograph a field five degrees in diameter, and can reach stars fainter than the 18th magnitude with an exposure of only nine minutes.

4·13. The Equatorial Mounting. Most telescopes are mounted so that they can turn on two axes to follow the circles of the equatorial system.

Fɪɢ. 4·13. The 36-inch Telescope of the Lick Observatory. This telescope, nearly sixty feet long, is equatorially mounted. The entire floor of the dome can be raised or lowered to a height convenient for observation.

The *polar axis* is parallel to the earth's axis and is therefore inclined to the horizontal at an angle equal to the latitude of the place. Around this axis the telescope is turned parallel to the celestial equator and so along the diurnal circle of the star. The *declination axis* is supported by the polar axis; around it the telescope is turned along an hour circle, from one declination to another.

Each axis carries a graduated circle. The one on the polar axis denotes the hour angle of the star toward which the telescope is pointing. In addition, there is often a dial on the pier, from which the right ascension of the star can be read directly. The circle on the declination axis is graduated in degrees of declination. With the aid of these circles the telescope can be quickly pointed toward a celestial object whose right ascension and declination are known. The telescope is then made to follow that object in its diurnal motion by the driving mechanism which is operated either mechanically or electrically.

In the standard type of equatorial mounting for refracting telescopes (Fig. 4·13), the polar axis is at the top of a single pier and the telescope must frequently be reversed from one side of the pier to the other. In the type used for most of the large reflecting telescopes the long polar axis is supported by two piers between which the telescope can swing from the east to the west horizon without reversal.

4·14. Light-Gathering Power. The brightness of the image of a star in the telescope increases in proportion to the area of the objective, or the square of its diameter. This defines the light-gathering power of the telescope, aside from the loss of light in the optical parts. Thus a star appears a hundred times as bright with the 100-inch telescope as with a 10-inch telescope, and 250,000 times as bright as with the eye alone, if we suppose the free aperture of the eye to be one fifth of an inch in diameter. By the concentration of the light, many stars become visible in the telescope which shine too feebly to be seen with the naked eye. Still fainter stars can be photographed by the cumulative effect of long exposures. By means of the driving clock and judicious manipulations of slow motions for slight adjustments, the telescope can be made to follow a star accurately, often for many hours, while the plate is being exposed.

It is easy to show that the surface brightness of an extended luminous area, such as the moon's surface, cannot be increased by the telescope. The light of the sky is no brighter than it appears to the eye alone. Since the light of a star is concentrated, it is possible to see the brighter stars with the telescope in the daytime.

4·15. Magnifying Power of the Telescope. The *linear scale of the image* formed by the objective increases with the focal length of the objective. Telescopes of long focus are best for observing the details of a planet's surface, or for separating very close double stars.   The *apparent size of the object* that is being observed depends also on the distance of the eye from the image.   The least distance of distinct vision for the normal eye is about 10 inches.   With the eyepiece the eye can be brought closer to the image, which accordingly appears larger.   *The magnifying power of a telescope is the focal length of the objective divided by the focal length of the eyepiece.*   If, for example, the focal length of the objective is 180 inches, and that of the eyepiece is a half inch, the object is magnified 360 times.

A telescope is usually equipped with eyepieces of different focal lengths, so that the magnification can be varied as desired.   The highest powers are useful only when atmospheric conditions are especially good; for unsteadiness of the image is magnified as well as the image itself. For this and other reasons, even under the best conditions there is little to be gained by increasing the magnification beyond fifty times for each inch of the aperture, and lower powers are usually more satisfactory. While the sun, moon, and planets appear larger with the telescope, no amount of magnification with present telescopes can show the *real* disk of a star.

4·16. Resolving Power.   The image of a star, or any other luminous point, is spread by *diffraction* of light in the telescope into a tiny disk which is brightest at the center, and is surrounded by faint concentric rings.   Two stars which are closer together than the diameter of the "spurious" disk cannot be separated by any amount of magnification. The *resolving power* of a telescope is the angular distance between two stars that can be just separated under the best conditions.   The least distance, d, in seconds of arc, is related to the aperture of the telescope, a, in inches, by the expression: $d'' = 4''.56/a$.   Thus with a $4\frac{1}{2}$-inch telescope a double star cannot be resolved if the separation is less than $1''$. With the 36-inch Lick refractor the minimum resolvable separation is $0''.13$, although double stars having somewhat smaller separations can sometimes be detected by the slight elongation of their images.

Aside from its ability to show fainter objects, the large telescope has the advantage of higher resolving power; it can show finer detail which runs together in the smaller instrument.   On the other hand, the blurring of the image by atmospheric disturbances is more pronounced in the large telescope.   In order to profit by the greater resolving power of the larger instrument, its site must be carefully chosen with respect to steadiness of the air.

The correctness of the formula for two stars of nearly equal brightness has been demonstrated by observations with telescopes of various apertures. For the eye alone the formula does not hold; it gives the resolving power as about $20''$, but the least separation the eye can resolve is several times greater. In fact, the eye is said to be a good one if it can separate the two stars of Epsilon Lyrae, which are $207''$ apart. The difference is ascribed to the coarse structure of the retina of the eye.

4·17. Value of the Telescope. As the fundamental instrument of astronomical research the telescope has many important uses, some of which we have already noted. It concentrates the light from a celestial body, forming a bright image which can be viewed and magnified with an eyepiece, or else photographed. The magnification and resolving power of the telescope permit observations of details of the sun, moon, planets, and other bodies, the separation of satellites from their·planets, and of star clouds into their individual stars. Owing to the enlarged scale the positions and motions of the celestial bodies can be determined more accurately than with the eye alone.

In addition to the direct study of the object, either visually or photographically, an important use of the telescope is to direct the concentrated light into special physical instruments, such as the spectroscope, photometer, and radiometer. Large telescopes are usually provided with a variety of auxiliary apparatus which can be attached at the eye end, or in some cases, as with the interferometer and objective prism, in front of the objective. Descriptions of a number of these instruments will be given in connection with the kind of investigation that each one promotes.

4·18. Great Telescopes. The 200-inch telescope on Mount Palomar will be the largest telescope in the world. Next in order are the 100-inch telescope of the Mount Wilson Observatory and the 82-inch telescope of the McDonald Observatory on Mount Locke in Texas. The 74-inch telescope of the Dunlap Observatory, near Toronto, the 74-inch telescope of the Radcliffe Observatory, near Pretoria, and the 72-inch telescope of the Dominion Astrophysical Observatory, Victoria, complete for the moment the list of giant telescopes six feet or more in diameter. All are reflecting telescopes.

Refracting telescopes have more moderate apertures. The largest are the 40-inch telescope of the Yerkes Observatory and the 36-inch telescope of the Lick Observatory. In addition, more than a dozen refracting telescopes have apertures of 25 inches or over; they are widely scattered geographically.

FIG. 4·18. Dome of the 100-inch Telescope of the Mount Wilson Observatory. The dome is 100 feet in diameter. It can be turned completely around, so that the telescope may look out in any direction. The top of the telescope is visible through the opened shutter.

4·19. The 100-inch Telescope. The objective of the great telescope on Mount Wilson is a circular block of glass 101 inches in diameter and 13 inches thick, weighing 4½ tons; the upper surface is concave and aluminized, having a focal length of 42 feet. The mirror is placed at the lower end of the skeleton tube which is characteristic of large reflecting telescopes. The tube is turned in declination in the massive yoke which forms the polar axis. The movable parts of the telescope weigh about 100 tons. A powerful driving clock moves the telescope around the polar axis to follow the stars in their diurnal motions. The telescope is supported by a concrete pier 52 feet wide at the top. When the mirror requires attention, the cell which holds it is detached from the tube and lowered by elevator into the room within the pier. The dome is 100 feet in diameter. The various motions of telescope, dome, shutters, and observing platforms are operated by motors, forty or more in all, which are controlled from a switchboard.

When photographs are taken with this telescope, the plate can be exposed in any one of four places: (1) directly at the focus of the objective, at the center of the tube near the upper end; (2) at the Newtonian focus, at the side of the tube near the upper end; (3) at the Cassegrainian focus, at the side of the tube near the lower end; and (4)

FIG. 4·19. The 100-inch Telescope of the Mount Wilson Observatory. The largest telescope in operation. It has an equatorial mounting of the English type. When the telescope is used in the Cassegrainian form, the observer occupies the platform to the left near the floor; the platform for the Newtonian form appears near the upper right corner of the picture.

in the laboratory to which the light is directed along the polar axis. This telescope is employed primarily in investigations of the stars, nebulae, and extragalactic systems by direct photography and with the aid of auxiliary apparatus, such as the spectrograph, thermocouple, and photoelectric cell.

4·20. The 200-inch Telescope of the California Institute of Technology is situated on Mount Palomar in southern California. It is housed in

FIG. 4·20. The 200-inch Reflecting Telescope. As it will appear when it is in operation on Mount Palomar in California. (*From a drawing by Russell W. Porter*)

a dome 135 feet in diameter. The telescope tube, 55 feet long and 20 feet across, moves in declination within a yoke which forms the polar axis. One of its novel features is that the observers will "ride the tube"; they will be carried by the telescope itself, either at the Cassegrainian focus below the mirror or at the principal focus in the upper end of the tube.

The great mirror is a circular disk of Pyrex glass nearly 17 feet in diameter and 2 feet in thickness, its concave upper surface coated with aluminum. The back of the disk is cast in a geometrical rib pattern, so that no part of the glass is more than two inches from the outside air. The weight of the glass is thereby reduced from 30 to 16 tons.

SPECTRUM ANALYSIS

Three factors have entered prominently in the progress of modern astronomy. They are: (1) The development of the telescope; (2) The greatly increased sensitiveness and range of the photographic plate; (3) The application of spectrum analysis to astronomical inquiry. While the uses of spectrum analysis will be encountered more often in our later studies of the sun, stars, and nebulae, its important contributions to knowledge of the planetary bodies will not be overlooked. A preliminary account of the spectroscope and what it does will be required, and this is as good a place as any to introduce it.

When a beam of light passes obliquely from one medium to another, as from air into a glass prism, the light is refracted and also dispersed to form a *spectrum*.

4·21. The Spectroscope. A familiar type of spectroscope consists of a prism of glass, quartz, or other transparent material, toward which two small telescopes are directed. The light enters the first telescope through a narrow *slit*, between the sharpened parallel edges of two metal plates. The slit is at the focus of the objective of this telescope, the *collimator*, so that the rays are parallel as they enter the *prism*. The light is refracted by the prism and dispersed into a spectrum, which is observed with the second telescope, the *view telescope*. Often the eyepiece of this telescope is replaced by a plate holder, so that the spectrum can be photographed.

If the light is monochromatic, the spectrum is simply the image of the slit in that particular color; if it is white light, composed of all colors, the spectrum is a band, violet at one end and red at the other, which is formed by overlapping images of the slit in the different colors. The absence of a particular wave length in the white light can be detected in the spectrum most easily when the separate images are so narrow that they overlap as little as possible. This is the reason for the narrow slit.

Thus the spectroscope is an instrument for analyzing light into its constituent colors.   Bright lines in the spectrum represent the presence of particular wave lengths in the light.   Dark lines show the absence

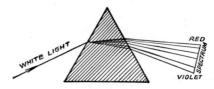

FIG. 4·21.   Formation of a Spectrum by a Prism.

of particular wave lengths, a circumstance that could otherwise entirely escape notice.   Integrated sunlight is like a set of books in many volumes piled in disorder.   But the spectrum of the light is like the set

FIG. 4·21A.   The Spectroscope.   (*By courtesy of Adam Hilger, Ltd.*)

arranged in order on a shelf; if a volume is withdrawn, the vacant space bears witness to the fact.

When the light is bright enough to be spread further, the scale of the spectrum can be increased by substituting for the single prism a train of prisms, or else a *grating;* this is a plate of speculum metal or transparent substance, on which many fine parallel grooves are ruled, perhaps 10,000 or more to the inch.   The grating forms the spectrum by the diffraction of light.   Its greatest use in astronomy has been in the study of the sun, where its wastefulness of the light, as compared with the prism, is of no consequence.   A new type of grating by R. W. Wood concentrates most of the light in one side of one order and is now preferred to the prism for many purposes.

4·22. Three Kinds of Spectra.   The spectra of all luminous bodies are of three kinds:

The bright-line spectrum is a succession of colored lines on a dark background.   The source of light is a glowing gas which radiates in a limited number of wave lengths characteristic of the chemical element of which the gas is composed.   Each gaseous element under the same conditions emits its particular selection of wave lengths, and can therefore be identified by the pattern of lines of its spectrum. A glowing neon tube, for example, produces a bright-line spectrum.

The continuous spectrum is a continuous array of colored light from violet to red. The source is a luminous solid or liquid; or it may be a gas so highly ionized that it cannot emit light selectively. The glowing filament of a lamp produces a continuous spectrum. Evidently this kind of spectrum tells nothing about the chemical composition of the source.

The dark-line spectrum is a spectrum that is continuous except where it is interrupted by dark lines. Cooler gas intervenes between

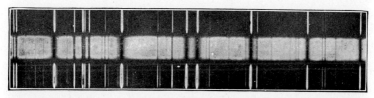

FIG. 4·22. Bright and Dark-Line Spectrum. A portion of the spectrum of an exploding iron wire. (*Photograph by J. A. Anderson, Mount Wilson Observatory*)

the source of the continuous spectrum and the observer. This intervening gas is opaque to precisely the wave lengths it emits under the same conditions. The spectrum is therefore the reverse of that of the gas itself; it is a pattern of dark lines which identifies the chemical composition of the gas. Sunlight produces a dark-line spectrum. This light has passed through the atmospheres of both the sun and the earth.

Spectra in which the lines are grouped in *bands* characterize some gases whose constituents are molecular, as in chemical compounds. Carbon dioxide and methane are examples of compounds that produce band spectra.

4·23. The Solar Spectrum. The visible solar spectrum is an array of colors from violet to red interrupted by thousands of dark lines. They are sometimes known as the *Fraunhofer lines* in honor of their discoverer. The German optician Fraunhofer, in 1814, was the first to clearly distinguish these lines; he mapped several hundred with considerable accuracy and labeled the most prominent ones with letters of the alphabet, starting at the red end of the spectrum. Thus the pair close together in the yellow are the D lines. The significance of the lines remained unknown until 1859, when it was understood that they are wave lengths abstracted from sunlight chiefly by a layer of gases surrounding the sun.

These lines are designated by their wave lengths expressed in angstroms, with the prefix λ. One *angstrom* is 10^{-8} centimeter. Thus

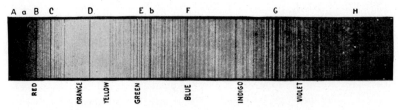

FIG. 4·23. Fraunhofer's Map of the Solar Spectrum.

λ4000 denotes a wave length of 4000 angstroms, or 4×10^{-5} cm. The visible part of the spectrum lies between about λ3900 and λ7500.

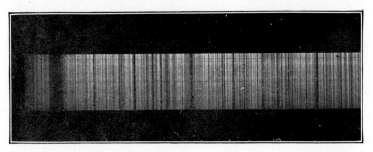

FIG. 4·23A. Part of the Solar Spectrum. The spectrum in the violet. The broad lines at the left are the H and K lines of calcium. (*Photographed at Allegheny Observatory*)

Some of the most conspicuous lines and bands in the visible part of the solar spectrum are the following:

Fraunhofer letter	Wave length	Identification
A	λ7594	oxygen (telluric)
B	6867	oxygen (telluric)
C	6563	hydrogen
D	5893	sodium (double)
E	5270	iron
F	4861	hydrogen
H	3969	calcium
K	3934	calcium

By far the strongest lines are the Fraunhofer H and K of calcium near the termination of the visible spectrum in the violet.

Not all the lines are of solar origin. There are also *telluric lines and bands* produced by absorption of sunlight in the earth's atmosphere. The Fraunhofer A and B are bands identified with terrestrial oxygen, and *a* with water vapor.

4·24. The Doppler Effect. When the source from which waves are spreading is approaching the observer, the distance between the wave crests reaching the observer is diminished and their frequency is increased. When the source is receding, the wave length is increased and the frequency is diminished. A familiar example in sound is the abrupt drop from the higher-pitched screech of the whistle of the approaching locomotive to the lower-pitched wail as it recedes. A similar effect can be noticed in the case of light. When the source of light is approaching the observer, the wave lengths become shorter, so that the lines in the spectrum of the source are displaced to the violet from their normal positions. When the source is receding, the wave lengths become longer, so that the lines are displaced to the red. Practically it does not matter whether it is the observer or the source that is moving. The *Doppler effect* as applied to the spectral lines is as follows:

When the source of light is relatively approaching or receding from the observer, the lines of its spectrum are displaced respectively toward the violet or red end by an amount proportional to the speed of approach or recession.

The amount of the displacement of a line in the spectrum is related to the relative speed of approach or recession as follows:

$$\frac{\text{change of wave length}}{\text{normal wave length}} = \frac{\text{relative speed}}{\text{speed of light}}.$$

If, for example, the source and observer are relatively approaching at the rate of 18.63 miles a second (remembering that the speed of light is 186,300 miles a second), the lines in the spectrum of the source are displaced to the violet a ten thousandth of their normal wave lengths. Thus a line at λ5000 is displaced 0.5 angstrom—an amount that can be easily observed.

4·25. Some Uses of Spectrum Analysis. The spectrum of a luminous celestial body gives information as to the *physical state* of that body. A bright-line spectrum is produced generally by tenuous gas, and a dark-line spectrum by gas intervening in the path of light. The pattern of lines identifies the *chemical composition* of the gas producing them.

The spectrum of a body such as the moon or a planet, which shines by reflected sunlight, tells nothing about the chemical composition of that body itself. But, if the planet has an atmosphere, any dark lines or bands in its spectrum which do not appear in the spectrum of direct sunlight can show something of the chemical constitution of that atmosphere.

The Doppler effect in the spectrum of a celestial body informs us about its *motion* in the line of sight, whether it is moving relatively toward or away from the earth, and how fast it is moving.   Other uses of spectrum analysis will be mentioned later.

REVIEW QUESTIONS

1. Now that we have noticed the effect of atmospheric refraction in increasing the altitudes of the stars, it is in order to reexamine some conclusions of Chapter I.   Modify the following statements:

(a) The duration of sunshine is 12 hours on days when the sun is at an equinox.
(b) The polar caps in which stars never rise or never set have radii equal to the observer's latitude.
(c) The midnight sun is visible only within the arctic circle.
(d) As seen from the north pole the celestial equator coincides with the horizon.

2. Distinguish between the refracting and the reflecting telescope.

3. Explain why the simple refracting telescope (having a single lens as an objective) gives blurred images.   How is the difficulty corrected in the achromatic objective?

4. Distinguish between the Newtonian and the Cassegrainian type of reflecting telescope.

5. In what respects does the Schmidt telescope differ from the types discussed in Question 4?   What advantage has this newer type over the older ones?

6. Why are all very large telescopes reflecting telescopes?

7. The following questions are frequently asked by visitors in the dome of the observatory.   How would you answer them?

(a) How much does the telescope magnify?
(b) How far can you see with it?
(c) How can you point the telescope to a star that is invisible to the naked eye?
(d) Why is this telescope better than a smaller one?
(e) What causes the color around the edge of the moon?
(f) Does the telescope magnify stars?

8. Describe what occurs when a beam of white light is passed through a glass prism.   Suppose that it is monochromatic red light instead.

9. Describe the appearance of (a) the continuous spectrum; (b) the bright-line spectrum; (c) the dark-line spectrum.   What is the nature of the source of light producing each kind of spectrum?

10. State and explain the effect in the spectrum when the source is approaching or receding from the observer.

PROBLEMS

1. The objective of a 12-inch telescope has a focal length of 15 feet. How much brighter does a star appear through this telescope than to the unaided eye?

Answer: 3600 times.

2. What is the magnifying power of this telescope with an eyepiece of one-inch focal length?

Answer: 180.

3. What is the theoretical resolving power of this telescope?

Answer: 0".38.

4. What is the diameter of the moon's image as photographed with this telescope?   (The moon's angular diameter is 0°.5.)

Answer: Diameter = 180 inches $\times$ 0.5/57.3 = slightly more than $1\frac{1}{2}$ inches.

5. A line at λ4000 in the spectrum of a star is displaced one angstrom to the red.   Calculate the star's velocity in the line of sight.

Answer: 46.6 miles a second, recession.

The 24-inch Schmidt-Type Telescope of Warner and Swasey Observatory, Cleveland.

CHAPTER V

THE MOON

MOTIONS OF THE MOON

The earth is accompanied in its revolution around the sun by its single satellite, the moon, whose diameter, 2160 miles, is a little more than one fourth the earth's diameter. Small as compared with the general run of visible celestial bodies, the moon nevertheless ranks sixth in size among all the satellites of the solar system. Moreover, it is larger and more massive in comparison with the earth than is any other satellite with respect to its primary. The earth-moon system has more nearly the characteristic of a double planet.

Next to the sun, the moon is the most conspicuous of the celestial bodies, owing to its small distance from the earth. The near equality in the apparent sizes of sun and moon arises from the interesting circumstance that the sun, while it is about 400 times as great in diameter as the moon, is also about that many times as far away.

5·1. Revolution of the Earth and Moon Around the Sun. The earth's revolution around the sun has been hitherto described without

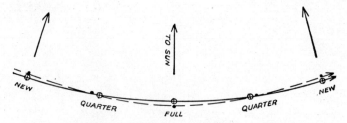

Fig. 5·1. Orbits of the Earth and Moon Around the Sun.

reference to the influence of the moon. Since these two bodies are moving together around the sun once in a year and mutually revolving

meanwhile once in a little less than a month, the orbit of each one relative to the sun has a slightly wavy character. What has been called the
earth's orbit is strictly the orbit of the center of mass of the earth-moon
system, around which the two make their monthly revolution. Imagine
them joined by a stout rod. The *center of mass* is the point of support
at which they would balance.

If the masses of the earth and moon were equal, the center of mass
would be halfway between their centers, and their orbits around the sun
would be identical, except that the waves would differ in phase by 180°,
so that the two bodies would be alternately within and without the
elliptical orbit of the center of mass. The moon's mass is in fact 1/81.56
of the earth's mass. The center of mass is therefore only 1/82.56 of
the way, or about 2900 miles, from the earth's center toward the moon,
and so is within the earth.

It is not an easy matter to show by means of a diagram (Fig. 5·1) the
paths of the earth and the moon around the sun. If the distance between
the earth and the sun is put equal to the length of this printed page, the distance between the earth and moon on the same scale scarcely exceeds the
diameter of one of the periods on the page. The reader is urged to be on
guard against being misled concerning the relative sizes and distances of
astronomical bodies by the limitations of the diagrams. A drawing exactly
to scale would show that *the paths of both the earth and moon are always
concave to the sun.*

5·2. The Moon's Orbit Relative to the Earth.

The moon's revolu-
tion may be considered in three ways: (1) Its annual revolution around the
sun, which is disturbed by the pres-
ence of the earth; (2) Its monthly
revolution around the center of mass
of the earth and moon, in which the
sun is a disturbing factor; or what
amounts to nearly the same thing in
this case: (3) Its monthly revolution with respect to the earth. It is
this relative motion with which we
are now concerned. The *orbit of
the moon,* for most purposes, is its
path around the earth—an ellipse of
small eccentricity, 0.055 on the average, with the earth at one focus.

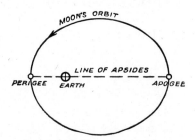

FIG. 5·2. The Moon's Orbit Relative to the Earth. The orbit is an
ellipse of small eccentricity (much
exaggerated in the Figure) with the
earth at one focus.

The moon's speed in its orbit averages somewhat more than half a
mile a second. By the law of equal areas (3·6), which applies to all

revolving celestial bodies, the speed is greatest at *perigee,* where the moon is nearest the earth, and is least at *apogee,* farthest from the earth. The major axis, or *line of apsides,* revolves eastward once in about nine years. This is only one of the many variations in the moon's orbit, which arise chiefly from the influence of the sun. The size of the orbit is determined by the moon's parallax.

5·3. Parallax; Relation to Distance. *Parallax* is the difference in direction of an object as seen from two places, or from the two ends of a *base line.* As an example of the parallax effect one may notice the

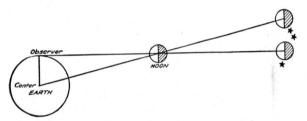

FIG. 5·3.   The Moon's Geocentric Parallax.   The horizontal parallax is about twice the moon's apparent diameter.

shifting of a near-by object against a distant background when the eyes are covered alternately. For the same base line the parallax becomes smaller as the distance of the object is increased. When the parallax of an object is measured, its distance may be calculated by the following relation:

$$\text{Distance} = \frac{\text{length of base line}}{\text{sine of parallax}},$$

supposing that the direction of the object is perpendicular to the base line as seen from one end of that line.

Here we have a means of measuring the distances of inaccessible objects such as the celestial bodies. The parallax of the relatively near-by moon can be determined by simultaneous observations of its positions among the stars from two places on the earth whose distance apart is known. Whatever stations are used, the observed parallax is standardized by calculating from it the parallax that would have resulted if the base line had been the earth's equatorial radius, and the moon had been on the horizon. This *equatorial horizontal parallax* is regarded as the *parallax* of the moon.

The relation between distance and parallax will be understood if it is remembered that the sine of an angle of a right triangle equals the length of the side opposite that angle divided by the length of the hypotenuse. The following example illustrates the relation:

Example: The moon's parallax at its mean distance from the earth is 57′ 2″.7. Required the mean distance.

$$\text{Distance} = \frac{\text{earth's equatorial radius}}{\text{sine of moon's parallax}} = \frac{3963.34 \text{ miles}}{0.016593}.$$

Answer: The moon's mean distance is 238,857 miles.

5·4. The Moon's Distance.

The moon's parallax at its mean distance from the earth is 57′ 2″.7, as has been said. This is also the apparent radius of the earth as viewed from the moon. Thus the earth fills an angle of two degrees in the lunar sky, or four times the moon's apparent diameter as we see it.

The mean distance between the centers of the earth and the moon is 238,857 miles, by our calculation, or about 60¼ times the earth's equatorial radius. The distance at perigee may be as small as 221,463 miles, while at apogee it may be as great as 252,710 miles.

5·5. Aspects of the Moon.

The *elongation* of the moon is its angular distance from the sun, measured east or west through 180°. Special values of the elongation receive distinctive names and are known as the *aspects* of the moon. The moon is in *conjunction* with the sun when these two bodies have the same celestial longitude; it is in *quadrature* when the difference in longitude is 90°, and in *opposition* when the difference is 180°. For the conjunctions of the planets with the moon and with one another the predicted times in the *American Ephemeris and Nautical Almanac* are the instants when the two bodies have the same right ascension.

5·6. The Moon's Phases.

The changing figures of the waxing and waning moon are among the most conspicuous of celestial phenomena, and were among the first to be understood. Like the earth, the moon is a dark globe shining only by reflected light. As the moon revolves around the earth, the sunlit hemisphere is presented to us in varying amounts. This is the cause of the phases.

At conjunction, when the moon is between the earth and the sun, the dark side is toward us and the phase is *new*. With increasing eastern elongation the illuminated hemisphere gradually comes into view; the phases are successively *crescent, first quarter,* near quadrature, *gibbous,* and finally *full*, when the moon arrives at opposition and the bright side faces fully toward us. The phases are then repeated in the reverse order with the same designations except that the phase near western quadrature is *last quarter*. The moon's *age* is the interval at any time since the preceding new moon.

The *terminator* is the line between the bright and dark sides of the moon; it is the sunrise line that we see before full moon, and the sunset line thereafter. Aside from irregularities in its course, which arise from

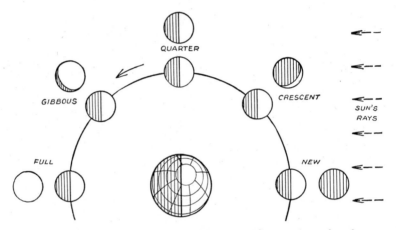

Fig. 5·6. The Phases of the Moon. The outer figures show the phases as seen from the earth.

the mountainous character of the lunar surface and which are often noticed without the telescope, the terminator is elliptical, because it is a circle seen in projection. The full circle coincides with the limb of the moon at the full phase, while at the quarter phases it is turned edgewise, appearing as a straight line.

The horns, or *cusps,* of the crescent moon point always away from the sun, whose direction is denoted by the perpendicular to the line joining the horns at its middle point. This is also nearly the course of the ecliptic in the moon's vicinity. It will be seen, therefore, that the positions of the crescent at moonrise and moonset depend on the angle between the ecliptic and horizon at those times (1·19). It is left to the reader to show that the horns of the crescent moon are most nearly vertical after sunset in the spring, and before sunrise in the autumn.

5·7. Earthlight on the Moon. The earth as viewed from the moon also exhibits the whole cycle of phases, and these are supplementary to the moon's phases. "Full earth" occurs at the time of new moon. Thus moonlight with us has its counterpart in earthlight on the moon. At the crescent phases the part of the lunar disk that is not in direct sunlight is made plainly visible by the sunlight reflected from the earth. Full earthlight on the moon is something like 40 times as bright as the

light of the full moon on the earth; for the earth is not only a larger mirror, but it is also a better one, since it reflects nearly one half of the light it receives from the sun.

The bright crescent, because of its greater brightness, appears to have a greater diameter than the earthlit part of the disk, and so to be wrapped around it. This illusion of the difference in scale of the two parts becomes more striking as the quarter phase is approached, although at this phase the earthlight has faded almost to invisibility.

Spectroscopic observations and photographs in different colors show that earthlight contains a greater percentage of blue light

FIG. 5·7. Earthlight on the Moon at the Crescent Phase in the Morning Sky. The bright crescent is lighted directly by the sun. The remainder of the moon's disk is illuminated by sunlight reflected from the earth. The planet Saturn appears near the moon. (*Photographed at Yerkes Observatory*)

than there is in direct sunlight. This result is not surprising, for a considerable part of the light is selectively reflected by the earth's atmosphere, and in this light the blue of the sky predominates.

5·8. Sidereal and Synodic Months. Astronomically, the month is the period of the moon's revolution. As in the cases of the day and year the different kinds of month arise from the different points to which the motion is referred. The *sidereal month* is the true period of the moon's revolution; it is the interval between successive conjunctions of the moon's center with the same star, as seen from the center of the earth. Its average length is $27^d 7^h 43^m 11^s.5$, or nearly $27\frac{1}{3}$ days, but it varies as much as seven hours owing to perturbations.

The *synodic month* is the interval between successive conjunctions of the moon and sun, from new moon to new moon again. This *month of the phases* is the period in which the moon gains a lap on the slower moving sun, and is therefore longer than the sidereal month. The average length of the synodic month is $29^d 12^h 44^m 2^s.8$, or a little more than $29\frac{1}{2}$ days; it varies, however, more than half a day.

Between the sidereal month, M, the synodic month, S, and the sidereal year, E, there is the simple relation: $1/M - 1/E = 1/S$. These reciprocals are mean daily motions. Thus the moon moves eastward among the constellations $360°/M$, or $13°.2$ daily; it gains on the sun $360°/S$, or $12°.2$ a day. In one hour it moves a little more than half a degree, or slightly more than its own diameter—a useful fact to remember.

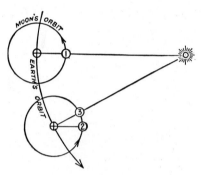

FIG. 5·8. The Synodic Month is Longer Than the Sidereal Month. Between positions 1 and 2 the moon has made one revolution, completing the sidereal month. The synodic month does not end until the moon has reached position 3.

5·9. The Moon Rises Later from Day to Day. When the eastward motion is considered, as we have just now done, the moon gains a lap on the sun in the course of a synodic month. But with respect to the diurnal motion the moon keeps falling behind the sun, so that it returns to upper transit 28.5 times in 29.5 solar days. The interval between upper transits is 29.5/28.5 times 24 hours, or about $24^h 50^m$ of mean solar time. Thus the moon transits 50 minutes later from day to day on the average.

The daily retardation of moonrise also averages about 50 minutes, but the actual retardation may differ greatly from this value, especially in high latitudes. In the latitude of New York the greatest possible delay may exceed the least by more than an hour. The variation depends chiefly on the angle between the moon's path, which is not far from the ecliptic, and the horizon; the smaller the angle at moonrise, the less is the delay in the rising from day to day. As we have already noticed (1·19), the ecliptic is least inclined to the horizon in northern latitudes when the vernal equinox rises. When the moon is near that point, its rising is least delayed, a circumstance that is especially conspicuous when the moon is also near its full phase.

5·10. The Harvest Moon is the full moon that occurs nearest the *time* of the autumnal equinox, September 23. Since the sun is then near the autumnal equinox, the full moon is near the vernal equinox, and is therefore in that part of its path which is least inclined to the horizon at moonrise. The peculiarity of the harvest moon, as distinguished from other occasions when the moon is near full, is its minimum delay in rising for a few nights. Thus there is bright moonlight in the early

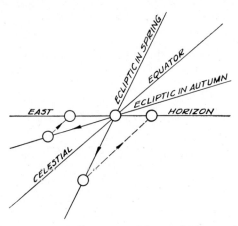

FIG. 5·10. Explanation of the Harvest Moon. Owing to the eastward motion along its path nearly coinciding with the ecliptic, the moon rises later from night to night. For the nearly full moon the delay is the least around September 23, in northern latitudes, because the ecliptic is the least inclined to the horizon at moonrise.

evening for an unusual number of evenings. This is true only in middle and higher northern latitudes.

5·11. The Moon's Apparent Path; Regression of the Nodes. The moon's path among the constellations may be determined by noticing the moon's position relative to the stars each night during the month, and recording the places on a suitable star map. Greater accuracy is obtained by use of the telescope, from whose circles the right ascension and declination may be read at each pointing; or these coordinates may be taken from the *Nautical Almanac* where they are tabulated at hourly intervals.

The moon's apparent path is nearly a great circle which is inclined about 5° to the ecliptic. It therefore intersects the ecliptic at two opposite *nodes*. The *ascending node* is the point where the moon crosses the ecliptic going north; the *descending node* is the point where it crosses going south.

Regression of the nodes is their westward displacement along the ecliptic, just as the equinoxes slide westward in their precessional motion, but at a much faster rate; for a complete revolution of the nodes is accomplished in 18.6 years. From this and other rapid changes in the moon's orbit, for which the sun's attraction is mostly responsible, the moon's apparent course among the constellations is considerably different from month to month.

5·12. The Moon's Range in Declination.

Since the moon's path on the celestial sphere departs only a little from the ecliptic, the moon

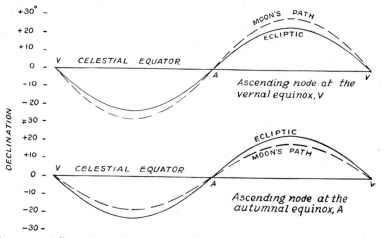

FIG. 5·12. Effect of Regression of the Nodes on the Moon's Range in Declination.

moves north and south during the month about as much as the sun does in the course of the year. Near the position of the summer solstice it rises in the northeast, sets in the northwest, and is high in the sky (in the northern hemisphere) at upper transit; near the winter solstice, about two weeks later, the moon rises in the southeast, sets in the southwest, and crosses the meridian at a lower altitude. An interesting example of the many compensations in nature is furnished by the full moon, which, being opposite the sun, rides highest in the long winter evenings and lowest in the summer.

When, however, the inclination of the moon's path to the ecliptic is taken into account, it appears that the range in declination varies perceptibly as the nodes regress. When the ascending node coincides with the vernal equinox, the moon's path is inclined to the celestial equator 23½° plus 5°, or 28½°; this will occur in 1950. Nine years earlier, when the ascending node coincided with the autumnal equinox, the inclination to the equator was $23\frac{1}{2}°$ minus $5°$, or $18\frac{1}{2}°$. Thus the moon's highest and lowest altitudes at upper transits in latitude $40°$ N. average in the first case $78\frac{1}{2}°$ and $21\frac{1}{2}°$ respectively, and in the second case $68\frac{1}{2}°$ and $31\frac{1}{2}°$—a decrease in range of about $20°$.

The variation of $10°$ in the moon's maximum declination in the 18.6-year cycle is chiefly responsible for nutation, the nodding of the earth's axis which accompanies its precessional motion.

5·13. The Moon's Rotation and Librations. *The moon rotates on its axis in the same period in which it revolves around the earth,* namely,

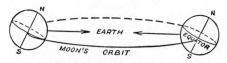

FIG. 5·13. The Moon's Libration in Latitude. Owing to the inclination of the moon's equator to the plane of its orbit, the poles of the moon are alternately presented to the earth.

the sidereal month of $27\frac{1}{3}$ days. In consequence of the equality of the two periods the moon presents nearly the same hemisphere toward the earth at all times. It is always the face of the "man in the moon" that we see at the full phase and never the back of his head. But an examination of the moon's surface throughout the month shows that features near the edge of the disk are turned sometimes into view and at other times out of sight. The moon seems to rock slightly; these apparent oscillations, or *librations,* arise from three causes:

(1) *The libration in latitude* results from the inclination of about $6\frac{1}{2}°$ between the moon's equator and the plane of its orbit. At intervals of two weeks the lunar poles are tipped alternately toward and away from us; at times we can see $6\frac{1}{2}°$ beyond the north pole, at others the same distance beyond the south pole. The explanation of this libration is similar to that of the seasons.

(2) *The libration in longitude* is brought about by the failure of the moon's rotation and revolution to keep exactly in step throughout the month, although they come out together at the end. The rotation, like the earth's, proceeds at a very nearly uniform rate; but the revolution is not uniform, because the moon's orbit is an ellipse, and the law of areas holds. Thus the moon seems to rock in an east and west direction, allowing us to see as much as $7\frac{3}{4}°$ farther around in longitude at each edge than we could otherwise.

(3) *The diurnal libration* is produced by the earth's rotation. Even
if the other librations were absent, so that the same hemisphere were
turned always toward the earth's center, we on the surface view the
moon from slightly different directions during the day, and therefore
see slightly different hemispheres. From the elevated position nearly
4000 miles above the center of the earth the observer can see, at most,

FIG. 5·13A. The Moon's Libration in Longitude. The prominent group of
seas is nearer the moon's limb in the picture at the right. (*From photographs
at the Paris Observatory, by courtesy of Carl Zeiss, Inc.*)

one degree farther over the western edge at moonrise, and the same
amount over the eastern edge at moonset.

These are the principal librations. When the sidereal month is completed, fully 59 per cent of the moon's surface has been visible. The
remaining 41 per cent is never seen; and throughout that region, of
course, the earth would always be invisible to lunar observers.

THE MOON'S SURFACE FEATURES

The unaided eye can discern only the dark areas of the moon's surface, which are known as the lunar seas, and occasional irregularities of

the terminator, which suggest that the moon is mountainous. The telescope shows the mountains themselves and other details of the moonscape as well. The mountains are clearest near the terminator, either
the sunrise or sunset line where shadows are long and the contrast between mountain and plain is therefore pronounced. Altogether, the
most pleasing views with the telescope are offered within two or three
days of the quarter phases.

Two factors are chiefly responsible for the differences between the
surface features of the moon and earth: (1) Surface gravity on the
moon has only one sixth of its value on the earth; (2) The moon has
no appreciable atmosphere.

5·14. The Moon's Atmosphere is so rare that no evidence of its existence is detected. There is no twilight; the division between day and
night is abrupt. The effect of twilight in prolonging the cusps of the
crescent moon beyond the diameter could be noticed if atmosphere near
the moon's surface were a ten thousandth as dense as air near the earth's
surface. There is no perceptible haze, even near the edge of the moon
where atmosphere would be most effective in dimming the view.

On the frequent occasions when a star is occulted by the moon, the
star does not first become fainter and redder, as it would behind a considerable amount of atmosphere. Instead, the star remains at its usual
brightness until it disappears instantly. These are some of the indica-
tions that the moon's atmosphere is extremely rare, if there is any at all.
The reason is found in the escape of the gases from the weak control of
the moon's attraction.

5·15. Escape of an Atmosphere. *The kinetic theory of gases* is concerned with the movements of the molecules of a gas. It views the
molecules as speeding in all directions and incessantly colliding, so that
some are brought momentarily almost to rest where others are impelled
to speeds far exceeding the average. *The average squared velocity of
the molecules varies directly as the absolute temperature of the gas and
inversely as its mean molecular weight.* The average velocity in miles
a second at 0° C is 1.2 for hydrogen, 0.4 for water vapor, and 0.3 for
nitrogen and oxygen. At 100° C the velocities are 17 per cent greater.

The ability of a celestial body to retain an atmosphere around it depends on the *velocity of escape* at its surface, that is to say, the initial
speed an object must have in order to overcome the pull of gravity and
to get away. The velocity of escape is 7 miles a second at the earth's
surface, but is only 1½ miles a second at the surface of the moon. Cal-

culations show that a celestial body will lose half of its atmosphere in a
few weeks if the velocity of escape is three times the mean velocity of
the molecules in that atmosphere. The required time increases to a few
thousand years if the factor is four, and to hundreds of million years if
it is five times the mean velocity of the molecules.

Putting these items together we have some understanding of why
the earth has retained more atmosphere and the moon less, perhaps none
at all. A more complete account would require data on the surface
temperatures of these bodies earlier in their history.

5·16. The Character of the Moon's Surface. The surface temperature varies gradually from $+100°$ C, when the sun is overhead, to
$-50°$ C at sunset, and is reduced to $-150°$ C at midnight. During a
lunar eclipse the temperature fell $150°$ C in an hour. Such rapid cooling of the surface when the sunlight is withdrawn is due partly to the
absence of an atmospheric blanket and partly to low heat conductivity;
in this respect the surface material has been likened to pumice or volcanic ash.

That the moon's surface is generally dark colored and broken is indicated by its low reflecting power and the character of the reflected light.
The *albedo* of a planet or satellite, as the term is ordinarily employed,
is the ratio of the light reflected by its whole illuminated hemisphere to
the light received from the sun. The average albedo of the moon is
only 7 per cent; it is comparable with that of rather dark brown rock.

Presumably it is not entirely bare, unbroken rock that we see. While
the rocks on the moon are not subject to ordinary weathering by action
of water and wind, their surfaces may have crumbled because of repeated expansion and contraction with the great range in their temperatures. The accumulation of meteorites and fragments of rocks shattered
by the fall of the meteorites may add to the rubble.

5·17. The Lunar Seas. The dark areas which form the face of the
"man in the moon," the profile of the "girl in the moon," and other
products of the lively imagination are the lunar *maria* (*seas*), so called
long ago when they were thought to be the beds of primitive seas. They
are also known as *plains*. Fourteen seas are recognized, the largest of
which is distinguished by the rank of ocean, and they have fantastic
names such as Mare Serenetatis (Sea of Serenity). Irregularities in
their shorelines occasionally have special names; Sinus Iridum (Bay of
Rainbows) is a familiar example.

Mostly connected, with the conspicuous exception of Mare Crisium,

FIG. 5·17. The Moon Shortly After the Full Phase. The sunset line is appearing at the left. The seas and bright rays are conspicuous; the longest ray system radiates from Tycho, near the upper edge. Many short, crooked rays surround the crater Copernicus, to the right of the center and a little below it. The mountains are not prominent near the full phase.

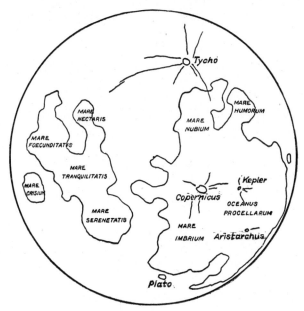

FIG. 5·17A. Key to Photograph of Nearly Full Moon.

the seas cover about one half of the moon's visible surface, and predominate in its northern hemisphere. The majority are roughly circular. Although they lack the extremely rugged scenery of the mountainous country to the south, the seas are far from monotonous as viewed with the telescope. They are broken by many pits and clefts and by the summits of partly submerged mountains. As further suggestion that they may once have been lava pools, the seas contain long, crooked ridges which resemble flow marks.

FIG. 5·18. The Moon About Two Days After First Quarter. The moon is inverted and reversed, as it appears ordinarily in the telescope. Near the terminator, which is here the sunrise line, the mountains show to the best advantage. In the upper part (near the south pole) the craters are especially numerous. A little more than halfway down along the terminator is the crater Copernicus, between the Mare Nubium, above, and the Mare Imbrium, below. (*Photographed at Yerkes Observatory*)

5·18. The Lunar Mountains. Among the few formations which have any resemblance to terrestrial mountain ranges are the three which form

the western border of Mare Imbrium. They are the Apennines, Caucasus, and Alps—designations that have survived from an early map in
which the names of mountains on the earth were given to those on the
moon. These mountains are evidently caused by igneous action and not
by folding. They slope more abruptly toward the sea and more gradually in the opposite direction; and they are surmounted by thousands of
sharp peaks, the highest ones rising nearly 20,000 feet above the plain.

Still greater heights are measured in the Leibnitz and Doerfel mountains near the south pole and almost beyond the moon's limb; some of
those peaks have elevations of 26,000 feet—comparable with but not as
high as Mount Everest. Heights on the moon, however, are not so
easily compared because they are referred to the neighboring plains; and
the plains themselves are at different levels.

The height of a lunar mountain is determined in one way by measuring
the length of its shadow and calculating the sun's altitude as seen from that
point on the moon. Or it may be determined by measuring the distance of
the summit from the terminator, as it catches the first rays of the rising sun
or the last rays of the setting sun; at that instant the illuminated top of the
peak looks like a little star out in the dark beyond the terminator. A sketch
of either situation will show that enough data are then known to make possible the calculation of the height of the mountain by solving a right triangle.

5·19. The Lunar Craters. The most remarkable characteristic of lunar
mountains is their preference for nearly circular formations. These
craters bear the names of distinguished philosophers and scientists of
former times, such as Plato and Copernicus. In number they exceed
30,000, and in size they range from the smallest pits and craterlets, 1000
feet or less across, that can be discerned with the largest telescopes, to
the walled plains. Clavius, near the moon's south pole, and Grimaldi,
near its eastern edge, are the largest walled plains; they measure nearly
150 miles in diameter. Characteristics of the craters are found in the
great plains, or seas, themselves.

The circumference of a lunar crater is a nearly circular mountain
wall, precipitous and often shelving on the inside and more gradually
sloping without. Lofty peaks surmount the wall, while lower peaks
appear near the centers of many craters. In some cases the crater floor
is depressed several thousand feet below the level of the surrounding
plain; in others it is elevated, notably in the crater Wargentin, where
the floor is raised nearly to the top of the wall. Some craters have
rough, bright, saucer-shaped floors; Aristarchus is the brightest. Others,
such as Plato, have floors as smooth and dark as the seas.

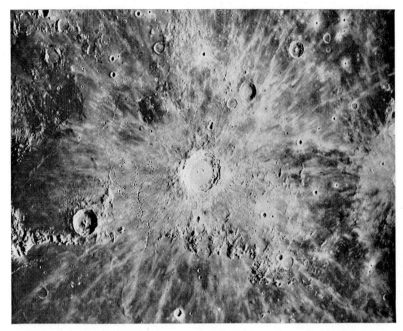

FIG. 5·19. The Crater Copernicus. (*Photographed at Mount Wilson Observatory*)

5·20. Rays and Rills. The lunar *rays* are bright streaks, often five or ten miles wide and up to 1500 miles long, which radiate from points near a few of the craters, and pass over mountain and plain alike without much regard for the topography. Best seen when the sun is high above them, the rays are prominent features of the full moon. The most conspicuous and longest ray system radiates from Tycho near the south pole, causing the full moon through a small telescope to appear something like an orange. A fine system of shorter, more crooked, and somewhat less brilliant rays centers in the crater Copernicus (Fig. 5·19).

There are many *rills,* or clefts—cracks of the order of half a mile wide and of unknown depth. Some are very tortuous, while others seem nearly straight for tens of miles and, like the rays, pay little attention to surface irregularities. A rather large telescope is needed to show the rills clearly.

A fine *fault* is easily seen with a small telescope near the southwest edge of Mare Nubium (Fig. 5·21). This is the Straight Wall some 70 miles long and rising more than a thousand feet above the plain.

5·21. The History of the Surface Formations is imperfectly under-stood. At first sight it may seem surprising that an object so open to minute inspection as the moon is should be mysterious in any way, until we reflect that scientists are not in entire agreement concerning the early

FIG. 5·21. Southern Portion of the Moon at Last Quarter. Above the center of the picture is the crater Tycho from which bright rays radiate. Above this crater, about halfway to the upper edge, is the walled plain Clavius, nearly 150 miles in diameter. The shadows lengthen as the terminator (sunset line) is approached. Part of the Mare Nubium is at the lower right. (*Photographed at Mount Wilson Observatory*)

history of the earth's surface. Vulcanism must have played an important part in the lunar formations. The fall of meteorites may have left scars as well. Ordinary weathering, gradation, and folding did not enter.

Two factors could make the igneous formations on the moon different from those on the earth: (1) *The lower surface gravity* permitted volcanic activity on a greater scale; (2) *The smaller mass* of the moon hastened the cooling, which tended to perpetuate the earlier igneous formations. *One version* of the lunar formations is the following:

When the moon cooled from a completely liquid state enough to establish a solid crust, great blisters appeared on its surface. When these healed, they left permanent scars which are the basins of the seas. Eventually the basins were partly filled by lava which welled up through fissures, dissolving and submerging many original features, and finally hardening to form the level surfaces of the seas.

As the moon's crust thickened, the circular formations diminished in size. Walled plains made their appearance, and later the normal craters such as Tycho and Copernicus. It is significant that in cases of overlapping craters the smaller one was the later to be formed, because it breaks through the wall of the larger crater. As the emergence of lava became more contained, mountain peaks rose, often near the centers of the craters; and some of these may have been explosive volcanoes.

If it could be established that the lunar rays radiate only from explosive volcanoes, that would support the view that the rays are lighter-colored lava erupted and distributed irregularly over the moonscape by the explosion. An explosion velocity of a mile a second, which is not excessive for a terrestrial volcano, would account for the longest lunar rays.

5·22. Conditions at the Moon's Surface. Two worlds have grown up in the same neighborhood with equal benefit of the sunlight. One, the earth, is the scene of activity of many kinds; on the other, the moon, there is absence of perceptible activity of any kind. The contrast, as we have seen, is due chiefly to difference of surface gravity. With its greater surface gravity the earth has retained an atmosphere extensive enough to sustain life and to promote by weathering persistent changes in the landscape. With its weaker attraction the moon has not retained sufficient atmosphere to accomplish these things.

If anyone could visit the moon, he would accordingly find conditions there quite different from those at home. The reduced surface gravity might suggest surprising athletic feats. Absence of considerable atmosphere would produce unfamiliar effects. The glaring sunlight would include dangerous ultraviolet rays. No twilight would intervene be-

FIG. 5·22. Northern Portion of the Moon at Last Quarter. A large part of the picture is occupied by the Mare Imbrium. This sea is bordered above by the Apennines, and at the left by the Caucasus and Alps. To the right of the Alps is the crater Plato whose floor is especially dark, and farther to the right is the Bay of Rainbows. (*Photographed at Mount Wilson Observatory*)

tween day and night. A black sky instead of a blue one would be set with stars day and night alike. The bare, lifeless landscape would be that of the perfect desert where practically nothing ever happens. If the visitor was an astronomer, he might well conclude that for steadiness, clearness, and continuity of view of the celestial bodies the moon would be the perfect site for an observatory.

THE TIDES

The rise and fall of the level of the ocean twice at any place in a little more than a day has been associated with the moon from early times. Newton correctly ascribed the tides in the ocean to the attractions of both the moon and the sun, and accounted for their general behavior by means of his law of gravitation.

5·23. Lunar Tides. To simplify the explanation of the tides, let us suppose, as Newton did, that the whole earth is covered by very deep water. Now the gravitational attraction between two bodies decreases as the distance between the bodies becomes greater, as we see more formally at a later time. The moon's attraction is accordingly more than average for that part of the ocean nearest the moon and less than average for the most distant part. Thus the ocean has the figure of an ellipsoid of revolution, whose longest axis would be directed toward the moon if additional effects were absent. This axis rotates slowly eastward, following the moon in its monthly revolution around the earth.

Meanwhile the earth is rotating eastward daily under the tide figure; it makes a complete rotation relative to a particular point of that figure once in a lunar day, which averages $24^h 50^m$ of civil time. At the place of observation *high tide* occurs at intervals of $12^h 25^m$, and *low tide* at equal intervals halfway between. These are the occasions when the ocean level is the highest and lowest in that particular cycle.

But the ocean is not deep enough to fulfill the assumed condition. Moreover, the earth's rotation is too rapid for the simple theory to apply; and other factors which have important effects on the tides have not been taken into account. High tide and the transit of the moon are generally far from simultaneous. The difference between these occurrences, which varies from place to place, is best determined by observation.

5·24. Spring and Neap Tides. The sun also causes tides in the ocean. It can be shown that the tide-producing force of a body varies inversely as the cube of its distance, and accordingly that the sun, despite its overwhelmingly greater mass, is less than half as effective as the moon in raising tides on the earth.

The two sets of tides may be considered as operating independently, the relative positions of their crests varying with the moon's phases. The *spring tide* occurs when the moon is new or full. Since the moon and sun are then attracting from the same or opposite directions, lunar and solar tides reinforce each other; the high tide is highest and the low tide is lowest. The *neap tide* occurs when the moon is at either quarter phase. Then the moon and sun are 90° apart, so that one set of tides is partly neutralized by the other. When the moon is new or full and

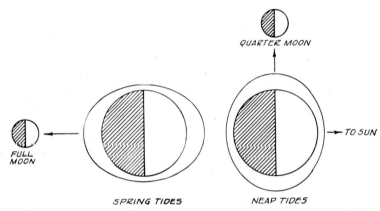

Fig. 5·24. Spring Tides and Neap Tides. Spring tides occur at new and full moon, when lunar and solar tides reinforce each other. Neap tides occur at quarter moon, when one set of tides is partly neutralized by the other.

also in perigee, the change in level between low and high tides is especially great.

The earth itself, like the ocean, is deformed by lunar and solar tides, but of course to a much smaller extent. Consequently, the observed tides in the ocean represent the differences between ocean and earth tides.

Since any point in the ocean is carried eastward by the earth's rotation relative to the tide figure, the tides may be regarded as a wave sweeping westward past the point. The succession of wave crests pass by at intervals of 12^{h} 25^{m}. In the open ocean the range in height between crest and trough is only two or three feet. Along coasts it may easily be six or eight feet, and in very favorable conditions, as in the Bay of Fundy, may be as much as fifty or sixty feet.

5·25. Tidal Friction. The tides act as a friction brake on the earth's rotation; they are held in position by the moon and sun, while the earth rotates under them. The incessant resistance of the water over the uneven floor of the ocean should gradually reduce the speed of the earth's rotation and therefore lengthen the day.

If the earth-clock is actually slowing down, other periodic occurrences, such as the revolution of the moon, ought to be forging ahead
of their schedules. Indeed, the moon seems to have advanced as much
as half its apparent diameter in the course of a thousand years beyond
its calculated place among the constellations at a particular time. The
discrepancy is explained if we suppose that the day is increasing in length
at the rate of a thousandth of a second in a century ($2 \cdot 12$).

Jeffreys has shown that an increase of this order in the length of the
day requires continuous dissipation of energy by the friction of the tides
at the rate of two billion horsepower. The question arises as to whether
the tides are capable of promoting this gigantic enterprise. According
to the same authority, friction in the open ocean and in the earth's interior is relatively negligible; but in the shallow seas and straits, for
which data are available, the average dissipation of energy by tidal friction is altogether 60 per cent of that required to lengthen the day $0^s.001$
a century, and two thirds of it takes place in Behring Sea. Assuming
the correctness of these results, it is not improbable that the full quota
of friction might be found if complete data were available.

5·26. Tidal Theory of the Earth-Moon System.

It can be shown
that retardation of the earth's rotation by tidal friction would be accompanied by increasing speed of the moon's revolution around the earth.
The increase of speed would cause the moon to spiral outward from the
earth; and as the size of the moon's orbit increased, the length of the
month would also increase. Such gradual variations in the day and the
month, when they operate over long periods of time, could greatly alter
the configuration of the earth-moon system.

G. H. Darwin, son of the celebrated naturalist, traced the possible
past and future history of the system. Beginning at the time when the
moon was about 10,000 miles from the earth, the length of the month
was then something less than a quarter of the present month, and the
day was a still smaller fraction of the present day. Under the action
of the tides, both month and day slowly increased in length, the month
faster than the day. After a time, however, the day will lengthen
faster than month, and will finally overtake it, when the day and
month become equal to 55 of our present days.

At this remote period in the future, when the moon is much farther
away than it is now, the earth-moon system will be internally stable,
the earth turning the same hemisphere always toward the moon, just as
the moon now presents one hemisphere to the earth. If it happens not
to be our hemisphere that is turned moonward, the moon may become

one of the sights to see on a trip abroad. At this stage lunar tides cannot alter the system; but solar tides still operate on it, and they will force the earth and moon out of step. The history of the system will then be repeated in reverse order, until the moon is brought close to the earth again.

As in the case of any theory that contemplates vast periods of time, the tidal theory of the earth-moon system may properly be regarded with considerable caution; for other factors, which may now seem inconsiderable, or for which experience has not yet prepared us, may eventually dominate the situation. The fact that the moon now turns one hemisphere toward us always is favorable to the theory. Owing to its smaller mass and to the greater tide-raising force of the earth, it is perhaps not surprising that equality of rotation and revolution has already come about on the moon, even though the more effective friction of ocean tides is absent there.

Review Questions

1. Name the terms which are defined as follows:

(a) The point of the moon's orbit that is nearest the earth.
(b) The aspect of the moon when its phase is new.
(c) The interval of time between two successive new moons.
(d) The westward movement of the nodes of the moon's path.
(e) The tide that occurs at new or full moon.

2. Explain the relation between the parallax and distance of an object.

3. Explain the moon's phases. Would the earth show the different phases as viewed from the moon?

4. Explain why the horns of the crescent moon are most nearly vertical in the evenings of spring and most nearly horizontal in the evenings of autumn, as viewed in middle northern latitudes (Refer to Sec. 1·19).

5. Why does the full moon pass nearest the zenith near the beginning of winter, in middle northern latitudes? What is its least possible distance from your zenith?

6. Give two reasons why you can see somewhat more than 50 per cent of the moon's surface in the course of a month.

7. From what observational evidence may we conclude that the moon has little or no atmosphere? Give a reason for the lack of atmosphere.

8. Describe the following features of the moon's surface: (a) the seas; (b) the craters; (c) the rays; (d) the rills.

9. If you could visit the moon, what conditions at its surface and in the heavens would you find different from those at home?

10. Explain the cause of the tides. Why do high tides occur at intervals of $12^h 25^m$?

11. Why do extremely high tides occur when the moon is new or full?

12. Show that the tides might be expected to gradually lengthen the period of the earth's rotation.

CHAPTER VI

ECLIPSES OF THE MOON AND SUN

Eclipses of the moon occur when the moon, at the *full* phase, passes through the earth's shadow, and is therefore darkened. Solar eclipses occur when the moon, then at the *new* phase, passes between the earth and the sun, so that its shadow falls on the earth; the observer within the shadow sees the sun wholly or partially hidden by the moon.

6·1. Shadows of the Earth and Moon. Since the earth and moon are globes smaller than the sun, the shadow of each one is a cone having its

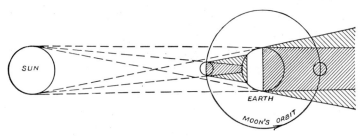

FIG. 6·1. The Cause of Lunar and Solar Eclipses. When the moon is opposite the sun, it is eclipsed by the earth's shadow. When the moon is between the earth and the sun, its shadow falls on a portion of the earth; within this region the sun is eclipsed.

apex directed away from the sun. This region, from which sunlight is geometrically entirely excluded, will be spoken of as the *shadow,* though it is in fact only one part of the shadow, the *umbra;* surrounding it is the larger inverted cone of the *penumbra,* from which the light is only partially excluded. There is no way of observing the shadows except as they encounter objects that shine by reflected sunlight. The dark arch of the earth's shadow on the atmosphere can be seen rising in the east at nightfall.

The average length of the earth's shadow is 859,000 miles, as anyone can easily verify by making a diagram and writing a proportion between two similar triangles. By a like procedure it is found that the length of the moon's shadow averages 232,000 miles when the moon is between the earth and the sun. Since these shadows are more than a hundred times as long as their greatest widths, they cannot conveniently be represented in diagrams in their proper proportions.

6·2. The Moon in the Earth's Shadow. If a screen could be placed opposite the sun at the moon's distance from us, the earth's shadow falling normally upon it would appear as a dark circle having a diameter of around 5700 miles. Since the shadow is always opposite the sun, it moves eastward around the ecliptic once a year. At intervals of a synodic month, the faster-moving moon overtakes the shadow and, whenever it then encounters the shadow, enters at the *west* side and moves through at the rate which is the difference between the speeds of the

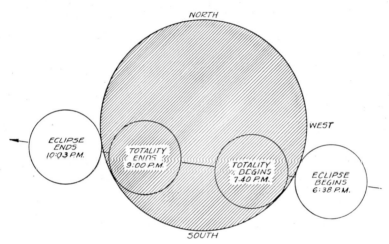

Fig. 6·2. Path of the Moon Through the Umbra of the Earth's Shadow During the Eclipse of the Moon, December 18, 1945. Central standard times are given.

moon and shadow; the hourly rate is about 30′, or very nearly the moon's diameter.

Eclipses of the moon are total and partial. The longest eclipses occur when the moon passes centrally through the shadow; the duration of the whole eclipse is then about $3^h 40^m$, and of totality $1^h 40^m$. Noncentral eclipses are shorter, depending on how nearly the moon's path approaches the center of the shadow. When the least distance exceeds the difference between the radii of shadow and moon, there is no total phase.

A lunar eclipse is visible wherever the moon is above the horizon during its occurrence, that is, over more than half of the earth, counting the region that is rotated into view of the moon while the eclipse is going on. The Greenwich civil times when the moon enters and leaves the penumbra and umbra, and of the beginning and end of totality, are published in advance in the various almanacs. To obtain the times at any other place it is necessary simply to add or subtract the difference between Greenwich time and the kind of civil time in use at the place.

6·3. Eclipses of the Moon. The moon is darkened so gradually in its passage through the penumbra of the shadow that this phase of the eclipse can be unnoticed. Soon after it enters the umbra, a dark notch appears at the moon's east limb and slowly overspreads the disk. So dark in contrast is the shadow that the moon might well be expected to vanish in total eclipse. But as totality comes on, the moon is usually plainly visible.

Even when it is entirely eclipsed, the moon is still illuminated by sunlight. The light filters through the earth's atmosphere around the

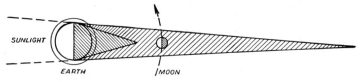

FIG. 6·3. Visibility of the Moon in Total Eclipse. Sunlight is refracted by the earth's atmosphere into the shadow and upon the eclipsed moon.

base of the shadow, and is refracted and diffused into the shadow and onto the moon. Red predominates in this light for the same reason that the sunset is red. The brightness of the moon in total eclipse depends on the degree of cloudiness around the base of the shadow. Often the surface features remain clearly visible. On rare occasions the moon itself becomes very dim.

In the ten year interval from 1945 to 1954 inclusive, there are 16 lunar eclipses, of which ten are total. The following nine, of which seven are total, are visible in the United States and southern Canada:

LUNAR ECLIPSES VISIBLE IN THE UNITED STATES

Date	C.S.T.	Eclipse	Total Eclipse
	Middle of Eclipse		Duration of
1945, Dec. 18	8^h 20^m P.M.	3^h 35^m	1^h 20^m
1949, Apr. 12	10 10 P.M.	3 40	1 30
1949, Oct. 6	8 55 P.M.	3 30	1 10
1950, Nov. 25	10 15 P.M.	3 25	0 45
1952, Feb. 10	6 40 P.M.	1 10	. . . . .
1953, Jan. 29	5 50 P.M.	3 35	1 20
1953, Aug. 26	6 20 A.M.	3 40	1 40
1954, Jan. 18	8 35 P.M.	3 20	0 40
1954, Aug. 15	6 20 P.M.	2 25	. . . . .

6·4. The Moon's Shadow on the Earth. Under average conditions the umbra of the moon's shadow fails to reach the earth. The average length of this shadow is 232,000 miles, which is almost 3000 miles less than the moon's average distance from the nearest point of the earth's surface. The fact that the umbra often extends to the earth at solar eclipse is owing to the eccentricity of the orbit of the earth-moon system around the sun and of the moon's orbit around the earth. At aphelion the length of the moon's shadow increases to 236,000 miles. At perigee the moon may be 217,500 miles from the earth's surface. Under these extreme conditions the umbra may fall on the earth 18,000 miles inside its apex.

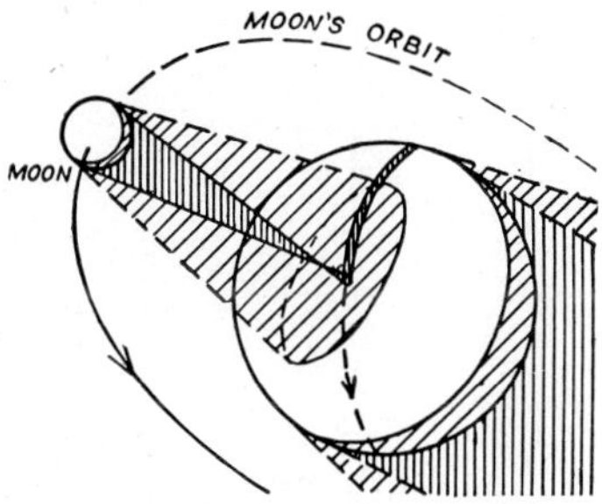

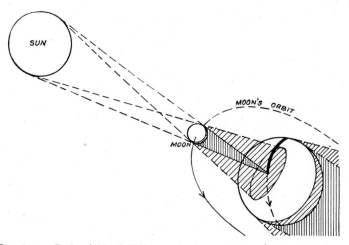

FIG. 6·5. Annular Eclipse of the Sun. The umbra of the moon's shadow does not reach the earth's surface. Within this shadow geometrically produced, a thin ring of the sun's disk remains visible around the moon.

6·5. Total and Annular Solar Eclipses. A *total eclipse* of the sun occurs when the umbra of the moon's shadow falls on the earth. If the observer is within the umbra, which can never exceed 167 miles in

FIG. 6·5A. Path of Total Eclipse. Owing to the moon's eastward revolution, the small shadow-dot moves in an easterly direction over the earth's surface. Within the shadow-dot the eclipse is total. Elsewhere within the larger circle of the penumbra the eclipse is partial.

diameter when the sun is overhead, he sees the dark circle of the moon completely hiding the sun's disk.

An *annular eclipse* occurs when the umbra does not touch the earth. If the observer is within the circle of the umbra produced beyond its apex (Fig. 6·5), he sees the moon's disk projected against the sun; the dark disk now appears slightly the smaller of the two, so that a bright ring, or annulus, of the sun's disk remains uneclipsed. Annular eclipses are 20 per cent more frequent than total eclipses.

Around the small area of the earth in which the eclipse appears total or annular at a particular time, there is the larger partly shaded region of the penumbra. This region is some two to three thousand miles in radius. Here the eclipse is partial; the moon hides only a fraction of the sun's disk, the fraction diminishing with increasing distance from the center of the region. When the axis of the shadow is directed slightly to one side of the earth, only the partial eclipse can be seen.

6·6. Path of the Moon's Shadow. As the moon revolves, its shadow moves generally eastward at the average rate of 2100 miles an hour. Since the earth's rotation at the equator is at the rate of 1040 miles an hour, also eastward, the effective speed of the shadow at the equator, when the sun is overhead, is 1060 miles an hour. In other parts of the earth where the speed of rotation is less, the effective speed of the shadow is greater; and it is still more when the sun is low, attaining a maximum of 5000 miles an hour. Considering the great speed of the shadow and its small size, it is evident that a total eclipse of the sun cannot last long in any one place. The maximum possible duration scarcely exceeds 7^m 30^s. An annular eclipse may last a little longer, while the partial phase accompanying either type of eclipse may have a duration of more than four hours from beginning to end.

The *path of total eclipse,* or of annular eclipse, is the narrow track of the shadow as it sweeps generally eastward over the earth's surface, from the time when it first touches the earth at sunrise until it departs at sunset. Meanwhile, the penumbra moves over the larger surrounding region in which the eclipse is partial.

Occasionally the shadow touches the earth at the middle of its path, but at the beginning and end fails to reach the surface. The eclipse begins as annular, changes to total, and later reverts to the annular type.

Oppolzer's *Canon der Finsternisse* contains the elements of solar and lunar eclipses between 1207 B.C. and 2163 A.D., and also maps showing the approximate tracks of total and annular solar eclipses during this interval.

More accurate data concerning eclipses are published in the various almanacs for the year in which each occurs.

TOTAL ECLIPSE OF JULY 9, 1945

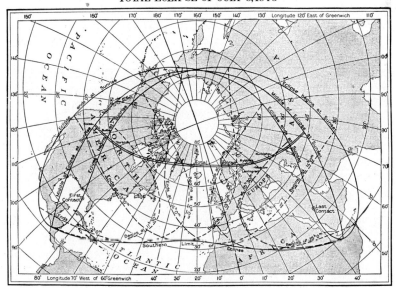

FIG. 6·6. Path of Total Solar Eclipse of July 9, 1945. The umbra of the
moon's shadow touched the earth in Idaho, and swept across Canada, Greenland, Scandinavia, and Russia. (From *The American Ephemeris and Nautical
Almanac*)

The dates, durations at noon, and land areas in which current total
eclipses are visible are as follows. The totality paths of the 1945 and 1952
eclipses begin at sunrise in northern United States.

TOTAL SOLAR ECLIPSES

Date	Duration (minutes)	Region
1945, July 9	1	Canada, Greenland, Russia
1947, May 20	5	Argentina, Central Africa
1948, Nov. 1	2	Central Africa
1950, Sept. 12	1	Siberia
1952, Feb. 25	3	Sudan, Persia, Siberia
1954, June 30	3	Canada, Scandinavia, Russia
1955, June 20	7	India, Siam, Philippines

6·7. The Sun in Total Eclipse. As a spectacle the total eclipse of the
sun ranks among the most impressive of celestial phenomena. While
the details vary considerably from one eclipse to another, depending on

the diameter of the shadow and other factors, the principal phenomena to be noted are much the same on all these occasions.

As the crescent of the sun becomes narrow, an unfamiliar pallor overspreads the sky and landscape, because the quality of the light from the sun's limb differs from that of normal sunlight. Immediately preceding totality the sky darkens rapidly; shadow bands, like ripples, ap-

FIG. 6·7. The Total Solar Eclipse of January 24, 1925. From a painting by Howard Russell Butler. (*By courtesy of the American Museum of Natural History, New York*)

pear on white surfaces; animals grow disturbed and some flowers close; and the shadow rushes in, while the last sliver of the vanishing sun breaks into brilliant "Baily's beads" and quickly disappears.

With the coming of totality the corona appears; it is pearly white, brilliant immediately around the moon and fading out in streamers. Flame-like prominences rise from the scarlet chromosphere of the sun. Their bases around the west limb are gradually uncovered, while those at the east limb are covered as the moon moves across. The brighter stars and planets are sometimes visible to the unaided eye. Totality ends as suddenly as it began, and the phenomena of the partial eclipse recur in reverse order.

6·8. Solar Eclipse Problems. During the brief occasions when the sun's disk is hidden in eclipse there is opportunity to observe things in the sun's vicinity. This opportunity has been the chief reason for scientific interest in total solar eclipses. Outer parts of the sun, such as the corona, become available for study—features that can be observed at other times only by use of special devices and some of them not at all. The visibility of planets and stars near the direction of the sun has permitted special studies. Prominent among these was an unsuccessful search for a suspected planet within the orbit of Mercury and a test of the theory of relativity.

The theory of relativity requires that stars close to the sun's place in the sky should be apparently displaced slightly away from the sun;

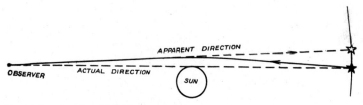

FIG. 6·8. Apparent Displacement of a Star Near the Sun's Limb. By the theory of relativity, starlight passing near the sun is deflected in such a way that the star is apparently displaced outward from the sun's position.

the maximum displacement, for a star at the sun's limb, is 1″.75. The delicate test was attempted by astronomers at a total solar eclipse in 1919. The procedure was to compare photographs of a field of stars immediately surrounding the eclipsed sun with other photographs of the same region of the sky taken at night at another time of the year. When the comparisons revealed something like the predicted displacement, Einstein and his theory became the subjects of much popular comment.

6·9. Eclipse Seasons. Eclipses of the sun and moon take place respectively when the moon is new and full. These phases recur every month, but eclipses are less frequent. The reason is that the moon's apparent path in the sky is inclined 5° 9′ to the ecliptic. Each time when the moon returns to conjunction with the sun, or with the shadow opposite the sun, both objects have moved eastward from their places at the preceding conjunction. Since they are traveling in different paths, the moon will pass north or south of the sun, or shadow, unless it is near one of the nodes; only then can the moon pass across the sun, or into the shadow.

Eclipses occur, therefore, not every month, but at nearly opposite seasons of the year, when the sun is in the vicinity of one of the nodes of the moon's orbit. These are the *eclipse seasons*. As the nodes regress rapidly westward, the eclipse seasons are more than half a month earlier

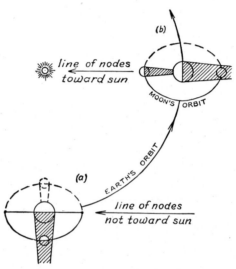

FIG. 6·9. Eclipse Seasons. Since the moon's orbit is inclined about 5° to the plane of the earth's orbit, eclipses can occur only at the two opposite seasons, as at (*b*), when the sun is near the line of nodes of the moon's orbit. At other times in the year, as at (*a*), the moon does not pass between the earth and the sun, or into the earth's shadow.

from year to year. The interval between two successive conjunctions of the sun with the same node of the moon's path is the *eclipse year;* its length is 346.620 days. The eclipse seasons in 1945 are around January and July.

6·10. Solar and Lunar Ecliptic Limits.

The *solar ecliptic limit* is the distance of the sun from the node, at which it is grazed by the moon, as seen from some station on the earth. Within this distance the sun will be eclipsed; beyond it no eclipse can occur. The value of this limiting distance varies with the changing distances, and therefore apparent sizes, of the sun and moon, and with the fluctuations in the angle between the moon's path and the ecliptic. The extreme values, or *major and minor limits,* are respectively 18° 31′ and 15° 21′. When the sun is beyond the major limit, an eclipse is impossible; when it is within the minor limit at the time of new moon, an eclipse is inevitable.

The *lunar ecliptic limit* is likewise the greatest distance of the sun from the node at which a lunar eclipse is possible. The major and minor limits are 12° 15′ and 9° 30′. At first sight it may seem that these limits should be greater, instead of less, than for solar eclipses. But we are concerned with the cone tangent to the sun and earth which terminates as the umbra of the earth's shadow. In order to eclipse or be eclipsed, except in the penumbra of the earth's shadow, the moon must enter this cone. The diameter of the cone, where the full moon

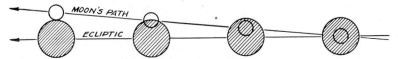

FIG. 6·10. The Lunar Ecliptic Limit. In order to eclipse the moon the earth's shadow must be near one of the nodes of the moon's path. The greatest distance of the center of the shadow from the node (or of the sun's center from the opposite node) at which an eclipse is possible is the lunar ecliptic limit.

passes through, is 5700 miles, as we have seen (6·2); but it is more than 10,000 miles across at the position of the new moon, so that the solar ecliptic limit is the greater if penumbral lunar eclipses are neglected.

6·11. Frequency of Eclipses. The number of eclipses during each eclipse season is determined by comparing the double ecliptic limits with the distance the sun moves along the ecliptic in a synodic month with respect to the regressing node; this distance is 29.5/346.6 of 360°, or 30°.6. The question is whether the sun, and the earth's shadow opposite it, can possibly pass through the eclipse region without encountering the moon. They can do so if the double ecliptic limit is less than 30°.6, although usually they may not escape. If the double limit is greater than 30°.6, one eclipse must take place at each node, and two are possible. Moreover, since the calendar year is over 18 days longer than the eclipse year, the first eclipse season may return at the very end of the year, and in this event *one* additional eclipse may result.

Two solar eclipses of some kind must occur every year; for twice the minor solar ecliptic limit is 30°.7. Five may occur. No lunar eclipse in the umbra of the earth's shadow or total (or annular) solar eclipse need occur during the year, although three of each kind are possible.

The minimum number of eclipses in a year is therefore two, both of the sun. This happens frequently, as, for example, in 1933. *The maximum number in a year is seven,* five of the sun and two of the moon (in 1935), or four of the sun and three of the moon (1982). Thus solar eclipses are more frequent than lunar eclipses for the earth as a whole. But at any one place lunar eclipses are seen the more often, owing to the greater area in which a lunar eclipse is visible.

6·12. Recurrence of Eclipses. The *saros* is the interval of $18^y \ 11\frac{1}{3}^d$ ($10\frac{1}{3}$ days if five instead of four leap years are included) after which eclipses are repeated. It is equal to 223 synodic months, which contain 6585.32 days, and is nearly the same in length as 19 eclipse years (6585.78 days). Not only have the sun and moon returned to nearly the same positions relative to each other and to the node, but their distances are nearly the same as before, so that the durations of succeeding eclipses in a series differ very little. Knowledge of the saros, as it applies to cycles of lunar eclipses at least, goes back to very early times.

The effect of the one third of a day in the period is to shift the region of the following eclipse 120° west in longitude; after three periods it is nearly the same again. At the end of each period the sun is a half-day's journey, or 28′, west of its former position relative to the node. Thus a gradual change in the character of succeeding eclipses is brought about, together with a shift in latitude of the regions in which they occur.

Eclipses occurring at intervals of the saros fall into series, each series of solar eclipses containing about 70 eclipses and having a duration of 1200 years. A new series is introduced by a small partial eclipse visible near one of the poles. After a dozen partial eclipses of increasing magnitude and decreasing latitude, the series becomes total or annular for 45 eclipses, reverts to about a dozen diminishing partial eclipses, and finally disappears at the opposite pole. At present, twelve notable series of total eclipses are in progress; the one that is represented by the eclipses of 1919, 1937, and 1955 is remarkable because the durations of totality are not far from the greatest possible. A series of lunar eclipses runs through about 50 periods in a total of 870 years.

REVIEW QUESTIONS

1. Solar eclipses occur at new moon, lunar eclipses at full moon. Why do not eclipses occur every time the moon is new and full?

2. Explain why eclipses occur only at two opposite seasons, and why those seasons come earlier from year to year.

3. There are more eclipses of the sun than of the moon. Most people can recall having seen a total eclipse of the moon, but the majority have never seen a total solar eclipse. Explain.

4. Why is the totally eclipsed moon visible? What conditions would cause it to be very dim, even in a clear sky?

5. Distinguish between the total and the annular eclipse of the sun, as to cause and appearance. Account for an eclipse which is partly total and partly annular.

6. Describe the appearance of the earth as viewed from the moon when a total solar eclipse is occurring.

7. What information about the sun and its surroundings can be best obtained during a total solar eclipse? Mention a problem that was solved at the time of an eclipse.

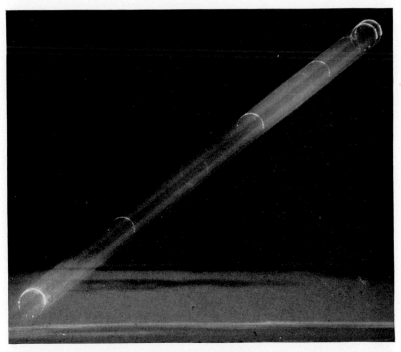

Spectrum of Sun's Chromosphere and Corona. Photographed at the total solar eclipse of July 9, 1945. (*Official photograph of Royal Canadian Air Force. Courtesy of P. M. Millman*)

CHAPTER VII

THE SOLAR SYSTEM

MOTIONS OF THE PLANETS — THEORIES OF PLANETARY MOTIONS — THE LAW OF GRAVITATION

The *solar system* consists of the sun and the many smaller bodies in its vicinity which revolve around the sun. This system includes the planets, like the earth, their satellites, such as the moon, and also the comets and the swarms of meteors. Its dimensions are great as compared with terrestrial standards; the outermost planet, Pluto, is forty times as far from the sun as we are, and the majority of the comets have the aphelion points of their orbits still more remote. But in comparison with the distance of even the nearest star the planetary spaces shrink to such insignificance that we look upon the solar system as our own community, and the other planets as our neighbors.

Motions of the Planets

In its original significance the word *planet* (wanderer) was used to distinguish from the many "fixed" stars the few celestial bodies (excepting comets and meteors) that move about among the constellations. Seven were known: the sun, the moon, and the five bright planets, Mercury, Venus, Mars, Jupiter, and Saturn, the last of which was supposed to be the outermost planet, and not far within the sphere containing the stars themselves. Thus Omar Khayyam ascended in his meditation "from earth's center through the seventh gate" to the throne of Saturn— from the center of the universe, as he understood it, almost to its limits.

The current meaning of the word "planet" began with the acceptance of the Copernican theory which added the earth to the list of planets revolving around the sun, and subtracted from the list the sun and the moon. Uranus, which is barely visible to the unaided eye, was discovered in 1781. Neptune, which is always too faint to be seen without the telescope, was found in 1846. The still fainter Pluto discovered in 1930 completes the list of the nine known *principal planets*. In the meantime, in 1801, Ceres, the largest of the asteroids, or *minor planets,* was the first to be discovered.

7·1. The Planets Named and Classified. The names of the planets in order of distance from the sun are:

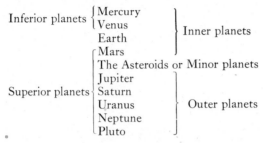

They are classified as inferior and superior planets, and also as inner and outer planets. The *inferior planets* are nearer the sun than we are, while the *superior planets* have orbits outside the earth's orbit. The four *inner planets,* including the earth, are nearer the sun; the five *outer planets* are farther from the sun, and, with the exception of Pluto, are larger than the others.

7·2. Planets Distinguished from Stars. Planets are cool, relatively small globes which revolve around the sun, and which shine by reflected sunlight. Five of the principal planets look like brilliant stars in our skies, while a sixth is faintly visible to the naked eye. Examined through the telescope, the larger and nearer planets appear as disks, some of them noticeably flattened at their poles by their rapid rotations. The stars themselves are remote suns shining by their own light; they appear only as glowing points of light even through the largest telescope.

The bright planets can often be recognized by their steadier light when the stars around them are twinkling. All planets can be distinguished by their motions among the constellations. The right ascensions and declinations of the principal planets, except Pluto, are tabulated in the *American Ephemeris and Nautical Almanac* for each day of the year; their positions in the constellations can be marked on the star maps for any desired date.

The planet Mercury is occasionally visible to the naked eye in the twilight near the horizon, either in the west after sunset or in the east before sunrise. Venus, the most familiar evening or morning "star," is the brightest starlike object in the heavens; it is sometimes brilliant enough to be seen in full daylight.

Mars is distinguished by its red color. At closest approach to the earth it is second in brightness only to Venus; at other times it is inferior to Jupiter. The giant planet Jupiter ranks next to Venus in brightness, as a general thing. Saturn rivals the brightest stars; it is the most remote of the five bright planets and therefore the most leisurely in its movement among the stars.

7·3. The Revolutions of the Principal Planets around the sun are characterized by the following regularities:

(1) *Their orbits are nearly circular.* They are ellipses of small eccentricity, but with more marked departure from the circular form in the cases of Pluto and Mercury.

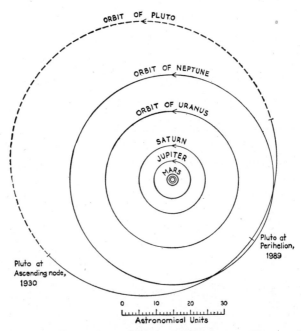

FIG. 7·3. Approximate Orbits of the Principal Planets. They are in general nearly circles with the sun at the common center, and nearly in the same plane. The orbits of Pluto and Mercury depart the most conspicuously from these regularities.

(2) *Their orbits are nearly in the same plane.* With the prominent exception of Pluto, the inclinations of their orbits to the ecliptic do not exceed 8°; so that the principal planets are located in the sky always near the ecliptic, and mostly within the boundaries of the zodiac.

(3) *The planets all revolve from west to east.* This is the usual direction of revolution, and of rotation as well, for all members of the solar system. Only a few exceptions are known.

The smaller of the principal planets conform less faithfully to these regularities than do the larger ones. Tiny Pluto is so extreme in the eccentricity and inclination of its orbit to the ecliptic that in these respects it might be listed as an asteroid. The asteroids themselves, particularly the small ones, present a number of cases of highly eccentric and highly inclined orbits, though all their revolutions are from west to east.

7·4. The Distances of the Planets from the sun are related approximately by the simple rule with which Bode, in 1772, anticipated the discovery of the first-known asteroid, Ceres.

Bode's law is obtained by writing the numbers 0, 3, 6, 12, 24, . . . , doubling the number each time to obtain the next one, then by adding 4 to each number and dividing the sums by 10. The resulting series of numbers, 0.4, 0.7, 1.0, 1.6, 2.8, . . . , represents the mean distances of the planets from the sun, expressed in astronomical units. The *astronomical unit* is the earth's mean distance from the sun.

There was at that time, however, one exception to the rule; the number 2.8 between the numbers for Mars and Jupiter corresponded to the mean distance of no known planet. Bode pointed out that the success of the "law" in other respects justified a search for the missing planet. The discovery of Uranus, in 1781, at a distance in satisfactory agreement with the series extended one term further, so strengthened his position that a systematic search was undertaken by a group of European astronomers.

As it turned out, the asteroid Ceres was discovered accidentally by Piazzi, in 1801, at the expected distance of 2.8 astronomical units. This is very nearly the average distance of the many hundreds of asteroids since discovered.

The law is not so successful in representing the distance of Neptune, and fails entirely in the case of Pluto; nor would it serve so well for Mercury if the rule of doubling the number had been adhered to at the beginning of the series. Bode's law has no known physical significance. It is at least an easy way of remembering the mean distances of most of the principal planets from the sun.

7·5. Sidereal and Synodic Periods. The *sidereal period* is the interval between two successive conjunctions of the planet with a star, as seen from the sun. It is the true period of the planet's revolution around the sun. This interval ranges from 88 days for Mercury to 248 years for Pluto.

TABLE 7·I.　DISTANCES AND PERIODS OF THE PLANETS

Name	Mean Distance from Sun			Period of Revolution	
	Bode's Law	Astron. Units	Million Miles	Sidereal	Mean Synodic
				days	days
Mercury	0.4	0.39	36	88	116
Venus	0.7	0.72	67	225	584
Earth	1.0	1.00	93	365¼	
Mars	1.6	1.52	142	687	780
				years	
Ceres	2.8	2.77	257	5	467
Jupiter	5.2	5.20	483	12	399
Saturn	10.0	9.54	886	29	378
Uranus	19.6	19.19	1782	84	370
Neptune	38.8	30.07	2793	165	367
Pluto	77.2	39.46	3670	248	367

The *synodic period* is the interval between two successive conjunctions of the planet with the sun, as seen from the earth; for an inferior planet the conjunctions must both be either inferior or superior (Fig. 7·6). It is the interval in which the faster-moving inferior planet gains a lap on the earth, or in which the earth gains a lap on the slower superior planet. The relation between the two periods for any planet is:

$$\frac{1}{\text{synodic period}} = \pm \frac{1}{\text{sidereal period}} \mp \frac{1}{\text{earth's sidereal period}},$$

where the upper signs are for an inferior planet and the lower signs for a superior planet. This is merely the statement of the fact that the rate of the earth's gain on the other planet, or of the planet's gain on the earth, is the difference of the angular rates of their revolutions around the sun.

As an example of the use of this relation, let us calculate approximately the mean synodic period of the planet Mercury: 1/synodic period = $1/88 - 1/365\frac{1}{4}$. Mercury's synodic period is therefore $365\frac{1}{4} \times 88/(365\frac{1}{4} - 88)$, or about 116 days.

Mars and Venus have the longest synodic periods of the principal planets (Table 7·I) because they run the closest race with the earth. The synodic periods of the outer planets approach the length of the year as their distances from the sun, and therefore their sidereal periods, increase.

7·6. Aspects and Phases of the Inferior Planets. Since the inferior planets, Mercury and Venus, complete their revolutions in less time

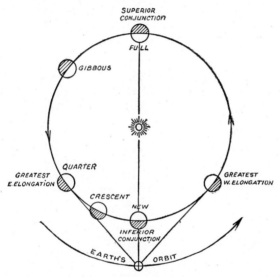

FIG. 7·6. Aspects and Phases of an Inferior Planet. The aspects differ from those of the moon; the phases are the same as the moon's.

than a year, they gain on the earth, and therefore appear to us to oscillate to the east and west with respect to the sun's position. *Their aspects are unlike those of the moon* (5·5) which has all values of elongation up to 180°. After passing *superior conjunction* beyond the sun, the inferior planet emerges to the east of it as an evening star, and moves out to *greatest eastern elongation.* Here it turns west and, apparently moving more rapidly, passes between us and the sun at *inferior conjunction* into the morning sky. Turning east again at *greatest western elongation,* it returns to superior conjunction. Greatest elongation does not exceed 48° from the sun for Venus, and 28° for Mercury.

The phases of the inferior planets resemble those of the moon (5·6);

as these planets revolve within the earth's orbit, their sunlit hemispheres are presented to the earth in varying amounts. Without allowance for the inclinations of their orbits, they show the full phase at the time of superior conjunction, the quarter phase at the elongations, and the new phase at inferior conjunction.

7·7. Aspects and Phases of the Superior Planets.

Since the superior planets have periods longer than a year, they move eastward in the sky

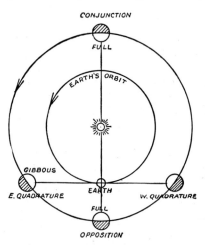

FIG. 7·7. Aspects and Phases of a Superior Planet. The aspects are similar to those of the moon. The only phases are full and gibbous.

more slowly than the sun appears to do, so that they are overtaken and passed by it at intervals. With respect to the sun's position they seem to move westward, and to attain all values of elongation from 0° to 180°. *The aspects of the superior planets are the same as those of the moon.*

Jupiter, as an example, emerges from conjunction to the west of the sun. It is then visible as a morning star, rising at dawn in the east. Moving westward continually with respect to the sun, it comes successively to western quadrature when it is in the south at sunrise, to opposition when it is in the south at midnight, and to eastern quadrature

when it is in the south at sunset. Setting earlier from night to night as it approaches the next conjunction with the sun, the planet is finally lost in the twilight in the west.

The superior planets do not exhibit the whole cycle of phases that the moon shows. At conjunctions and oppositions their disks are fully illuminated, and in other positions they do not depart much from the full phase; for the hemisphere turned toward the sun is nearly the same as the one presented to the earth. The *phase angle* is the angle at the planet between the directions of the earth and sun; divided by 180°, it gives the fraction of the hemisphere turned toward the earth that is in darkness. The phase angle is greatest when the planet is near quadrature; for the nearest superior planet, Mars, its value may be as much as 47°. The maximum phase angle of Jupiter is 12°, and the values for the more distant planets are smaller. Thus the superior planets show nearly the full phase at all times, with the exception of Mars which near quadrature resembles the gibbous moon.

7·8. Apparent Motions Among the Stars. It is instructive not merely to notice that the planets change their places among the constellations, but also to observe the paths they follow. Mars serves well as an example. Observe its position in the sky relative to near-by stars, and mark the place and the date on a star map. Repeat the observation about once a week as long as the planet remains in view in the evening

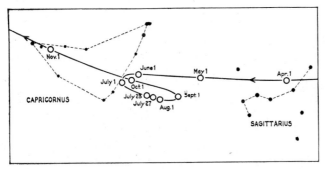

FIG. 7·8. Retrograde Motion of Mars Near the Favorable Opposition of 1939. During July and August the planet moved westward among the stars.

sky. A smooth curve through the points, as in Fig. 7·8, represents the apparent path.

Against the background of the stars the planet's motion is for the most part eastward, or *direct,* the same as the direction of its course around the sun. Once during each synodic period the planet turns and moves westward, or *retrogrades,* for a time before resuming the eastward motion. On the turns the planet is said to be *stationary.* Thus all the planets appear to move among the stars in a succession of loops, making progress toward the east and never departing far from the ecliptic.

As long as the earth was regarded as stationary, these looped paths had necessarily to be ascribed entirely to the motions of the planets themselves. Complex motions such as these called for a complex explanation. The problem was finally simplified by the acceptance of the earth's revolution around the sun.

7·9. Retrograde Motions Explained. Owing to the earth's swift movement in its orbit around the sun, the planets are shifted backward.

toward the west, against the more distant background of the stars. It is the same effect that one observes as he drives along the highway; objects near the road fly past more rapidly than those in the distance. This effect combines with the planet's real eastward movement to produce the looped path that is observed.

A superior planet, such as Mars, retrogrades near the time of opposition; for the earth then overtakes the planet and leaves it behind. The direct motion becomes most rapid near conjunction, where the planet's

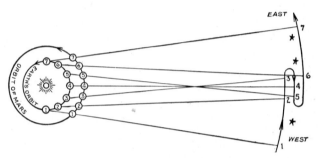

FIG. 7·9. Retrograde Motion of a Superior Planet. Positions of the earth at intervals of a month are numbered on the inner circle. Positions of Mars in its orbit at the same times are similarly numbered on the outer circle. As seen from the faster-moving earth, Mars describes a looped path among the constellations, retrograding, at positions 4 and 5, around the time of opposition.

orbital motion and its displacement due to the earth's revolution are in the same direction. An inferior planet retrogrades near inferior conjunction. This can be shown by extending the lines in Fig. 7·9 in the reverse direction, whereupon it is evident that the earth—an inferior planet relative to Mars, and then near inferior conjunction—is retrograding in the Martian sky. Mercury and Venus exhibit this effect to us. In general, a planet retrogrades when it is nearest the earth.

Theories of Planetary Motions

7·10. The Rotating Celestial Sphere. The first step toward an understanding of the earth's relation to the rest of the universe was taken when primitive folk discarded purely fanciful ideas of nature and began to picture the world as it seemed to them. The earth was represented as a flat surface, either oblong, if they dwelt in valleys, or circular in form. The sky was either a flat canopy appropriately supported at its corners, or like an inverted bowl resting around the circle of the horizon.

The stars marched across the sky daily in unchanging formations, while the sun, moon, and planets were observed to be more independent in their movements.

The first important advance was made by Greek scholars as early as the sixth century B.C. The earth then came to be regarded as a stationary globe, and the sky as a hollow, concentric globe supported by an axis through the earth's center, on which the sky rotated daily from east to west, causing the stars to rise and set. Within the celestial sphere the sun, moon, and five bright planets shared in the daily rotation; but they moved about in unexplained ways against the turning background of the constellations. This geocentric theory remained almost unchallenged for more than two thousand years, though it was amplified in attempts to account for the movements of the planets.

During that long period, however, there was an undercurrent of opinion that the earth is not stationary. Philolaus (about 420 B.C.) declared that the daily turning of the celestial sphere might be only apparent; it might be due to a movement of the earth, about which his ideas were somewhat fantastic. Heracleides (about 370 B.C.) seems to have definitely favored the earth's daily rotation from west to east. Aristarchus of Samos, in the third century B.C., is said to have further maintained that the annual motion of the sun along the ecliptic is owing to the earth's revolution around the sun.

7·11. Concentric Spheres of Eudoxus. By what combinations of uniform circular motions can the movements of the celestial bodies be represented? This problem, which was destined to have a prominent place in astronomy through the following two thousand years, was proposed by Plato (427-347 B.C.).

One solution of the problem was explained by the mathematician Eudoxus of Cnidus (408-355 B.C.), pupil of Plato, in his work *On Velocities* which has been lost together with all his other writings.

Each planet, including the sun and moon, was supposed to be moved by a series of concentric spheres around the earth, which rotated uniformly, one inside another, on different axes—a sort of gimbal arrangement. The outer sphere of each group rotated daily from east to west along with the sphere of the stars, causing the planet to rise and set. The sphere next inside rotated more slowly from west to east on an axis inclined to the first, producing the planet's eastward motion along the ecliptic. Other spheres represented additional motions. The planet itself was attached at the equator of the innermost sphere of the group.

Twenty-seven spheres were required in the original plan, including the sphere of the stars. The number was increased to 55 when Aristotle (384-322 B.C.) elaborated the plan in order to make it conform more nearly to the observed motions of the planets. Unlike many who preceded him, and practically all the Greek scholars who followed him, Aristotle regarded the spheres as actual physical machinery, and not as mathematical conventions.

The rotating spheres of Eudoxus represented fairly well the observed movements of the planets as they were not very accurately recorded in those early times. It gave a more convincing reason for the daily risings and settings of the planets than did the plan that succeeded it. But it kept the planets at invariable distances from the earth, and therefore could not account for the conspicuous changes in brightness of some of them.

7·12. The Plan of Epicycles. A second solution of Plato's problem is ascribed to Apollonius of Perga (third century B.C.) who is also known

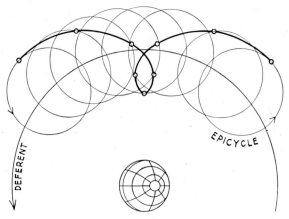

FIG. 7·12. The Motion of a Planet in the Ptolemaic System. The planet revolved in an epicycle whose center revolved in a larger circle around the earth.

for his work on conics. It involved circles instead of spheres, and gave a choice of the alternate plans of epicycles and eccentrics.

In the first plan the planet revolved in a smaller circle whose center moved meanwhile in a larger circle around the central earth. In the second plan the planet revolved in a large circle whose center was at some distance from the earth, either stationary or moving in a circle around the earth. Though both plans were subsequently employed, the first one proved the more generally useful, and in the interest of clearness will be the only one considered here.

The small circle in which the planet moved uniformly was called the *epicycle.* Its center, the *fictitious planet,* moved around the earth in the larger circle, or *deferent.* Fig. 7·12 shows how the plan could be employed to interpret the looped path of a planet among the constellations.

Hipparchus, whose work was done on the island of Rhodes chiefly between 146 and 126 B.C., adopted the plans of epicycles and eccentrics, and applied them in representing the motions of the sun and moon. An observer of remarkable ability, Hipparchus improved the astronomical instruments of the time, especially the astrolabe which is a combination of graduated circles and of sights like those still used on rifles. With these he determined the places of the celestial bodies with a precision that was not improved in any important way until the time of Tycho Brahe, seventeen centuries later. To facilitate the reduction of the observations, Hipparchus invented the subject of spherical trigonometry.

7·13. The Ptolemaic System. After three centuries had elapsed, the work of Hipparchus was continued by Ptolemy (Claudius Ptolemaeus),

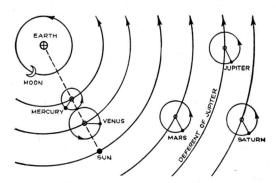

FIG. 7·13. The Ptolemaic System of Planetary Motions.

the last of the important Greek astronomers, who lived at Alexandria around the middle of the second century A.D.

In his great book, the *Syntaxis,* usually known by its later Arabian title, the *Almagest,* Ptolemy improved the theory of epicycles as applied to the sun and the moon, and extended it to the motions of the five planets. The whole theory is known, therefore, as the Ptolemaic system; its chief feature is the resolution of the complex observed motions into uniform circular ones centered at the earth.

In the simplest form of the theory (Fig. 7·13) each planet moved from west to east on the circumference of a small circle, once around, counted from apogee to apogee, in the planet's synodic period. The center of the epicycle circled from west to east around the earth; the period of this motion was the sidereal year for an inferior planet, and not far from its sidereal period for a superior planet. The main features of the planets' movements among the constellations, including the loops, were thus represented by two uniform circular motions in the same direction, the circles being appropriately inclined to the ecliptic.

The chief epicycles of the sun and moon (not shown in the diagram) accounted for their variable speeds which are really caused by the eccentric orbits of the earth and moon. The motions in these epicycles were from east to west, once around in a sidereal year and sidereal month respectively, counting the period again from apogee to apogee, as the ancients did. The westward daily motions of all these bodies was shared somehow with that of the sphere of the stars out beyond the deferent of Saturn.

Notice in the Figure that the centers of the epicycles of Mercury and Venus remained on the line joining the earth and sun, and that the line from the superior planet to the center of its epicycle was parallel to the earth's direction from the sun. It seems strange that these requirements did not sooner promote the simplification effected by putting the sun in the center of the system.

The problem of representing the planetary motions by circles centered at the earth, when these motions really center at the sun, was an exceedingly difficult one. Ptolemy's work went further than has been described here; and during the long period from his time to the revival of learning in Europe, Arabian scholars in Persia, Egypt, Spain, and elsewhere sought to bring the geocentric system more nearly into accord with the observed motions. Epicycles were piled upon epicycles, until the whole construction became extremely cumbersome, but without satisfactory improvement in its effectiveness.

7·14. The Copernican System. Nicolas Copernicus (1473-1543) inaugurated a new era in astronomy by discarding the ancient theory of the central, motionless earth. In his book, *On the Revolutions of the Celestial Bodies,* published shortly before his death, he showed that all these motions can be interpreted more reasonably on the theory of the central sun. He assumed that the earth revolves around the sun once a year, and rotates daily on its axis.

In the Copernican system the sun was stationary at the center.

Around it the planets revolved *uniformly* in *circles* as before, including the earth and its attendant, the moon. Epicycles were therefore still required, but their number was smaller than before. With the assumption of the earth's rotation from west to east, the daily circling of all the celestial bodies from east to west became simply the scenery passing by.

No longer required to rotate around the earth, the sphere of the stars could be imagined larger than before. This altered condition and the sun's new status as the dominant member of the system prepared the way for the thought that the stars are remote suns.

It is not surprising that the heliocentric theory met with disapproval on almost every hand; for it was a radical departure from the common-sense view of the world that had persisted from the very beginning of reflections about it. The new theory was supported at the outset by no convincing proof; its greater simplicity in representing celestial motions was the only argument Copernicus could offer in its defense. Moreover, it seemed to be discredited by the evidence of the celestial bodies themselves, as Tycho presently discovered.

7·15. Tycho's Observations.

Tycho Brahe (1546-1601), native of the extreme south of Sweden, then a part of Denmark, spent the most fruitful years of his life at the fine observatory which the king of Denmark had built for him on the island of Hven, about 20 miles northeast of Copenhagen. During the last two years of his life, his observations were made at a castle near Prague.

The instruments of Tycho's observatory were mostly constructed of metal; they had larger and more accurately divided circles than any previously used. His improved methods of observing and his allowance for effects of refraction, which observers before him had neglected, made it possible to determine the places of celestial bodies in the sky with the average error of an observation scarcely exceeding a minute of arc. This was remarkable precision for observations made through the plain sights that preceded the telescope.

Tycho was unable to detect any annual variations in the relative directions of the stars, which he believed would be noticeable if the earth revolved around the sun. Either the stars were so remote (at least 7000 times as far away as the sun) that their very small parallaxes could not be observed with his instruments, or else the earth did not go around the sun. Since the first alternative required stellar distances that seemed impossibly great, Tycho rejected the Copernican assumption of the earth's revolution.

As a substitute for the Copernican system, the *Tychonic system* again placed the earth stationary at the center. In the new system, the sun and moon circled around the earth, but all the other planets revolved around the sun. Aside from slight effects such as parallax and aberration, the Tychonic and the Copernican systems were identical for calculations of the relative positions of the celestial bodies at any time.

Tycho's most noteworthy contribution to the improvement of the planetary theory was his long-continued determinations of the positions of the planets in the sky (their right ascensions and declinations at different times). These data provided the material for Kepler's studies which resulted in his three laws of planetary motions.

7·16. Kepler's Laws. John Kepler (1571-1630), a German, joined Tycho at Prague in 1600, and as his successor inherited the records of

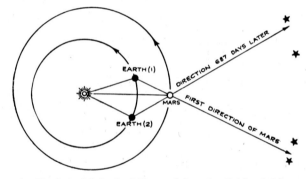

FIG. 7·16. Kepler's Method of Determining the Orbit of Mars. Pairs of apparent positions of Mars separated by its sidereal period of 687 days gave the planet's direction and distance in astronomical units from the sun.

Tycho's many observations of the places of the planets. Beginning with the recorded places of Mars, Kepler at first undertook to represent them in the traditional way by combinations of epicycles and eccentrics, but was unable to fit them all as closely as their high accuracy seemed to require. Experimenting finally with ellipses having the sun at one focus, he was astonished to see the large discrepancies between theory and observation disappear.

Tycho's observations of the planets' right ascensions and declinations gave only their directions from the earth at the various dates. Kepler required for his studies their directions and distances from the sun. This he accomplished by the following device, as Fig. 7·16 is intended to show.

Consider the case of Mars whose sidereal period is 687 days, and neglect for the present purpose the inclination of its orbit to the ecliptic. Compare two observations of the planet made 687 days apart. At the end of this interval Mars has returned to the same place in its orbit, while the earth is 43 days' journey west of its original place. Accordingly, the observed directions of Mars on the two occasions differ widely, and by their intersection show where the planet is situated in space. By comparing pairs of observations in different parts of the planet's orbit it is possible to determine the form of the orbit and its size relative to the earth's orbit.

Kepler's first two laws were published in 1609, in his book entitled *Commentaries on the Motion of Mars;* the third, or harmonic law, whose formulation gave him greater trouble, appeared in 1618, in his book on *The Harmony of the World.* Kepler's laws are as follows:

1. *The orbit of each planet is an ellipse with the sun at one of its foci.*

2. *Each planet revolves so that the line joining it to the sun sweeps over equal areas in equal intervals of time.*

3. *The squares of the periods of any two planets are in the same proportion as the cubes of their mean distances from the sun.*

These laws assert that the planets revolve around the sun, but they do not necessarily include the earth as one of the planets. It was not yet possible to choose between the Copernican and Tychonic systems. The laws bring to an end the practice, that had prevailed since its proposal, of representing planetary movements only by combinations of uniform circular motions.

The third law determines the mean distances of all the planets from the sun in terms of the distance of one of them, when their sidereal periods of revolution have been observed. The usual yardstick is the earth's mean distance from the sun, which is accordingly known as the astronomical unit.

7·17. The Scale of the Solar System. The problem of determining the scale of the solar system as accurately as possible may be called the solar parallax problem, because the sun's geocentric parallax is often regarded as the constant that is required. Unlike the parallax of the moon (5·3), the sun's parallax cannot be determined satisfactorily by observing the difference between the directions of the sun's center from two stations on the earth. The sun's parallax is smaller, while the error in measuring it is likely to be greater owing to the unavailability of stars in the daytime to serve as reference points.

Since the relative dimensions of planetary orbits are given by Kepler's third law, one observed distance provides the scale of miles as well as another. Mars at its closest approach and some even more neighborly asteroids, such as Eros, are more suitable than the sun itself for this purpose; their parallaxes are greater and their places among the stars can be accurately observed. When the parallax of one of these bodies has been determined, it can serve for the calculation of the sun's parallax. There are also gravitational methods and others involving the velocity of light, which we do not examine here.

The recent reliable determinations of the solar parallax have given values not far from 8″.80. By international agreement *The American Ephemeris and Nautical Almanac* and the astronomical almanacs of other nations have adopted 8″.80 as the value of the solar parallax. The sun's mean distance from the earth is accordingly 92,900,000 miles.

It is important to mention that an extensive undertaking to determine the solar parallax from observations of the asteroid Eros at its close approach in 1931 resulted in a somewhat smaller value of the parallax. This program was arranged by the Solar Parallax Commission of the International Astronomical Union. The report of this Commission (1941) gave the value of the solar parallax as 8″.790 ± 0″.001. The corresponding value of the astronomical unit is 93,000,000 miles.

7·18. Galileo; the Motions of Bodies. While Kepler was engaged in his studies of planetary orbits, Galileo Galilei (1564-1642), in Italy, was finding new evidence with the telescope in favor of the Copernican system.

Galileo's discovery of four bright satellites revolving around the planet Jupiter dispelled the objection that the moon would be left behind if the earth really revolved around the sun. His discovery that Venus exhibits phases like those of the moon discredited the specification of the Ptolemaic system (Fig. 7·13) which kept the planet always on the earthward side of the sun, where it could never increase beyond the crescent phase. His explanation that the movements of the spots across the sun's disk are owing to the sun's rotation provided an argument by analogy for the earth's rotation as well.

But Galileo's chief contribution to our knowledge of the planetary movements was his pioneer work on the motions of bodies in general. His conclusion that an undisturbed body continues to move uniformly in a straight line, or to remain at rest, and his studies of the rate of change of motion of a body not left to itself prepared the way for a new viewpoint in astronomy. The interest was beginning to shift from the kinematics to the dynamics of the solar system—from the courses of the planets to mighty forces controlling them.

THE LAW OF GRAVITATION

7·19. Force Equals Mass Times Acceleration. The concept of forces acting throughout the universe originates in our own experience with the things around us. If an object at rest, that is free to move, is pulled or pushed, it responds by moving in the direction of the pull or push. We say that force is applied to the object, and, with allowance for disturbing factors such as air resistance and surface friction, we estimate the force by the mass of the object that is moved, and the acceleration, or rate at which its motion changes. In general, the acceleration of a body anywhere in any direction implies a force acting on it in that direction, and the amount of the force is found by multiplying the mass of the body by its acceleration, or $f = ma$.

Acceleration is defined as rate of change of velocity. Since *velocity* is not merely speed, but *directed speed,* acceleration may appear as changing speed or changing direction, or both.

A falling stone illustrates the first case. Its behavior is represented by the relations:

$$v = v_0 + at; \qquad s = v_0 t + \tfrac{1}{2} at^2,$$

where v_0 is the speed when first observed, a is the acceleration toward the earth (about 32.2 feet/sec^2), v and s are its speed and the distance it has fallen after t seconds. If the stone starts at rest ($v_0 = 0$), it will fall 16.1 feet in the first second, 48.3 feet in the next second, and so on, getting up speed at the rate of 32.2 feet/sec^2.

A planet moving in a circular orbit illustrates acceleration in direction only; its speed is constant. If the planet describes an elliptic orbit, the speed also changes in accordance with Kepler's second law.

7·20. The Laws of Motion. The conclusions of Galileo and others concerning the relations between bodies and their motions were consolidated by Newton (1642-1727), in the *Principia* (1687), into three statements which form the basis of all mechanics. They are:

1. *Every body persists in its state of rest or of uniform motion in a straight line unless it is compelled to change that state by a force impressed on it.* In this event:

2. *The acceleration is directly proportional to the force, and inversely to the mass of the body, and it takes place in the direction of the straight line in which the force acts.*

3. *To every action there is always an equal and contrary reaction;* or, *the mutual actions of any two bodies are equal and oppositely directed.*

The First Law states that a body subject to no external influences moves uniformly in a straight line forever, unless it happens never to have acquired any motion. It contradicts the traditional view that rest is the natural state, and motion the enforced one. Up to the time of Galileo, the continued motion of a planet required explanation; since that time, uniform motion is accepted as no more surprising than the existence of matter. Changing motion demands an accounting.

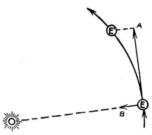

FIG. 7·20. The Earth's Revolution Explained by the Laws of Motion. At the position *E* the earth if undisturbed would continue on to *A*, by the first law of motion. It arrives at *E'* instead, having in the meantime fallen toward the sun the distance *EB*.

The Second Law defines force in the usual way. Since nothing is said to the contrary, it implies that the effect of the force is the same whether the body is originally at rest or in motion, and whether or not it is acted on at the same time by other forces.

The Third Law states that the force between any two bodies is the same in the two directions. The earth attracts the sun just as much as the sun attracts the earth, so that $f_S = f_E$, or $m_S a_S = m_E a_E$. But the effects of the equal forces, that is to say, the accelerations, are not the same if the masses are unequal; the ratio of the accelerations is the inverse ratio of the masses affected.

7·21. The Law of Gravitation. By means of his laws of motion and by mathematical reasoning, Newton succeeded in reducing Kepler's geometrical description of the planetary system to a single comprehensive physical law. It will serve our present purpose to simply outline the sequence and chief results of Newton's inquiry, reserving the details for a more advanced study.

According to Kepler's first law, the path of a planet is an ellipse; it is continually curving. Consequently, the planet's motion is continually accelerated and, by the second law of motion, *a force is always acting on the planet.*

Since the planet moves, by Kepler's second law, so that a line joining it to the sun describes equal areas in equal times, it is easily proved that *the force is directed toward the sun.* Kepler had suspected that the sun had something to do with the planet's revolution around it, but he did not understand the connection.

Again from Kepler's first law, since the orbit is an ellipse with the sun at one focus, it can be proved that *the force varies inversely as the square of the planet's distance from the sun*. An elliptic orbit would also result if the force varied directly as the distance, but in this event the sun would be at the center of the ellipse, not at one focus.

From Kepler's third law and the third law of motion it can be shown that *the attractive force between the sun and any planet varies directly as the product of their masses*. In addition, the moon's revolution is controlled by precisely the same force directed toward the earth. While Newton's experience did not extend beyond the solar system, he concluded that the same force operates everywhere. These were the steps that led to the formulation of the *law of gravitation*:

Every particle of matter in the universe attracts every other particle with a force that varies directly as the product of their masses, and inversely as the square of the distance between them.

7·22. Examining the Law of Gravitation.

The law of gravitation provides the key for the interpretation of the physical universe as an orderly system. Since it constitutes the "rules of the game," the importance of understanding its meaning cannot be urged too strongly. The statement is:

$$f = Gm_1m_2/d^2,$$

where f is the force; m_1 and m_2 are the masses of the two particles whose distance apart is d.

(1) *The constant of gravitation, G,* is defined as the force of attraction between two unit masses at unit distance apart. If $m_1 = m_2 = 1$ gram, and d is 1 centimeter, then $G = f$. This constant is believed to be the same wherever in the universe the experiment may be tried, regardless of other physical characteristics of the particles, or of surrounding conditions. It is a universal constant, like the speed of light; but it is even more remarkable as a constant, for the speed of light is reduced by an interposing medium, such as glass, while the force of gravitation is unaffected by anything placed between the attracting bodies.

The value of G is best determined in the physical laboratory by the method first tried by Cavendish about 1798. It consists in measuring the minute attractions of metallic balls, or cylinders. Heyl's determination (1930) at the United States Bureau of Standards is:

Constant of gravitation = 6.670×10^{-8}

in the c.g.s. system. Thus the attraction between gram masses 1 cm apart is a 15-millionth of a dyne. While it is very feeble between ordinary bodies, the gravitational force becomes important between the great masses of celestial bodies. The *Gaussian constant of gravitation* is much used in astronomical calculations; it is the acceleration due to the sun's attraction at the earth's mean distance from the sun.

(2) *The attraction of a sphere is toward its center,* as though the whole mass were concentrated there. Owing to their rotations the celestial bodies are not spheres, but the flattening at their poles is usually so small and the intervening spaces are so great that the distances between their centers may be used ordinarily in calculating their attractions. The attraction of a spheroid in the direction of its equator exceeds that of a sphere of the same mass, and it is smaller in the direction of its poles; but the difference becomes very slight with increasing distance.

(3) *The acceleration of the attracted body is independent of its mass.* If the attractive force, f_1, on this body is replaced by the equivalent $m_1 a_1$ in the statement of the law of gravitation, the mass, m_1, cancels out, and the acceleration:

$$a_1 = Gm_2/d^2$$

of the attracted body does not depend on its own mass. Galileo is said to have demonstrated this fact by dropping large and small weights from the leaning tower in Pisa. They fell together, thereby discrediting the traditional idea that heavy bodies fall faster than light ones.

The second, or attracting body, as we have chosen to consider it, is itself attracted and has the acceleration $a_2 = Gm_1/d^2$ in the direction of the first. In Galileo's experiment this factor need not be taken into account. It becomes important when the two bodies have comparable masses. The acceleration of one body with respect to the other is the sum:

$$a_1 + a_2 = G\frac{(m_1 + m_2)}{d^2}.$$

Thus *the relative acceleration of two bodies varies as the sum of their masses.*

(4) *Two bodies, such as the earth and the sun, mutually revolve* around a common center. Imagine the earth and the sun joined by a stout rod. The point of support at which the two bodies would exactly balance is their *center of mass;* it is the point around which they revolve in orbits of the same shape. If the masses of the earth and the sun were equal, this point would be halfway between their centers. Since the sun's mass is 332,000 times as great as the earth's mass, the center of mass is not far from the sun's center. The relation is:

$$\frac{\text{sun's center to center of mass}}{\text{earth's center to center of mass}} = \frac{\text{earth's mass}}{\text{sun's mass}}.$$

The distance from the sun's center to the center of mass of the earth-sun system is therefore 92,900,000 miles divided by 332,000, which equals 280 miles. Thus the ancient problem of whether the earth or the sun revolves no longer concerns us. Both revolve, though the center of mass is within the sun.

7·23. Kepler's Third Law Restated. In its original form (7·16) Kepler's harmonic law gave a relation between the periods and distances of the planets. As it is now derived from the law of gravitation, the relation involves the masses of the planets as well; it is as follows:

The squares of the periods of any two planets, *each multiplied by the sum of the sun's mass and the planet's mass,* are in the same proportion as the cubes of their mean distances from the sun.

Consider two planets, Mars and the earth, revolving around the sun. Let m represent the mass, P the sidereal period of revolution, and d the mean distance from the sun. The revised harmonic law is in this case:

$$\frac{(m_S + m_M)P^2{}_{MS}}{(m_S + m_E)P^2{}_{ES}} = \frac{d^3{}_{MS}}{d^3{}_{ES}}.$$

The law in its original form was not far from correct, because the masses of all the planets are so small in comparison with the sun's mass that the ratio of the sums of the masses is nearly unity.

Let the units of time, distance, and mass in the above relation be respectively the sidereal year, the earth's mean distance from the sun, and the combined mass of sun and earth. The denominators then disappear because their terms are all unity. Further, in place of Mars and the sun take any two mutually revolving bodies *anywhere,* denoting them by the subscripts 1 and 2. They may be the sun and a planet, a planet and its satellite, or a double star. In the more general form Kepler's third law becomes:

$$(m_1 + m_2) = \frac{d_{12}{}^3}{P_{12}{}^2}.$$

The sum of the masses of any two mutually revolving bodies equals the cube of their mean linear separation divided by the square of their period of revolution.

In this way, and in others, the masses of the sun and of planets having satellites have been determined. The law does not serve for the solitary planets, such as Mercury and Pluto, nor for the asteroids, the satellites themselves, the comets, and the meteor swarms. Their masses become known only in case they noticeably disturb the orbits of their neighbors.

7·24. The Relative Orbit of Two Bodies. We have seen (7·22) that two bodies, such as the earth and sun, mutually revolve around their common center of mass, which is nearer the more massive body, so that the less massive component has the larger orbit. It can be shown (1) that the orbits are independent of any motions of the center of mass, that is to say, of the system as a whole; (2) that they are the same in form, and that this is also the form of the *relative orbit* of one body with respect to the other. The relative orbit is often the only one that can be calculated; it is the one understood when one body is said to revolve around another.

Kepler's first law states that the orbits of the planets are ellipses. Newton proved that the orbit of a body revolving in accordance with the law of gravitation must be a conic, of which the ellipse is an example.

The *conics,* or conic sections, are the ellipse, parabola, and hyperbola. They are sections cut from a circular cone, which for this purpose is the surface generated by one of two intersecting lines when it is revolved around the other as an axis, the angle between them remaining the same.

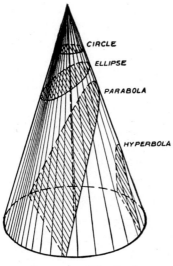

The ellipse (eccentricities o to 1) is obtained when the cutting plane passes entirely through the cone, so that the section is closed; when it passes at right angles to the axis the eccentricity is zero, and the section is a *circle.*

The parabola (eccentricity = 1) results when the cutting plane is parallel to an element of the cone. This curve extends an indefinite distance, its direction at the two ends approaching parallelism. The orbits of many comets are nearly parabolas. All parabolas, like all circles, have the same form, but not the same size.

FIG. 7·24. The Conics.

The hyperbola (eccentricity greater than 1) is obtained when the cone is cut at a still smaller angle with the axis. It is an open curve like the parabola, but the directions of the two ends approach diverging lines. When a star passes another and is deflected by attraction from its original course, the orbit is hyperbolic; if it were repelled instead, its path would be the other branch of the hyperbola.

7·25. Form of the Relative Orbit. The particular conic in which a celestial body revolves is determined by the central force and the velocity with which the body is started; for it is evident that the curvature of the orbit depends on the deflection of the body in the direction of its companion, and the distance it has moved forward meanwhile in the orbit. This conclusion, among others, is derived formally from the *equation of energy:*

$$V^2 = G\,(m_1 + m_2)\left(\frac{2}{r} - \frac{1}{a}\right),$$

where V is the velocity of revolution when the two bodies are the distance r apart, and a is the semi-major axis of the resulting relative orbit.

It can be seen from this equation that the semi-major axis lengthens as the velocity is increased. For a moderate speed the orbit is an ellipse; for increasing speeds the length and eccentricity of the orbit grow greater, until a critical speed is reached at which the orbit becomes parabolic.

If the orbit is a circle, then $a = r$ in the above formula, so that V^2 is proportional to $1/r$. If it is a parabola, a is infinite and V^2 is proportional to $2/r$. There- fore, if the speed of a body revolving in a circular orbit is multiplied by the square root of 2, or about 1.41, its orbit becomes a para- bola. Since the earth's orbit is nearly circu- lar, the *parabolic velocity* at our distance from the sun is the earth's velocity, 18½ miles a second, multiplied by 1.41, or 26 miles a second. If its velocity should ever become as great as this value, the earth would depart from the sun's vicinity. Many comets and meteor swarms, whose aphelion points are far beyond the orbit of Neptune, cross the earth's orbit with speeds of this order.

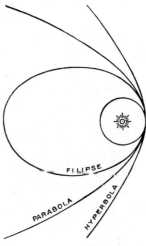

FIG. 7·25. Orbits Having the Same Perihelion Dis- tance. The size and eccen- tricity of the orbit increase with the speed of the revolv- ing body at perihelion.

7·26. The Elements of the Orbit are the specifications necessary to define it uniquely, and to fix the place of the revolving body in the orbit at any time. The elements of the elliptical orbit of a planet, with their symbols, are the following:

(1) *Inclination to ecliptic, i.* If the plane of the orbit is inclined to the ecliptic plane (*i* denotes the numerical value of the inclina- tion), the line of their intersection is the *line of nodes*, which passes through the sun's posi- tion. The *ascending node* is the point at which the planet crosses the ecliptic plane going from south to north.

(2) *Longitude of the ascending node,* ☊. It is the celestial longitude of this node as seen from the sun, that is, the angle between the line of nodes and the direction of the vernal equinox. It fixes the orientation of the orbit plane, and, together with the inclination, defines this plane precisely.

(3) *Angle from the ascending node to the perihelion point, ω.* It is meas- ured from the ascending node along the orbit in the direction of the planet's motion, which must be specified; it gives the direction of the major axis of the orbit with respect to the line of nodes, and thus describes the orientation of the orbit in its plane.

(4) *Semi-major axis, a.* This element, which is also known as the planet's *mean distance* from the sun, defines the size of the orbit and, very nearly, the period of revolution; for by Kepler's third law, P^2 is propor- tional to a^3 regardless of the shape of the ellipse.

(5) *Eccentricity, e.* The eccentricity of the ellipse is the ratio c/a, where c is the sun's distance from the center of the ellipse (one half the distance between the foci). These five elements define the relative orbit uniquely.

(6) *Time of passing perihelion, T.* This element and the value of the period of revolution permit the determination of the planet's position in the orbit at any time.

If the orbit is circular, the longitude of perihelion drops out; if it is a parabola, the semi-major axis, which is then infinite, is replaced as an element by the *perihelion distance, q,* which defines the size of the parabola.

When the elements become known, the position of the planet or comet at any time can be computed; this, combined with the earth's position in its

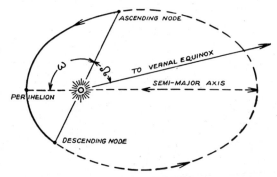

FIG. 7·26. The Orbit of a Planet. The plane of the planet's orbit is inclined to the plane of the earth's orbit, represented by the plane of the paper.

orbit at that time, gives finally the apparent place of the object as seen from the earth, its right ascension and declination. A tabulation of such places at regular intervals, often of a day, is an *ephemeris.* The astronomical almanacs give such tabulations for the sun, moon, and principal planets for each year in advance.

7·27. Perturbations.

Thus far we have dealt with the revolution of a planet around the sun as though the planet were acted on only by the sun's attraction. This is the *problem of two bodies,* which is solved directly and completely in terms of the law of gravitation. But the planet is subject to the attractions of all the other members of the solar system as well, so that it departs in a complex manner from simple elliptic motion. Thus we have in practice the *problem of three or more bodies,* whose solution is much more troublesome. It is fortunate for the orderly description of planetary movements that the masses of the planets are very small in comparison with the sun's mass, and that their distances apart are very great. If it were not so, the mutual disturbances of the revolving bodies would introduce so much confusion that simple approximations, such as Kepler's laws, would have been impossible.

Since the sun's mass is dominant in the solar system, it is possible to derive at first the planet's orbit with reference to the sun alone, and then to consider the departures from this simple elliptic motion that are imposed by the attractions of other members of the system. *Perturbations* are the alterations so produced. As examples, the eccentricities and inclinations of planetary orbits fluctuate, perihelia advance, and nodes regress. All perturbations are oscillatory in the long run, so that they are not likely to permanently alter the arrangement of the solar system.

7·28. The Theory of Relativity. In Newtonian mechanics the emphasis is on the *force* that causes a planet to revolve around the sun. The relativity theory of Einstein directs the attention to the *course* the planet pursues. In otherwise perfectly empty space a body would move in accordance with the first law of motion. But the presence of a second body alters the properties of the space. In the vicinity of the sun the natural path of a planet is a conic, just as its path in otherwise empty space is a straight line. No attractive force is acting in either case. This is one aspect of the theory of relativity.

The mathematical developments of the theory are so complex that we leave them to the specialist in this field and simply notice some results. Under ordinary conditions in the laboratory and in space the occurrences are represented practically as well whether the formulae of Newton or Einstein are employed. A few exceptional cases are known in which predictions of phenomena on the two theories differ widely enough to be subject to the test of observation. These cases involve the presence of large masses or velocities great enough to have some significance in comparison with the velocity of light. They relate mostly to celestial phenomena.

Three astronomical test cases of the theory of relativity will be mentioned in later Chapters. In each case the observational evidence appears to support this theory. They are: (1) The apparent outward displacements of stars near the sun; (2) The faster advance of Mercury's perihelion than is predicted by the law of gravitation; (3) The displacement toward the red of the lines in the spectrum of the companion of Sirius.

REVIEW QUESTIONS

1. State three ways in which the bright planets are distinguished in the sky from the stars.

2. Explain the difference between the sidereal and the synodic period of a planet. Name the two principal planets having the longest synodic periods, and explain why they are the longest.

3. State the phase of the planet Venus at (a) inferior conjunction; (b) superior conjunction; (c) greatest elongation; (d) greatest brilliancy.

4. Describe and explain the apparent motion of a planet among the stars.

5. State the chief contribution to knowledge of planetary motions made by each of the following: (a) Copernicus; (b) Tycho; (c) Kepler; (d) Galileo; (e) Newton.

6. Distinguish between the Ptolemaic, Copernican, and present view of the planetary motions.

7. Why is the sun's mean distance determined more reliably from the parallaxes of certain planets than directly from the sun's parallax?

8. Explain that a planet moving uniformly in a circular orbit is continuously accelerated.

9. Show that Newton's first and second laws of motion contain little more than the definition of force.

10. State the law of gravitation. How is the force between two bodies affected (a) if the original distance between them is doubled? (b) if the distance is unaltered, but the mass of each body is doubled?

11. Supposing that Galileo actually made the experiment of dropping objects of different weights simultaneously from the leaning tower in Pisa, explain by means of the law of gravitation (neglecting air resistance) that they reached the ground at the same instant.

12. Why is it easier to determine the mass of a planet having a satellite than of one without a satellite?

13. It is improbable that the orbit of a body revolving around the sun can be either a circle or a parabola. Explain.

14. Supply the term that is defined by each of the following:

(a) A planet revolving within the earth's orbit.
(b) The westward movement of a planet among the stars.
(c) An early view of the planetary system, which supposed that the sun revolved around the earth and that the other planets revolved around the sun.
(d) Rate of change of velocity.
(e) The force of attraction between two one-gram masses one centimeter apart.
(f) The specifications that define the orbit of a planet and the planet's position in the orbit at any particular time.

PROBLEMS

1. The sidereal period of Venus is 224.7 days. Calculate the synodic period of this planet.
   Answer: 583.9 days.

2. Taking as examples the orbits of the sun, the earth, and Mars, show by diagrams that the relative positions of the three bodies at a particular time can be represented equally as well by the Ptolemaic, Copernican, or Tychonic systems.

3. A ball near the earth's surface falls from rest 16 feet in the first second, or one half the acceleration. The moon's distance from the earth's

center is about 60 times the radius of the earth. Neglecting the masses of moon and ball, show (7·22) that the moon "falls" toward the earth about a twentieth of an inch in a second.

4. Employing Kepler's third law in its general form and neglecting the masses, calculate the period of a satellite revolving close to the earth's surface. (Compare this satellite with the moon. Take the moon's sidereal period as $27\frac{1}{3}$ days).

Answer: $1^h 24^m$.

5. The mean distance of Jupiter's ninth satellite from the planet is about one sixth the earth's distance from the sun, and its period of revolution around the planet is about 2.1 years. Neglecting the mass of the satellite, show that Jupiter is about a thousandth as massive as the sun.

Saturn, October 21, 1941. (*Photographed by B. Lyot at Pic du Midi, France*)

CHAPTER VIII

THE OTHER PLANETS

MERCURY — VENUS — MARS AND ITS SATELLITES — THE ASTEROIDS — JUPITER AND ITS SATELLITES — SATURN; ITS RINGS AND SATELLITES — URANUS AND NEPTUNE; THEIR SATELLITES — PLUTO — TABLES OF THE PLANETS AND SATELLITES

MERCURY

Nearest the sun, at the mean distance of 36 million miles, Mercury therefore revolves the most rapidly of all the planets; its speed at perihelion is 36 miles a second, or twice the speed of the earth's revolution, and its period of revolution is only 88 days. Its orbit has greater eccentricity (0.2) and higher inclination to the ecliptic than has any other principal planet except Pluto. Mercury is the smallest of the principal planets; its diameter, 3100 miles, is only 50 per cent greater than the moon's diameter. Mercury is the only planet whose periods of rotation and revolution are the same.

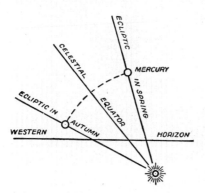

FIG. 8·1. Mercury as Evening Star. It is most conspicuous as evening star at greatest eastern elongations in the spring.

8·1. As Morning and Evening Star. Mercury is occasionally visible to the naked eye for a few days near the times of its greatest elongations, which take place, on the average, 22 days before and after inferior conjunctions. Since the synodic period is only 116 days, three western and as many eastern elongations may occur in the course of a year. They are by no means equally favorable. The apparent distance from the sun at greatest elongations varies from 28°, when the planet is at aphelion, to as little as 18° at perihelion.   Moreover, since the planet is never far from the ecliptic, it is highest in the sky at sunrise and sunset when the ecliptic is most inclined to the horizon.   This condition is fulfilled (1·19) for us in middle northern latitudes when the autumnal equinox is rising and the vernal equinox is setting.

As a morning star, therefore, Mercury is most conspicuous at greatest western elongations in September and October, and as evening star at greatest eastern elongations which occur in March and April.   It then appears in the twilight near the horizon as a star of the first magnitude—at times nearly as bright as Sirius, twinkling like a star because of its small size and low altitude.   Although most people have never seen it, this planet was known to astronomers of very early times.

The terms "morning star" and "evening star" are applied generally to appearances of the inferior planets, especially Venus because it is the more noticeable of the two.   But they are employed for the superior planets as well, to designate that they rise before or set after the sun.

8·2. Telescopic Appearance and Rotation.   Through the telescope Mercury shows phases as an inferior planet should (7·6).   The phase

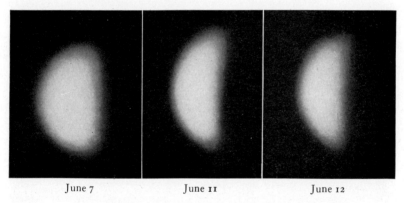

June 7   June 11   June 12

FIG. 8·2.   Mercury Near Eastern Elongation in 1934.   The phases are seen, but the markings on the disk can be glimpsed only on the original negatives. (*Photographed at Lowell Observatory*)

is full at superior conjunction, quarter near greatest elongation, and new at inferior conjunction.   The best views are likely to be obtained in the daytime, when the planet can be observed at a higher altitude.   Faint dark markings on the disk of Mercury have been discerned by experienced observers and have even been made out on some of the photographs.   These markings remain stationary on the sunlit hemisphere of the planet. The conclusion is that the period of Mercury's rotation is 88 days, the same as that of its revolution around the sun.

Mercury is so near the sun that it is evidently constrained by powerful sun-raised tides to rotate and revolve in the same period, just as the moon does in relation to the earth. If it were not for librations, the planet would have the same face always turned toward the sun. Owing to the considerable eccentricity of the orbit, the libration in longitude leaves scarcely 30 per cent of the planet's surface in permanent darkness.

8·3. Mercury Resembles the Moon. This planet does not greatly exceed the moon in diameter and mass, and therefore in surface gravity. The low velocity of escape (2.3 miles a second as compared with 1.5 miles a second at the moon's surface) suggests scarcely better success in retaining an atmosphere. The low albedo (0.07) is about the same as the moon's, and this small efficiency as a mirror probably has the same cause—the reflection of sunlight from a broken airless surface. That the planet is at least as mountainous as the moon is inferred from the similar or somewhat greater increase in its brightness between the quarter and full phases.

The surface of Mercury is subjected to even greater extremes of temperature than that of the moon. Radiometric measurements at the Mount Wilson Observatory indicate a maximum of 410° C (about 770° Fahrenheit) on the sunward side of the planet, which is hotter than the melting points of tin and lead. No radiation at all could be detected from the dark side; evidently the temperature there is extremely low. Mercury appears to contain both the hottest and the coldest places in the planetary system.

8·4. Advance of Perihelion. The major axis of Mercury's orbit rotates eastward at the rate of some 570″ a century, owing to the disturbing effects of Venus and other planets, which are subject to calculation. The French mathematician Leverrier, in 1845, found that the observed advance of the perihelion exceeded the predicted advance by about 40″ a century. This planet, which "seems to exist for no other reason than to throw discredit on astronomers," had to be reckoned with. Either the observations were at fault, or the planet was further disturbed by an unknown body, or else the law of gravitation, the basis of the calculations, had finally failed.

Leverrier reached the conclusion that the excessive motion of Mercury's perihelion was caused by an undiscovered planet revolving within the orbit of Mercury. But, despite careful searching for its transits

across the sun and for its appearance near the sun at times of total solar
eclipse, the supposed intra-Mercurial planet was not seen. Evidently it
did not exist. The problem remained.

Scientific and popular interest in the perihelion advance was re-
awakened, in 1915, when Einstein's general theory of relativity (7·28)
was successful in requiring an advance above that predicted by Newton's
theory of gravitation; the difference was in practical agreement with the
observed excess. This was the first physical test of the theory of relativity. It is one of the very few known differences between predictions
of the same effect by the two theories, which are great enough to be
tested by observation.

8·5. Transits of Mercury and Venus. The inferior planets usually
pass north or south of the sun at inferior conjunction, because their or-

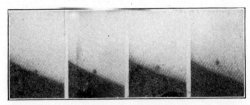

FIG. 8·5. Transit of Mercury. The planet appears as a small dot against
the sun's disk. The interval of time between the first and fourth exposures was
less than five minutes. (*Photographed at the Royal Observatory, Greenwich*)

bits are slightly inclined to the ecliptic. Occasionally they *transit,* or
cross the sun's disk. The additional condition necessary for a transit is
similar to the requirement for solar and lunar eclipses, namely, that the
earth must be near the line of the nodes of the planet's orbit.

The earth, as viewed from the sun, passes Mercury's nodes on May 8
and November 10. Transits are possible only within 3 days of the
former date, and within 5 days of the latter; this difference, owing to
the eccentricity of the planet's orbit, makes the November transits twice
as numerous as those in May. There are about 13 transits of Mercury
in a century. The latest one, on November 11, 1940, was partly visible
in the United States and Canada. The next transit, on November 14,
1953, will be wholly visible here. Transits of Mercury cannot be seen
without the telescope.

Transits of Venus are possible only within about two days before or
after June 7 and December 9, the dates when the earth passes the nodes
of this planet's path. They are much less frequent because the limits

are narrower, and also because conjunctions come less often.   At present
the transits of Venus come in pairs having a separation of eight years.
A pair of transits occurred in 1874 and 1882.   The next ones are due
June 8, 2004, and June 6, 2012.   Transits of Venus are visible without
the telescope.

VENUS

Venus, the familiar morning and evening star, is the brightest of the
planets.   It outshines all the celestial bodies except the sun and moon,
and near the times of greatest brilliancy it is plainly visible to the naked
eye at midday, when the attention is directed to it.   The second in order
from the sun, this planet revolves next within the earth's orbit at the
mean distance of 67 million miles from the sun, completing the circuit
of the sun in 225 days.   Its orbit is the most nearly circular in the
planetary system.   Its diameter is 7700 miles.   While Venus resembles
the earth in size, and also in mass and surface gravity, it is quite dis-
similar in its rotation and in the constitution of its atmosphere.

8·6. As Morning and Evening Star.   Since the orbit of Venus is
within the earth's orbit and nearly in the same plane with it, this planet,

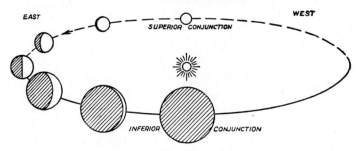

FIG. 8·6. Changing Phase and Apparent Size of Venus.

like Mercury, appears to oscillate with respect to the sun's position.   At
superior conjunction its distance from the earth is 160 million miles, or
the *sum* of the earth's and its own distance from the sun.   From this
position Venus emerges slowly to the east of the sun as the evening star;
it appears a little higher from night to night, and sets a little later after
sunset, until it reaches greatest eastern elongation, 220 days after the
time of superior conjunction.

The entire westward swing to greatest western elongation is accomplished in 144 days.   Midway, the planet passes nearly between the sun

and the earth into the morning sky. At inferior conjunction it is only 26 million miles from the earth, or the *difference* between the earth's and its own distance from the sun. This is the closest approach to us of any of the principal planets, although some of the asteroids come at times still closer to the earth. Turning eastward again after greatest western elongation, Venus moves slowly back to superior conjunction, again requiring 220 days for this part of the journey. The synodic period is accordingly 584 days.

Greatest brilliancy, as the evening or the morning star, occurs about 36 days preceding or following the times of inferior conjunction. On these occasions Venus is six times as bright as the planet Jupiter, and fifteen times as bright as Sirius, the brightest star.

TABLE 8·I.   DATES OF CONJUNCTIONS AND ELONGATIONS OF VENUS

Superior Conjunction	Greatest Elongation East (Evening Star)	Inferior Conjunction	Greatest Elongation West (Morning Star)
1944, June 27	1945, Feb. 2	1945, Apr. 15	1945, June 24
1946, Feb. 1	1946, Sept. 8	1946, Nov. 17	1947, Jan. 28
1947, Sept. 3	1948, Apr. 15	1948, June 24	1948, Sept. 3
1949, Apr. 16	1949, Nov. 20	1950, Jan. 31	1950, Apr. 11
1950, Nov. 14	1951, June 25	1951, Sept. 3	1951, Nov. 14
1952, June 24	1953, Jan. 31	1953, Apr. 13	1953, June 22

8·7. Through the Telescope; the Phases.

As a visual object with the telescope the most interesting feature of Venus is its phases, which Galileo, in 1610, was the first to observe. As an inferior planet, Venus exhibits the complete cycle of phases; it is full at superior conjunction, quarter at elongation, and new at inferior conjunction, although a thin illuminated crescent usually remains at the last named aspect, because as a rule the planet crosses a little above or below the sun.

Unlike the moon which is brightest at the full phase, Venus attains greatest brilliancy when its phase resembles that of the moon two days before the first quarter. At the full phase the planet's apparent diameter is 10″; at the new phase it has increased over six times, because the distance from the earth is then reduced to less than one sixth of the former value. Diminishing phase is more than offset by increasing apparent size, until the crescent phase is reached. At greatest brilliancy, the sunlit crescent sends us two and a half times as much light as does the smaller, fully illuminated disk at superior conjunction.

A small telescope gives a satisfactory view of the phases of Venus; but even the largest telescopes fail to reveal visually any conspicuous markings on the planet's surface. Indeed, to many observers the silvery disk has seemed always perfectly blank.

FIG. 8·7. Venus at Different Phases. (*Photographed at Lowell Observatory*)

8·8. The Problem of Venus' Rotation. The failure to observe well-defined and permanent markings on the planet's disk was responsible in former times for conflicting views about the rotation period. Some observers decided that the period was about a day, while others concluded that it was 225 days, equal to the revolution period. The present evidence seems to require the rejection of both.

Spectroscopic studies of Venus leave no doubt that the rotation is considerably slower than the earth's. If the period were less than two weeks, Doppler displacements of the lines of the spectrum could be detected. On the other hand, a period of rotation as long as 225 days seems improbable. If Venus turned one hemisphere always away from the sun, that hemisphere should be very cold. Yet the radiometric measurements give the temperature in the stratosphere of the dark side as $-25°$ C, which is much higher than the temperature of a similar region of the earth's atmosphere in the daytime. Venus' period of rotation is somewhere between these extremes; it may be around a month.

8·9. Cloudy Atmosphere of Venus. The appearance of a twilight zone is evidence that this planet has a considerable atmosphere. Near inferior conjunction the horns of the crescent are prolonged more than halfway around the disk, and at times a faint arc of the illuminated atmosphere extends entirely around the edge of the darkened side. If further evidence is needed, it is found in the high albedo, 0.59, of the planet and also in the invisibility of surface markings.

If the atmosphere of Venus were cloudless, any surface markings would be most likely to appear on photographs through red and infrared filters. This procedure gives the clearest views of the earth's surface from airplanes at high altitudes. But red and infrared photographs of Venus, made by Ross with the Mount Wilson telescopes, show no mark-

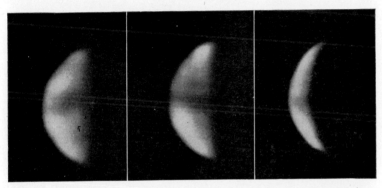

FIG. 8·9. Venus Photographed in Ultraviolet Light. The markings are in the planet's atmosphere. (*Photographed at Mount Wilson Observatory*)

ings at all. Some of the plates exposed behind blue filters show weak markings, and all those made with the ultraviolet light reveal considerable detail. The markings are cloud formations.

The planet's surface cannot be observed by present methods. Evidently we can look through the planet's atmosphere only as far as the upper levels of dense clouds. The cloud markings shown in the photographs change so rapidly that they are not helpful in determining the rotation period of Venus.

8·10. Abundance of Carbon Dioxide. Free oxygen and water vapor are not present in the atmosphere of Venus in sufficient amounts to leave their impression in the spectrum. A study of the infrared spectrum of Venus by Adams and Dunham at Mount Wilson confirms the conclusion and adds a significant discovery. Bands due to absorption by carbon dioxide appear, and in such strength as to indicate a surprising abundance of this compound. There may be ten thousand times as much carbon dioxide above the cloudbanks of Venus as in the entire atmosphere of the earth. Under such a heavy blanket the surface of the planet could have a temperature as high as the ordinary boiling point of water.

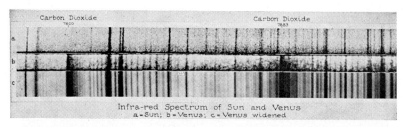

FIG. 8·10. Spectra of Sun and Venus Compared. Bands of carbon dioxide are prominent in the spectrum of Venus. (*Photographed at Mount Wilson Observatory*)

Sometimes called the "earth's twin sister," Venus appears to have little family resemblance after all, and to be unattractive as an abode for people like ourselves.

Mars and Its Satellites

The red planet Mars is next in order beyond the earth. It revolves in its rather eccentric orbit at the mean distance of 142 million miles from the sun, completing the sidereal revolution in 687 days. The synodic period is 780 days. Inconspicuous at times, it occasionally becomes a brilliant object and sometimes outshines Jupiter, its lurid light contrasting in a striking way with the pale yellow hue of that planet. Its diameter is scarcely more than half the earth's diameter. Through its fairly transparent atmosphere the surface features can be viewed with the telescope more clearly than those of any other planet.

8·11. Favorable Oppositions of Mars. A superior planet is best placed for observation when it is opposite the sun; the planet is then nearest the earth and is visible throughout the night. In the case of Mars another factor is introduced by the considerable eccentricity of the orbit (0.09) and the resulting range in its distance at the different oppositions. *Favorable oppositions* occur when the planet is also near perihelion. On these occasions the distance from the earth may be less than 35 million miles and the brightness exceeds that of any other planet except Venus.

Oppositions of Mars recur at intervals of the synodic period, which

is nearly two months longer than two years. Thus each opposition is
two months later than the preceding one. Favorable oppositions recur
at intervals of 15 or 17 years, usually in August or September; on
August 28 the earth has the same heliocentric longitude as the perihelion
of Mars. The next favorable opposition will occur in 1956.

On these favorable occasions the planet may attain an apparent diameter of 25″, so that a telescope magnifying only 75 times makes Mars

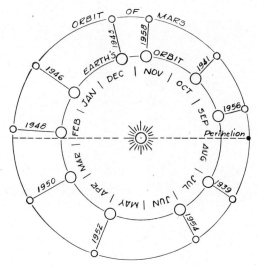

FIG. 8·11. Varying Distances of Mars at Opposition. The latest favorable
opposition occurred in 1939. The next will occur in 1956.

appear as large as the moon does to the unaided eye. Much of our
knowledge of Mars has been gained around the times of favorable
opposition.

8·12. Viewed with the Telescope under ordinary atmospheric conditions and by an inexperienced observer Mars is likely to be disappointing. What is glimpsed seems meager in contrast with the varied detail
that astronomers describe and exhibit in their drawings and photographs.
These observers have made use of moments of exceptionally steady
atmospheric conditions. In many places such moments rarely come.

Three fifths of the surface of Mars has a fairly uniform orange hue,
which accounts for the ruddy glow of the planet in our skies. White
caps appear alternately around the poles. Each cap expands rapidly as
winter comes on in that hemisphere and shrinks with the approach of

summer. The southern cap, which is somewhat the larger, has attained
a diameter of 3700 miles; it then extended more than halfway from the
pole to the equator. As a cap retreats toward the pole, the main body
may leave behind a small white spot isolated for a time as though on
the summit or the cooler slope of a hill. Transient white spots make
their appearance over other regions of the planet.

Dark markings are seen in a variety of sizes and shapes and colors.
They are permanent features of the surface, though they vary in inten-

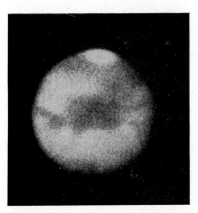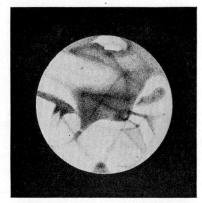

FIG. 8·12. Photograph and Drawing of Mars. The south polar cap is at
the top. The large "sea" in the center is Mare Erythraeum. Several canals are
clearly shown. (*Photograph with red filter, and drawing by R. J. Trumpler,
Lick Observatory*)

sity and in color. Formerly supposed to be bodies of water, they were
accordingly named seas, lakes, bogs, canals, and so on; and these designations on the early maps have survived, like the lunar "seas." Prominent among them are Syrtis Major (Great Bog) and Solis Lacus (Lake
of the Sun).

8·13. Mars Photographed Through Filters. Photographs through
filters of different colors are effective in distinguishing between surface
and atmospheric features. The principle involved has been mentioned
before (8·9). The reddening of the sun as it sinks toward the horizon
demonstrates the ability of red light to penetrate farther through our
atmosphere than blue or violet light. The latter colors are more readily
scattered by the air, as is also shown by the blue of the sky. Accordingly, the clearest views of a planet's surface ought to be obtained on
photographs through red filters; its atmospheric features ought to be
emphasized when violet filters are employed.

The white polar caps are more conspicuous when photographed in their violet light. They appear to be surface features with fog banks above them. Transitory bright spots, which last only a few hours, are patches of fog; others, which persist for a few days and are conspicuous in photographs with yellow filters, appear to be dust clouds. The dark markings are clearest in red and infrared light and are accordingly surface markings, as would be expected from their permanence.

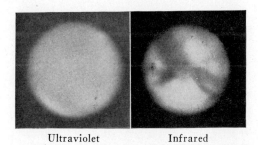

Ultraviolet   Infrared

FIG. 8·13. Photographs of Mars in Ultraviolet and Infrared Light. The polar caps are shown in ultraviolet light, while the dark surface markings are brought out clearly in infrared light. (*Photographed at Lick Observatory*)

8·14. Rotation of Mars. The period of rotation is $24^h 37^m 22^s.58$. The rotation of Mars has the same direction as the earth's rotation, and its period so nearly equals the earth's period that at the same hour from day to day almost the same face of the planet is presented to us, except that everything has stepped backward ten degrees. Thus the various markings pass slowly in review, completing their apparent backward revolutions in about 38 days. The permanence and definiteness of the dark markings, and the fact that they have been observed and mapped for 275 years, allows the rotation period to be determined with a high degree of accuracy.

The inclination of the planet's equator to the plane of its orbit is nearly the same as the angle between the earth's equator and the ecliptic plane. But the orientation of the axis differs about 90° from the earth's; its northern end is directed toward the neighborhood of the star Alpha Cephei, not far from the position our own north celestial pole will have 6000 years hence.

Notwithstanding the slightly longer rotation period, the oblateness of Mars (1/192) is more pronounced than the earth's polar flattening. This is a consequence of smaller density, and perhaps also of less rapid increase in density toward the center of the planet.

8·15. The Seasons of Mars. Mars presents its poles alternately to the sun in much the same way that the earth does, owing to the similarity of its axial tilt. The seasons resemble ours geometrically, although they are nearly twice as long. The winter solstice of Mars occurs when the planet has the same heliocentric longitude that the earth has about September 10, and not long after the time of perihelion, when Mars has the same direction from the sun as the earth has on August 28. Summer in the southern hemisphere is therefore warmer than the northern summer which comes when the planet is near the aphelion point, while the southern winters are colder than the northern ones. For the same reason, the earth's southern hemisphere would have the greater seasonal range in temperature if there were no compensating factor (2·27).

While the whole variation in our distance from the sun is only 3 per cent, Mars in its more eccentric orbit is fully 20 per cent (more than 26 million miles) farther from the sun at aphelion than at perihelion. The seasonal difference in the two hemispheres is marked. The southern polar cap becomes larger than the northern cap in the winter season, and it disappears completely in summer, which the other has not been observed to do.

8·16. Seasonal Changes. Not only the polar caps, but also the dark surface markings, including the canals, exhibit conspicuous seasonal changes, which have been carefully studied for many years at Lowell Observatory and elsewhere. The darkening, or the appearance, of the dark markings occurs in both hemispheres during the Martian seasons corresponding to our late spring. They become more intense in early summer, remain near maximum intensity for 50 days or more, and begin to fade as the fall season approaches. The fading, which extends into the winter, is in color as well as intensity; the blue-green of the spring and summer turns to chocolate brown. The dates of the changes in the intensity and color of the dark markings are such as would be expected if these changes are produced by the growth and decline of vegetation.

8·17. Life on Mars Considered. The question as to the presence of life in other worlds can be answered with a degree of confidence if the discussion is restricted to the solar system and to life as we know it. With a single possible exception, all the other members of this system are at once withdrawn from consideration; they are either too small to retain atmospheres, or their atmospheres are unsuitable, or their temperatures are too extreme. The possible exception is Mars.

Life, as we know it, requires air of appropriate composition and density, water, and temperatures within rather narrow limits. It is worth inquiring whether conditions on this planet seem to meet these demands.

An atmosphere is certainly present. The photographs through filters (8·13) give conclusive evidence. The appearance of a twilight zone on the hemisphere turned away from the sun is equally conclusive.

Martian
Date

Martian
Date

May 11

June 23

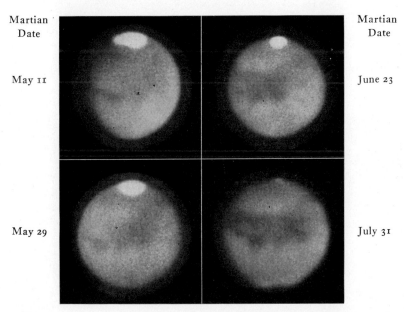

May 29

July 31

FIG. 8·16. Seasonal Changes on Mars. The series of photographs shows the shrinking of the south polar cap and the gradual darkening of the dark markings with the advance of the summer season in the southern Martian hemisphere. (*Photographed by E. C. Slipher, Lowell Observatory*)

The atmosphere of Mars is considerably rarer than ours. The low albedo, 0.15, and the distinctness of the surface markings lead to this conclusion, while the smaller surface gravity, 0.38 of the earth's, and the consequently smaller velocity of escape, 3 miles a second, give reason for it.

No trace of oxygen or of water vapor could be detected by a sensitive spectroscopic analysis at Mount Wilson Observatory. The atmosphere of Mars contains less than five per cent of the water vapor and one per cent of the free oxygen in the earth's atmosphere. The suggestion has been made that the lowering of a former ozone layer in the rare atmosphere of Mars accelerated oxidation at the surface until the free oxygen was depleted. Thus the red color of Mars may be the red of iron rust. As for water, there might still be enough to form thin snow caps at the poles, and some fog here and there.

The surface temperature rises at times above the ordinary freezing point of water, according to the radiometric measures.

The absence of adequate supplies of oxygen and water on Mars seems to preclude the existence of animal life as we know it. But the seasonal changes are explained by the growth and decline of vegetation more convincingly than by any other cause yet suggested.

8·18. The Two Satellites of Mars, discovered at the favorable opposition of 1877, are named Phobos and Deimos (Fear and Panic, the

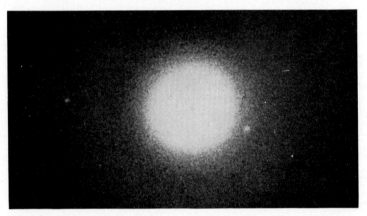

FIG. 8·18. The Satellites of Mars. Phobos is close to the planet at the right. Deimos, at the left, is considerably fainter and farther from the planet. (*Photographed at Lowell Observatory*)

companions of Mars). They are very small (perhaps not exceeding 10 miles in diameter), and so near the planet as to be invisible except with large telescopes at favorable times.

Phobos, the inner satellite, revolves at the distance of 5800 miles from the center of Mars, and 3700 miles from the surface; it completes a sidereal revolution in only $7^h 39^m$, a period less than one third that of the planet's rotation. As viewed from the planet, therefore, it rises in the west and sets in the east. *No other known satellite in the solar system revolves in a shorter interval than the rotation period of its primary.*

The distance of Deimos from the center of Mars is 14,600 miles, and its period of revolution is $30^h 18^m$. It is smaller than the inner satellite, and only one third as bright.

More than a hundred years before the discovery of these satellites, Voltaire mentions them in the story of Micromegas; and Swift's Gulliver, in reporting the scientific achievements of the Laputans, refers to their observation of two satellites of Mars, "whereof the innermost is distant from the center of the planet exactly three of his diameters, and the outermost five; the former revolves in the space of ten hours, and the latter in twenty-one and a half."

The Asteroids

The *asteroids,* or *minor planets,* are the many small planets which revolve around the sun mostly between the orbits of Mars and Jupiter. With a single exception they are always invisible without the telescope. The name "asteroid" (starlike) describes the appearance of most of them with the telescope; a few show tiny disks when viewed with large telescopes. Although lacking in telescopic interest, the asteroids present problems of considerable theoretical importance in their groupings and in the variety of their movements. At least five asteroids come closer to the earth than do any of the principal planets.

8·19. Discovery of the Asteroids. Ceres, the largest of the asteroids and the first to become known, was discovered accidentally by Piazzi, in Sicily, on the first evening of the nineteenth century, January 1, 1801. Its motion from night to night relative to stars he was observing showed that it was not one of them. Its orbit proved to be that of a planet revolving around the sun at the mean distance 2.8 times the earth's distance, in close agreement with the distance required by Bode's law (7·4). The discovery of another asteroid, Pallas, the following year by an observer who was looking for Ceres, led to the search for others.

For many years the discoveries of additional asteroids were entirely visual. The observer at the telescope compared the stars in a region of the sky with those previously charted in that region. If an uncharted star was seen, it was watched hopefully for movement among the stars, which would reveal its planetary character. Photography is now substituted for that slow procedure. The plate is exposed to the sky for an hour or so in a large camera which is mounted equatorially and provided with appropriate driving mechanism. On the developed plate the stars appear as dots, while any asteroid in that region is shown as a short streak, because of its motion among the stars while the exposure is in progress (Fig. 8·19). Slow-moving asteroids may be found by comparing two plates of the same region taken at different times.

About one in five of the asteroids that are discovered are often enough observed to permit the calculation of a reliable orbit. When the orbit is determined and the asteroid proven to be a new one, a number and name are assigned it. The numbers now exceed 1500. It is the

FIG. 8·19.   Trails of Three Asteroids.   (*Photographed at Königstuhl-Heidelberg*)

custom to employ the feminine form in the naming, except for a few asteroids in the extreme edges of the group, such as Eros and Achilles.

8·20. Characteristics of the Asteroids.

The largest asteroid, Ceres, is 480 miles in diameter. Pallas is second with a diameter of 300 miles. Vesta is half the size of Ceres, but under the same conditions outshines Ceres because its surface is a better reflector of sunlight. Vesta is occasionally barely visible without the telescope. Most of the asteroids are less than fifty miles in diameter and some are around a mile; these are estimates based on brightness and distance. The combined mass of all the asteroids can scarcely exceed five per cent of the moon's mass.

The large asteroids, with the exception of Vesta, have about the same reflecting power as the moon, which suggests that they have rough surfaces and no atmosphere. Some and perhaps most of the smaller ones fluctuate rather rapidly in brightness. Eros is an example. While the period of the fluctuation, about five hours and a quarter, has been constant, its extent has varied from a full magnitude to a barely perceptible amount. The fluctuation is evidently caused by the rotation of the asteroid. The variation can be accounted for if the asteroid is irregularly shaped; the maximum variation would occur when the plane of its equator passes through the earth. The irregular shapes could mean that these asteroids are fragments of a larger body which was shattered by the tidal effect of Jupiter during a close approach of the body to the great planet.

8·21. The Orbits of the Asteroids exhibit more variety than those of the principal planets. While the majority are not far from circular and only slightly inclined to the ecliptic, some depart considerably from the circular form and are not confined within the bounds of the zodiac. As an extreme case, the orbit of Hidalgo has an eccentricity of 0.66 and is inclined 43° to the ecliptic; its aphelion point is as far away as Saturn. The direction of revolution of all the asteroids is from west to east. The periods of revolution are mostly between 3½ and 6 years.

Through the region between the orbits of Mars and Jupiter which most asteroids frequent, the asteroid orbits are not distributed at random. There are wide gaps in the neighborhoods of distances from the sun where the periods of revolution would be one third, two fifths, and one half of Jupiter's period; and there are also well-defined gaps corresponding to other simple fractions. Any period of an asteroid commensurate with that of the chief disturbing planet must be unstable, because the same types of disturbances recur frequently. We shall notice divisions in Saturn's rings which suggest a similar cause. But for asteroids whose periods equal that of Jupiter there are two regions of considerable stability.

8·22. The Trojan Asteroids. Long ago, the mathematician Lagrange explained a particular solution of the problem of three bodies, and concluded that when the three bodies occupy the vertices of an equilateral triangle the configuration is stable. Since no celestial example was then known, he took as a hypothetical case a small body moving around the sun in such a way that its distances from Jupiter and the sun remained equal to the distance separating those two bodies. If the small body is disturbed, it will oscillate around its vertex of the triangle.

Twelve asteroids are now known which are not far from examples of this interesting case. Achilles was the first of these to be discovered, in 1904. Named after the Homeric heroes, they are accordingly known as the *Trojan group*. In their revolutions around the sun they oscillate about points which are equally distant from Jupiter and the sun. Their claim to permanent tenure of these positions, however, can be disputed by Saturn.

8·23. Close Approaches of Asteroids. Seven asteroids are known to come within the orbit of Mars. The five that make the nearest approach to the earth are as follows:

Eros, discovered in 1898, is 105 million miles from the sun at perihelion. Its least distance from the earth's orbit, also near the perihelion,

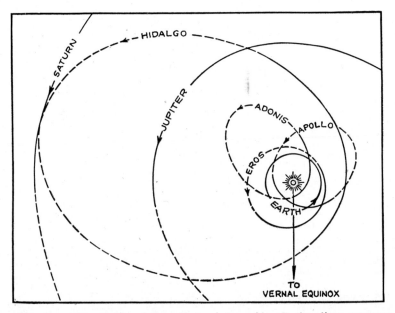

Fig. 8·23. The Orbits of Four Unusual Asteroids. Broken lines represent the parts of the orbits below the plane of the earth's orbit. (*Adapted from a diagram by Dirk Brouwer*)

is less than 14 million miles. The most favorable oppositions of this 20-mile asteroid are infrequent; the latest occurred in 1931, and the next will come in 1975. These occasions can provide data for more accurate determinations of the sun's distance and the moon's mass. *Amor,* discovered near the time of its favorable opposition in 1932, comes to perihelion 10 million miles outside the earth's orbit.

Apollo, also discovered in 1932, is about a mile in diameter; it has its perihelion inside the orbit of Venus, and passes within 3 million miles of the earth's orbit. *Adonis,* discovered in 1936, is also about a mile in diameter. Its perihelion distance is only slightly greater than Mercury's mean distance from the sun, and it passes about a million miles from the orbits of Venus, the earth, and Mars. *Hermes,* discovered in 1937, scarcely a mile in diameter, may come even nearer us than the others. The chance of discovering such tiny bodies is so small as to suggest that there must be many of them.

JUPITER AND ITS SATELLITES

This great planet is brighter than any of the stars or other planets, except Venus and occasionally Mars. Its banded disk and four bright satellites can be viewed through a small telescope. Jupiter has more known satellites than any other planet, eleven in all, though seven are very faint. At somewhat more than five times the earth's distance, it revolves in a little less than twelve years; the synodic period is about a year and a month, so that from year to year this planet advances among the stars about one constellation of the zodiac. *Jupiter is the largest planet* and more massive than all the others combined.

8·24. Jupiter's Bands and Other Markings. Viewed and photographed with large telescopes, Jupiter exhibits a great variety of detail and a surprising amount of color. The broad yellow equatorial band is paralleled by a succession of dark and bright *bands* to the north and

September 14   October 6   November 30

Fig. 8·24. Cloud Markings of Jupiter. Three photographs of the same face of Jupiter, in 1928, showing rapid changes in its southern (upper) hemisphere. Note the rapid advance of the white spot in the north tropical belt. The great red spot is seen at the left side of the disk. (*Photographed at Lowell Observatory*)

south. These bands, which are parallel to the planet's equator, appear to be atmospheric currents produced by its rapid rotation. *Jupiter's period of rotation, slightly less than ten hours, is the shortest of all the principal planets;* the speed of the rotation at its equator exceeds 25,000 miles an hour.

Irregular bright clouds and bright and dark patches break the continuity of the bands. Some of these are short-lived and change noticeably in form from day to day, suggesting considerable turmoil beneath the thick atmosphere whose upper levels are observed. Other spots persist for a very long time. Especially remarkable in this respect is the *Great Red Spot,* first announced in 1878, though drawings made previously show that it was present as early as 1831. This elliptical brick-red spot in the south tropical zone was 30,000 miles long; it is still a prominent marking, but its color has faded considerably.

The positions of the markings vary as well as the forms, so that the rotation periods determined from two spots are not likely to agree precisely. The South Tropical Disturbance, which is somewhat south of the Spot, has a period of rotation twenty seconds shorter than that of the Spot; it drifts by the Spot and gains a lap on it in about two years.

8·25. Methane and Ammonia in the Atmosphere of Jupiter are revealed by spectroscopic analysis. The temperature at the levels that can

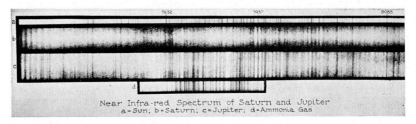

Near Infra-red Spectrum of Saturn and Jupiter
a=Sun; b=Saturn; c=Jupiter; d=Ammonia Gas

Fɪɢ. 8·25. Spectra of Saturn and Jupiter Compared with the Spectrum of Ammonia. The dark lines of ammonia are weak in the spectrum of Saturn and are conspicuous in the spectrum of Jupiter. (*Photographed at Mount Wilson Observatory*)

be observed is $-130°$ C. Methane (CH_4) is gaseous at this temperature; its boiling point is $-162°$ C. But ammonia (NH_3) must be present in the clouds of Jupiter as crystals, just as our own cirrus clouds are composed of ice crystals; for ammonia freezes at $-78°$ C. The suggestion has been offered that the white ammonia crystals might be tinted red by the action of metallic sodium, thus producing the red coloring that is observed.

Hydrogen is presumably the chief constituent of Jupiter's atmosphere. This abundant element cannot get away from the giant planet, for which the velocity of escape is 37 miles a second, as it seems to have done from the earth's atmosphere. Carbon and nitrogen must have combined with part of the hydrogen to form methane and ammonia. Oxygen, also an abundant element everywhere, must have combined with hydrogen to produce a great amount of ice around the surface of the planet itself.

8·26. Physical Constitution of Jupiter.   The centrifugal effect of Jupiter's rapid rotation should cause a considerable bulge at the planet's

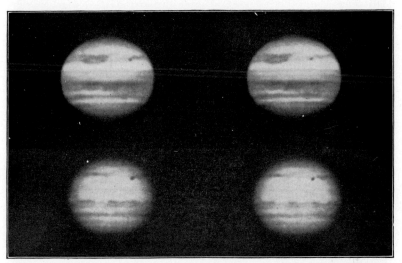

FIG. 8·26. Jupiter Photographed in Ultraviolet and Extreme Red Light. In ultraviolet (upper pair) the planet shows a sharper edge, larger disk, and different surface details than in red light (lower pair). The great red spot is prominent in the upper photographs, and scarcely visible in the lower ones. The exposures at the right were made eleven minutes later; in the meantime, the planet had rotated 6¾° toward the left, and the shadow of satellite II, which was in transit, had moved noticeably toward the left. (*Photographed at Lick Observatory*)

equator, despite the competition of a surface gravity 2.6 times as great as that at the earth's surface. The bulge is in fact considerable, as the photographs (Fig. 8·26) show; the oblateness is one fifteenth. But calculations indicate that the bulge should be still greater unless the mass of the planet is highly concentrated toward its center. This is one clue to the constitution of Jupiter. Another is the low mean density, only

1.3 times the density of water, which requires extremely low density in the outer part of the planet.

Wildt has constructed a theoretical model of Jupiter (Fig. 8·30), which meets these requirements and is intended to represent the other observational data. In this model the outer 18 per cent of the radius is composed chiefly of hydrogen compressed to the density 0.35 times water. The next 39 per cent of the radius is a layer of ice compressed under the very great pressure down there to the density 1.5 times water. The remaining 43 per cent of the radius of the model is a rocky core having a mean density 6.0 times water.

8·27. The Inner Satellites. Jupiter's eleven known satellites are sharply divided into three groups: the inner satellites and two groups of

FIG. 8·27. Jupiter's Four Bright Satellites. Photographed on two occasions. The four satellites are visible with a small telescope. (*Photographed at Lowell Observatory*)

outer satellites. The five inner satellites revolve from west to east in orbits which are nearly circular and nearly in the planes of the planet's equator and orbit. Four of these are so bright that they can be easily seen with a very small telescope.

The four bright satellites were discovered by Galileo early in 1610. They have received names but are oftener designated by number in order of distance from the planet. The first and second satellites are about as large as the moon. The third and fourth are 50 per cent greater in diameter; they are probably the largest of all satellites, even surpassing the planet Mercury. At their greater distance from the sun, however, their combined light upon Jupiter is not more than thirty per cent of the light of the full moon on the earth. Their periods of rotation and revolution are the same. After the four bright ones the numbering of the other satellites is in order of their discovery.

The fifth satellite, discovered in 1892, differs from the others of its group in its small size. Nearest of all to the planet, and difficult to observe on this account, it is the swiftest of all satellites, revolving at the rate of a thousand miles a minute.

8·28. The Outer Satellites have orbits (Fig. 8·28) of considerable eccentricity and inclination to the ecliptic. All six are small and very

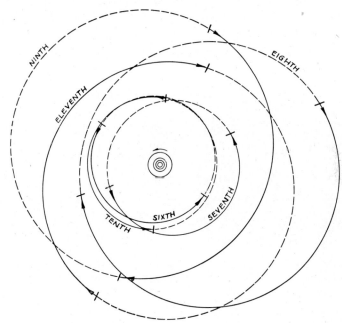

FIG. 8·28. Orbits of Jupiter's Satellites. The outer satellites are in two groups. The sixth, seventh, and tenth satellites revolve from west to east. The eighth, ninth, and eleventh revolve from east to west. (*Adapted from a diagram by Nicholson*)

faint. They were discovered photographically, the latest two by Nicholson at the Mount Wilson Observatory, in 1938; he remarks that the faintest one, the tenth satellite, is not brighter than the light of a candle at a distance of 3000 miles. From Jupiter itself only the sixth satellite would be visible without a telescope.

These satellites are divided into two groups. One group contains *the sixth, seventh, and tenth satellites,* which revolve from west to east at the average distance of a little more than 7 million miles from the planet and in periods around 260 days. The other group contains *the eighth, ninth, and eleventh satellites; these revolve from east to west* at the average distance of 15 million miles from the planet and in periods around 700 days. They are *the most distant of all satellites from the primary.* Jupiter's control over these remote satellites is disputed by the sun, whose attraction greatly disturbs their orbits.

8·29. Eclipses and Transits of the Bright Satellites. The orbits of the bright satellites are presented always nearly edgewise to us. As these satellites revolve around Jupiter, they accordingly appear to move back and forth in nearly the same straight line. The forward movement takes them behind the planet and through its shadow (the fourth satellite often clears them); the backward movement takes them in front of

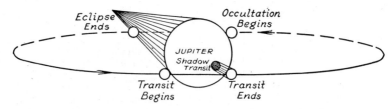

FIG. 8·29. Phenomena of a Satellite of Jupiter.

the planet, when their own shadows are cast upon its disk. These occultations, eclipses, transits, and shadow-transits of the satellites add interest to observations of Jupiter with the telescope. The times of their frequent occurrences are predicted in some of the astronomical almanacs.

SATURN; ITS RINGS AND SATELLITES

Saturn is the most distant of the bright planets from the sun, and the most remote planet known to early astronomers. At nearly twice the distance of Jupiter, it revolves around the sun in the period of 29½ years. This planet ranks second to Jupiter in size, mass, and number of known satellites. Saturn has the *least density* (0.7 times that of water) and the *greatest oblateness* of all the planets. It is unique in the possession of a system of rings which encircle the planet and make it one of the most impressive of celestial objects, when viewed with the telescope.

8·30. The Constitution of Saturn resembles that of Jupiter in many respects. The atmospheric markings are likewise arranged in bands which are here more regular and less distinct. A broad yellowish band overlies the equator, and large greenish caps surround the poles. The absorption of ammonia in the spectrum is much weaker while that of methane is stronger than in Jupiter's spectrum. At the lower temperature of Saturn, $-150°$ C, the ammonia clouds appear to be mostly frozen out, so that the sunlight analyzed in the spectrum has penetrated farther down through the methane of the planet's atmosphere.

Saturn's period of rotation at its equator is $10^{\text{h}} 02^{\text{m}}$, as determined spectroscopically by Moore at Lick Observatory; spots, which are rarely seen on this planet, have had periods up to $10^{\text{h}} 38^{\text{m}}$. The short period

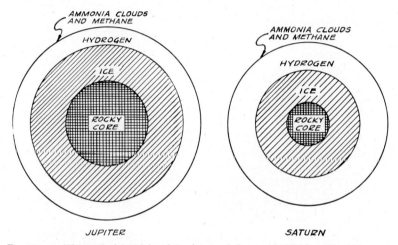

FIG. 8·30. Theoretical Models of Jupiter and Saturn (Wildt). The low mean density of Saturn is accounted for by the small volume of the rocky core.

of rotation combined with the large size and low density of Saturn cause its conspicuous oblateness. That the equatorial bulge is not even more pronounced indicates that the material of Saturn, as in the case of Jupiter, is strongly concentrated toward the center. The extremely low mean density, 0.7 times the density of water, offers an additional clue to the internal structure of the planet. The atmosphere consisting mostly of the very lightest gases extends nearly halfway from the outer cloud level to the center of the planet, in Wildt's theoretical model (Fig. 8·30).

8·31. Saturn's Rings. Saturn is encircled by three concentric rings in the plane of its equator. They are designated as the *outer ring,* the middle or *bright ring,* and the inner or *crape ring.* The rings are invisible to the unaided eye, and were therefore unknown until after the invention of the telescope. The diameter of the entire ring system is

171,000 miles, or 2.3 times the equatorial diameter of the planet (74,100 miles). Since they have nearly twice the diameter of Jupiter and are about twice as far away from us, the rings have about the same apparent diameter as that of Jupiter.

The bright ring is 16,000 miles wide, half again as wide as the other two; its outer edge is as luminous as the brightest parts of the planet

FIG. 8·31. Saturn. (*From a drawing by Keeler, Lick Observatory, and a photograph by Barnard at Mount Wilson Observatory*)

itself. It is separated from the outer ring by the prominent gap, some 3000 miles wide, known after the name of its discoverer as *Cassini's division*. Other narrower divisions in the rings have been observed. The crape ring is much fainter than the other two. Though it was not certainly noticed until 1850, this ring can be seen with telescopes of moderate size.

A surprising feature of the rings is that they are extremely thin. Their appreciable thickness can scarcely exceed ten miles. They are proportionately thinner than one of the sheets of paper of this book.

8·32. Saturn's Rings at Different Angles. The rings are inclined 27° to the plane of Saturn's orbit, and keep the same direction as the planet revolves around the sun. Thus their northern and southern faces are presented alternately to the sun and also to the earth; for as viewed from

February 11, 1916

Fig. 8·32. Saturn's Rings at Different Angles. The southern side of the rings was presented in 1916, the northern side in 1933 and 1934, and in 1936 the earth crossed the ring plane to the southern side again. Cassini's division is clearly shown between the two bright rings. In the first photograph the crape ring can be seen against the ball of the planet. In the second photograph the great white spot which suddenly appeared in 1933 can be clearly seen to the left of the center. In 1934 an unusually broad yellow band appeared in the tropical zone. The considerable oblateness of the planet, the parallel bands across its disk, and the shadows are to be noted. (*Photographed by E. C. Slipher, Lowell Observatory*)

August 9, 1933

September 18, 1934

October 1, 1937

Saturn these two bodies are never more than 6° apart. Twice during the sidereal period of 29½ years the plane of the rings passes through the sun's position. It requires nearly a year on each occasion to sweep across the earth's orbit. Meanwhile, owing to the earth's revolution, the rings become edgewise to us from one to three times, when they appear through large telescopes as a very narrow bright line. The latest edgewise appearance of the rings occurred in February, 1937, having barely missed in July of the previous year.

When the rings are widest open, as they were late in 1943, their apparent breadth is 45 per cent of their greatest diameter, and one sixth

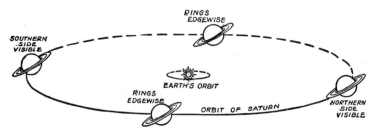

FIG. 8·32A. Explanation of the Different Appearances of Saturn's Rings. The plane of the rings is inclined about 27° to the plane of Saturn's orbit.

greater than the planet's polar diameter. On these occasions Saturn is much brighter than usual, for the rings at this angle can reflect 1.7 times as much sunlight as the planet alone. When it is also near perihelion and in opposition, the planet appears twice as bright as Capella. But when the rings are closed it is not brighter than Altair.

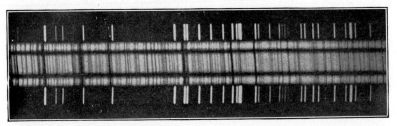

FIG. 8·33. Spectrum of Ball and Rings of Saturn. The direction of the red end of the spectrum is toward the right. In the spectrum of the ball of the planet, in the middle, the lines slant because of the planet's rotation. In the spectrum of the rings (above and below) the lines have the opposite slant. This shows that the rings are revolving more rapidly at their inner edges, proving their meteoric nature. The bright "pickets" are comparison spectra. (*Photographed by V. M. Slipher, Lowell Observatory*)

8·33. Meteoric Composition of the Rings.

Saturn's rings are composed of many separate particles, most of them presumably like grains of dust. They may be said to resemble a compact swarm of meteors revolving in a practically circular orbit and presenting the appearance of a continuous surface, aside from the divisions, because of the great distance from us. This conclusion is known to be correct, because *the inner parts of the rings revolve around the planet faster than the outer parts,* just as a planet that is nearer the sun revolves faster than one that is farther away. The reverse would be the case if the rings were continuous surfaces; for all parts would then rotate in the same period, and the outside, having farther to go, would move the fastest.

The Doppler effects (4·24) in the spectrum of Saturn (Fig. 8·33) show not only the meteoric constitution of the rings, but also that the

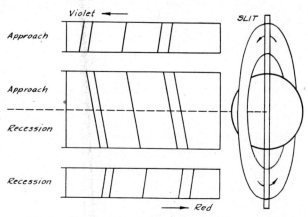

FIG. 8·33A. Doppler Effects in the Spectrum of Saturn. An explanation of Fig. 8·33.

rings and the planet rotate in the same direction. The behavior of the spectrum lines is explained by Fig. 8·33A, where the slit of the spectroscope is placed along Saturn's equator. The upper parts of the planet and the rings are rotating toward the observer, while the lower parts are receding from him.

The rotation periods of the outer edge of the outer ring and the inner edge of the bright ring are respectively $14^h 27^m$ and $7^h 46^m$, while the material in the crape ring goes around in still shorter periods. Since Saturn's equator rotates in about ten hours, it is evident that outer parts of the ring system move westward across the sky of Saturn. But a considerable part of the bright ring and all of the crape ring must rise in the west and set in the east as seen from the surface of the planet, duplicating the behavior of Phobos (8·18) in the sky of Mars.

8·34. The Cause of Saturn's Rings seems to be associated with their nearness to the planet. According to the theory, which was invoked in this respect long before the spectroscopic evidence was available, a solid ring so close to the planet would be shattered by the strains to which it would be subjected, while a ring of many small satellites would be reasonably stable. A *liquid* satellite of the same density would be torn into small pieces by the tide-raising force of the planet if its distance from the center of the planet were as small as 2.4 times the planet's radius.

All parts of Saturn's rings are well within this limit. The nearest satellite is safely outside. It is a matter for speculation whether the rings were formed from the material of a disrupted satellite, or from material that could not assemble into a satellite, or, of course, in some other way. The total mass of the rings is of the order of a hundredth the mass of the moon.

The divisions in the rings of Saturn remind us of the gaps in the asteroid zone (8·21), and are doubtless similar resonance effects. Thus a small satellite revolving in the Cassini division would have a period of revolution one half that of Saturn's nearest satellite.

8·35. The Satellites of Saturn. Saturn has nine known satellites. The largest, Titan, is somewhat larger than the moon, and is visible through small telescopes as a star of the eighth magnitude; its spectrum contains absorption bands of methane. Five or six other satellites can be seen with telescopes of moderate aperture; they appear as faint stars in the vicinity of Saturn, and are easily identified by means of convenient tables in some of the astronomical almanacs. Phoebe, the most distant satellite, revolves from east to west, like Jupiter's outer group of satellites (8·28).

Some of Saturn's satellites are known to rotate and revolve in the same period. This is shown by their variations in brightness in the same periods as their revolutions. Evidently their surfaces are uneven in reflecting power. Iapetus is most remarkable in this respect; it is five times as bright at western elongation as at eastern elongation.

URANUS AND NEPTUNE; THEIR SATELLITES

8·36. At distances nineteen and thirty times the earth's distance from the sun, these two planets complete their revolutions in periods of 84 and 165 years respectively. Uranus is barely visible to the unaided eye, while Neptune appears through the telescope as a star of the eighth magnitude. Through the telescope they show small greenish disks on which markings are not clearly seen. They are nearly alike in size, having diameters about 30,000 miles, and probably in most other respects. Physically they appear to resemble the other giant planets, Jupiter and Saturn.

With increasing distance from the sun the giant planets show progressively weaker ammonia and stronger methane absorption in their spectra, and also less variety in their atmospheric markings. Diminished temperature is assigned as one important factor. As the ammonia clouds are frozen out, the view penetrates deeper into the methane-contaminated atmosphere.

8·37. Discoveries of Uranus and Neptune.

Uranus was the first planet to be discovered. It was discovered accidentally, in 1781, by the English astronomer William Herschel who was observing in the region of Gemini and came upon an object which appeared larger than a star. An examination of the records showed that Uranus had been seen fully twenty times in the hundred years preceding its discovery; each time the position had been measured and set down as that of a star.

Since the old observations extended over a complete revolution of the planet, they were at once employed in the calculation of the orbit. But no orbit could be found to fit them perfectly. At length, the old positions were discarded, and an orbit was derived, in 1821, from the new observations alone, with proper allowance for the disturbing effects of known planets. It was not long, however, before Uranus began to depart appreciably from the assigned course, until in 1844 the difference between the observed and calculated positions amounted to something over 2', an angle scarcely perceptible to the unaided eye, but regarded as an "intolerable" discrepancy by astronomers. There seemed no longer any room for doubt that the motion of Uranus was being disturbed by a planet as yet unseen.

Leverrier, in France, discovered Neptune in 1846. From the discrepancies in the motion of Uranus he was able to calculate the place of the disturbing body in the sky. All that remained was to observe it. An astronomer at the Berlin Observatory searched with the telescope for the new planet and soon found it within a degree of the specified place in the constellation Aquarius. It was a great triumph for the law of gravitation, on which the calculations were based, and a notable example of the so-called "astronomy of the invisible"—the detection of celestial bodies before they are seen, by their gravitational effect on known bodies.

The account of Neptune's discovery is not complete without mention of the English astronomer, J. C. Adams, who also successfully solved the problem, and was indeed the first to determine the planet's position.

But those to whom he applied for telescopic aid did not have a suitable chart of this region of the sky, and perhaps also did not fully recognize the knock of opportunity.

8·38. Satellites of Uranus and Neptune. Uranus has four known satellites which are fainter than most satellites, owing to their moderate size and great distance from us.

FIG. 8·38. Neptune and Its Satellite. (*Photographed at Yerkes Observatory*)

Their orbits are practically circular and in the plane of the planet's equator. These orbits are inclined 98° to the plane of the ecliptic if we regard the revolutions as direct, or 82° if we regard them as retrograde. At any rate, the orbits are nearly perpendicular to the ecliptic. As the planet revolves, they are presented to the earth at various angles; they were edgewise to us in 1924 and flatwise in 1945.

Neptune's single satellite is somewhat larger than the moon and slightly nearer the planet than the moon's distance from the earth. *It revolves from east to west,* though Neptune's rotation is from west to east.

PLUTO

8·39. Discovery of Pluto. On March 13, 1930, the Lowell Observatory announced the discovery of a faint starlike object in the constellation Gemini, whose slow motion relative to neighboring stars distinguished it as a planet beyond the orbit of Neptune. The planet was first detected, by Tombaugh, by comparison of photographs taken in January. Further observations were required, however, before the character of the object could be definitely established. The first two letters of the planet's name are appropriately the initials of Percival Lowell who instituted the search for this planet, the search which extended over a quarter of a century.

After the discovery of Neptune, small departures in the motion of Uranus from the calculated orbit remained to suggest the presence of a planet beyond Neptune. On the basis of these departures, Lowell, in 1915, had calculated the orbit of the suspected planet. When the planet was discovered, its position and motion were in reasonable agreement with the calculated orbit.

Fig. 8·39. Pluto Near the Time of Its Discovery. The arrows point to the planet which appeared as a star of the fifteenth magnitude. The bright star below the planet is Delta Geminorum. (*Photographed at Lowell Observatory*)

8·40. Pluto and Its Orbit. Pluto appears as a star of the fifteenth visual magnitude; it can be seen only through large telescopes. It has a yellowish hue rather than the greenish color of its nearer neighbors. Its mass is 0.8 times the earth's mass, and its size may not differ greatly from that of the earth. The temperature at its surface can scarcely be 50 centigrade degrees above the absolute zero. This constitutes the available information about Pluto itself.

The orbit of Pluto is *more eccentric* and *more inclined* to the ecliptic than that of any other principal planet. The high eccentricity (0.25) introduces still another unique feature. While Pluto's mean distance from the sun is the greatest of all the planets, this planet at its aphelion comes 35 million miles *within the orbit of Neptune.* Owing to the high inclination of Pluto's orbit there is no present danger of

THE OTHER PLANETS

TABLE 8·I. THE PLANETS

Name		Symbol	Mean Distance from Sun		Period of Revolution		Eccentricity of Orbit	Inclination to Ecliptic
			Astron. Units	Million Miles	Sidereal	Synodic		
Inner	Mercury	☿	0.3871	35.96	days 87.969	days 115.88	0.206	7° 0′
	Venus	♀	0.7233	67.20	224.701	583.92	0.007	3 24
	Earth	⊕	1.0000	92.90	365.256	......	0.017	0 0
	Mars	♂	1.5237	141.6	686.980	779.94	0.093	1 51
	Ceres	①	2.7673	257.1	years 4.604	466.60	0.077	10 37
Outer	Jupiter	♃	5.2028	483.3	11.862	398.88	0.048	1 18
	Saturn	♄	9.5388	886.2	29.458	378.09	0.056	2 29
	Uranus	♅	19.1910	1783	84.015	369.66	0.047	0 46
	Neptune	♆	30.0707	2794	164.788	367.49	0.009	1 47
	Pluto	♇	39.4574	3670	247.697	366.74	0.249	17 9

Name	Equatorial Diameter in Miles	Mass ⊕ = 1	Density Water = 1	Period of Rotation	Inclination of Equator to Orbit	Oblateness	Stellar Magnitude at Greatest Brilliancy
Sun ☉	864,000	331,950	1.41	24^d.65	7° 10′	o	−26.7
Moon ☾	2,160	0.012	3.33	27 .32	6 41	o	−12.6
Mercury	3,100	0.04	3.8	88		o	−1.2
Venus	7,700	0.81	4.86	30?		o	−4.3
Earth	7,927	1.00	5.52	23^h 56^m	23 27	1/296	......
Mars	4,215	0.11	3.96	24 37	24	1/192	−2.8
Jupiter	88,640	316.94	1.34	9 50	3 7	1/15	−2.5
Saturn	74,100	94.9	0.71	10 02	26 45	1/9.5	−0.4
Uranus	32,000	14.7	1.27	10 45	98	1/14	+5.7
Neptune	31,000	17.2	1.58	15 48	29	1/40	+7.6

TABLE 8·II. THE SATELLITES

Name	Discovery		Mean Distance in Miles	Period of Revolution			Diameter in Miles	Stellar Magnitude at Mean Opposition
Moon			238,857	27^d	7^h	43^m	2160	−12

	SATELLITES OF MARS							
Phobos	Hall,	1877	5,800	0	7	39	10?	+12
Deimos	Hall,	1877	14,600	1	6	18	5?	13

	SATELLITES OF JUPITER							
Fifth	Barnard,	1892	112,600	0	11	57	100?	13
1. Io	Galileo,	1610	261,800	1	18	28	2300	5
2. Europa	Galileo,	1610	416,600	3	13	14	2000	6
3. Ganymede	Galileo,	1610	664,200	7	3	43	3200	5
4. Callisto	Galileo,	1610	1,169,000	16	16	32	3200	6
Sixth	Perrine,	1904	7,114,000	250	16		100?	14
Seventh	Perrine,	1905	7,292,000	260	1		40?	16
Tenth	Nicholson,	1938	7,340,000	264				
Eleventh	Nicholson,	1938	14,000,000	692				
Eighth	Melotte,	1908	14,600,000	739			40?	16
Ninth	Nicholson,	1914	14,900,000	758			20?	17

	SATELLITES OF SATURN							
Mimas	Herschel,	1789	115,000	0	22	37	400?	12
Enceladus	Herschel,	1789	148,000	1	8	53	500?	12
Tethys	Cassini,	1684	183,000	1	21	18	800?	11
Dione	Cassini,	1684	234,000	2	17	41	700?	11
Rhea	Cassini,	1672	327,000	4	12	25	1100?	10
Titan	Huyghens,	1655	759,000	15	22	41	2600	8
Hyperion	Bond,	1848	920,000	21	6	38	300?	13
Iapetus	Cassini,	1671	2,210,000	79	7	56	1000?	11
Phoebe	Pickering,	1898	8,034,000	550			200?	14

	SATELLITES OF URANUS							
Ariel	Lassell,	1851	119,000	2	12	29	600?	16
Umbriel	Lassell,	1851	166,000	4	3	28	400?	16
Titania	Herschel,	1787	272,000	8	16	56	1000?	14
Oberon	Herschel,	1787	364,000	13	11	7	900?	14

	SATELLITE OF NEPTUNE							
Nameless	Lassell,	1846	220,000	5	21	3	3000?	13

collision; the nearest possible approach of the two planets is 240 million miles.

In the diagram (Fig. 8·40) the plane of the page represents the ecliptic plane, and very nearly the plane of the orbit of Neptune. The portion of Pluto's orbit south of the ecliptic plane is indicated by the broken line. At the time of its discovery Pluto was near the ascending node of its orbit. It will reach its perihelion in 1989.

8·41. Tables of the Planets and Satellites.

In Tables 8·I and 8·II the elements of the planetary orbits are taken from *The American Ephemeris and Nautical Almanac,* to which the reader is referred for a more complete tabulation. The adopted length of the astronomical unit is 92,900,000 miles. To express any distance in kilometers, multiply the value in miles by 1.6093. The other data are taken from what seem to be the most reliable sources.

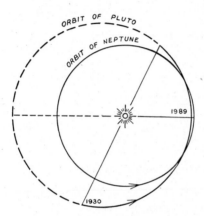

FIG. 8·40. The Orbit of Pluto.

The diameters of the majority of the satellites are subject to great uncertainty. With the exceptions of the moon, Jupiter's four bright satellites, and Titan, they do not show appreciable disks in the telescope; the diameter has been calculated from the observed brightness and assumed albedo of the satellite.

REVIEW QUESTIONS

1. Name the principal planets in order of distance from the sun. State a unique feature of each.

2. Name the principal planets described by each of the following:

(a) Occasionally transit the sun.
(b) Probably have no atmosphere.
(c) Unknown to ancient people.
(d) Surface markings visible.
(e) Rotation periods unknown.
(f) Have no known satellites.
(g) Atmospheres contain methane and ammonia.

3. As viewed with the telescope, what is the most conspicuous feature of Venus? Mars? Jupiter? Saturn?

4. Why is Venus brighter at crescent than at full phase?

5. In what respects does Venus resemble the earth? In what other respects does it differ so much from the earth as to suggest its unavailability for human life?

6. Mars seems unsuitable for animal life, but may perhaps support plant life. Explain.

7. In what respect does the inner satellite of Mars differ from all other satellites?

8. Why is Mars brighter than usual at intervals of 15 or 17 years?

9. Describe the motions (a) of asteroids such as Eros and Adonis; (b) of the Trojan asteroids.

10. Contrast the physical constitutions of Jupiter and the earth, including their atmospheres. Explain the chief differences.

11. Jupiter's satellites are sharply divided into three groups. Explain.

12. Why are Saturn's rings presented to us at different angles? Why are they edgewise to us at intervals of about 15 years?

13. Describe the spectroscopic evidence of the meteoric constitution of Saturn's rings.

14. Discuss the discoveries of Uranus, Neptune, and Pluto.

Problems

1. Aspects of Venus recur on nearly the same date at intervals of eight years (Table 8·1), and transits of Venus occur in pairs separated by an interval of eight years. Explain.

Answer: Five times the synodic period (583.92 days) equal very nearly eight years.

2. Though the orbit of Venus is inclined less than $3\frac{1}{2}°$ to the ecliptic, this planet is at times outside the zodiac (more than 8° from the ecliptic). Explain.

Answer: The inclination is the angle at the sun. When Venus is nearest the earth, its observed angular distance from the ecliptic may exceed 8°. This can be shown by a diagram drawn to scale.

3. A planet's distance from the sun at perihelion is $a(1 - e)$ and at aphelion is $a(1 + e)$, where a is its mean distance and e is the eccentricity of its orbit (Table 8·1). How much farther from the sun is Mars at aphelion than at perihelion?

Answer: About 26 million miles.

4. The diameter of a satellite of Saturn, which is too small to appear as a disk, is calculated as 1000 miles. Suppose that the satellite's albedo (reflecting power) is actually one half the assumed value. What is the actual diameter?

Answer: 1400 miles.

5. Show that the acceleration of gravity at the surface of Jupiter is about 2.6 times that at the earth's surface, neglecting the centrifugal effects of the rotations. Jupiter's mass is about 317 times the earth's mass and its radius is about 11 times the earth's radius.

6. The plane of Saturn's rings requires about a year to sweep across the earth's orbit. Show by diagrams that the rings are presented edgewise to us from one to three times in that interval.

CHAPTER IX

THE SOLAR SYSTEM, Continued

COMETS — METEORS AND METEOR STREAMS — METEORITES AND METEOR CRATERS — THE PROBLEM OF THE ORIGIN OF THE SYSTEM

In addition to the planets and their satellites, there are the multitudes of very small bodies in the solar system to be considered. We have already noticed an instance of these in the meteoric constitution of Saturn's rings. This Chapter is concerned chiefly with the assemblages of small bodies in the form of comets and meteor swarms, and with the meteors that encounter the earth. The account of the sun itself is left for the following Chapter.

COMETS

The appearance of a great comet was long ago viewed with alarm as an omen of some impending disaster, perhaps a pestilence or a war. In more recent times it brought the apprehension of damage that might result if the comet should collide with the earth. The unfounded fear of comets is now replaced by the interest everyone has when one of those spectacles is displayed in the sky. Great comets, such as Donati's comet of 1858, the comet of 1882, and Halley's comet at its latest appearance in 1910, are rare. Most comets are never bright enough to be seen without the telescope.

9·1. Discovery of Comets. Comets are sometimes discovered at the observatories, either accidentally in the course of other investigations or in routine examinations of photographic plates. They are frequently found by amateurs who like to hunt for them. The chief requirements for a comet hunter are a small telescope, much perseverance, and a catalog of nebulae and star clusters which could be mistaken for comets, though the motion of a comet among the stars should soon identify it. The western sky after nightfall or the east before dawn are the most promising regions for the search.

The announcement of the discovery of a comet, giving the comet's position and the direction of its motion, is usually communicated to Harvard Observatory, the central station in this country for such astronomical news, which forwards it to other observatories. As soon as three positions have been measured at intervals of a few days, the preliminary orbit is calculated; then it is often possible to decide whether

FIG. 9·1. Donati's Comet, October 5, 1858. As it appeared to the naked eye. Not long before this drawing was made, the comet passed over Arcturus (to the right of the comet's head) without obscuring it. (*From a drawing by Bond at Harvard Observatory*)

the comet is a new one, or the return of a comet that has appeared before, and what may be expected of it. Further observations provide data for the calculation of the definitive orbit.

An average of five or six comets are now picked up each year; about a third of these are returns of previously observed comets, and two thirds are new ones. Comets that are bright enough to be seen without the telescope average less than one a year, and only rarely is one spectacular enough to attract the attention of those who are not astronomers.

9·2. The Orbits of Comets. A comet has no permanent individuality by which it may be distinguished from other comets. The only identification mark is the path it pursues around the sun. The orbits of five hundred comets are known with varying degrees of precision. They fall into two groups, with a somewhat indefinite dividing line between them:

(1) *Nearly parabolic orbits.* The orbits of many comets are so nearly parabolas that it is difficult to tell the difference, from the small portions of the orbits near the sun in which the comets can be seen. These orbits extend far out beyond the planetary orbits, and the periods of revolution are so long that only one appearance of each comet has thus far been recorded. The orbits are mostly highly inclined to the ecliptic. Half the comets revolve from west to east and the other half from east to west.

(2) *Definitely elliptical orbits.* The orbits of "periodic comets," having periods not exceeding a few hundred years, are more closely allied to the organization of the rest of the solar system. While most of them are still highly eccentric, they are more moderately inclined to the ecliptic, and the revolutions of the comets are mostly from west to east.

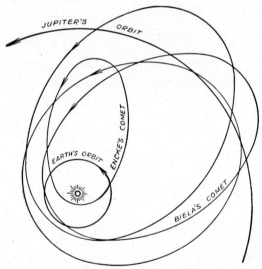

FIG. 9·3. Orbits of a Few Comets of Jupiter's Family. Encke's comet has the smallest orbit of all.

9·3. Jupiter's Family of Comets. Two dozen or more comets of very short period have orbits closely related to the orbit of Jupiter. In each case the aphelion point and one of the nodes are near the orbit of Jupiter, so that the comets often pass close to the planet itself. These comets are members of *Jupiter's family of comets*. Their close approaches to the giant planet result in such great perturbations of their orbits that the configuration is not stable.

The periods of revolution of these comets around the sun are mostly between five and nine years, averaging a little more than half of Jupiter's period. The orbits are generally not much inclined to the ecliptic and the revolutions are all from west to east. The comets themselves are never conspicuous objects. A few become faintly visible without the telescope when they pass near the earth.

Encke's comet was the first member of Jupiter's family to be recognized, in 1819. Its period of revolution, 3.3 years, is *the shortest of any known comet*. The aphelion point is a whole astronomical unit inside Jupiter's orbit. Since 1819 the comet has not been missed at a single return; the return in 1941 was the forty-first to be observed.

9·4. The Capture of Comets. The relation between Jupiter and its family of comets makes it seem probable that the planet has acquired the comets by capturing some of those that chanced to be passing by. The low inclinations of the orbits and the direct motions of all the comets in the family suggest that the process is selective. The theory seems to show that comets whose original orbits have sufficiently large perihelion distance and low inclination, so that they may move nearly parallel to Jupiter, are most likely to be captured; their orbits are made progressively smaller by successive encounters until they become members of Jupiter's family.

In former times, the capture theory was invoked to account for all periodic comets. It was supposed that comets were casual visitors from outside the solar system and that only those captured by planets prolonged their stay with us. Further study of their orbits makes it highly probable that all the comets we see are natives of this system.

9·5. Halley's Comet. This famous comet, *the first known periodic comet,* is named in honor of the English astronomer who predicted its return. Halley calculated the orbit of the bright comet of 1682 and noticed its close resemblance to the orbits which he had also calculated for the comets of 1531 and 1607. Concluding that these were appearances of the same comet, which must therefore be moving in an ellipse, Halley predicted that it would return again in 1758. The comet was sighted in that year according to prediction, and returned again in 1835 and 1910. Halley's comet is the only conspicuous comet having a period less than a hundred years. The revolution is from east to west.

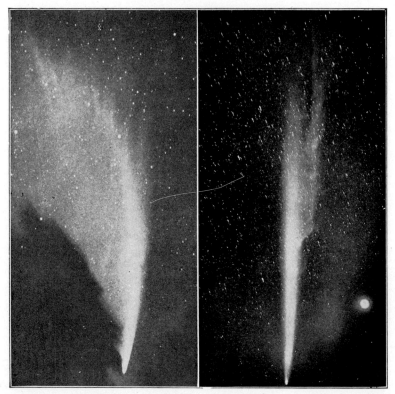

FIG. 9·5. Comet 1910a. Photographed January 26, 1910. Part of the comet is hidden by the pine trees in the lower left corner. (*Photographed at Lowell Observatory*)

Halley's Comet. Photographed May 13, 1910, when the comet was visible in the east before dawn. The bright object at the right is the planet Venus. (*Photographed at Lowell Observatory*)

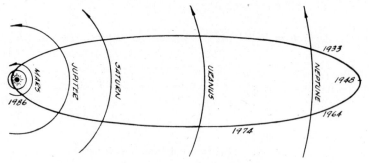

FIG. 9·5A. Orbit of Halley's Comet. The comet remains for nearly half the time in the small portion of its orbit beyond Neptune's orbit. It passes aphelion in 1948, and will return to the sun in 1986.

Twenty-eight observed returns of this comet have been recorded, as far back as 240 B.C. It was Halley's comet that appeared in 1066, at the time of the Norman conquest of England. The period has varied nearly five years meanwhile, owing to disturbing effects of planets. The average interval between perihelion passages is 77 years. The comet is now near its aphelion beyond the orbit of Neptune. It will return to perihelion in 1986.

9·6. The Schwassmann-Wachmann Comet (Comet 1925 II), discovered in 1927, is unique among known comets in respect to its nearly circular orbit. It looks like a comet and travels like a planet. This very faint comet revolves entirely between the orbits of Jupiter and Saturn. The eccentricity of the orbit is 0.14, which is considerably less than that of Mercury. It was the first comet to be observed around its aphelion. Normally about the eighteenth magnitude, it occasionally exhibits surprisingly great and rapid flareups in brightness; in the course of four days in 1934 (Fig. 9·6) the brightness increased a hundredfold.

March 10, 1934

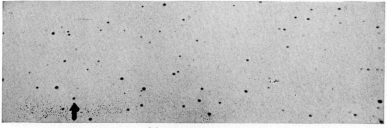

March 14, 1934

FIG. 9·6. Rapid Change in the Brightness of Comet 1925 II. (*Photographed by G. Van Biesbroeck, Yerkes Observatory*)

9·7. A Remarkable Group of Comets includes the great comets of 1668, 1843, 1880, 1882, and 1887. These comets passed unusually close to the sun and their orbits seemed practically identical. They were probably parts of a single comet which was disrupted at a previous close approach to the sun. The separate parts were dispersed in orbits of various sizes, and therefore with periods of revolution of various lengths. But all the orbits still closely resemble the orbit of the original comet in the vicinity of the sun.

The great September comet of 1882, the most spectacular of the group, was one of the finest comets of modern times, plainly visible in full daylight. It passed through the sun's corona, within 300,000 miles of the sun's surface, with a speed exceeding a million miles an hour. Effects of the tidal disruption during the close approach were evident soon afterwards. The nucleus divided into four parts which spread out in the direction of the comet's motion. These are expected to return as four comets between the 25th and 28th centuries.

FIG. 9·8. Finsler's Comet, August 9, 1937. This comet was faintly visible to the unaided eye. (*Photographed at Mount Wilson Observatory*)

9·8. The Comets Themselves. Characteristic of all comets is the *coma,* the foggy disk that distinguishes the distant comet from a star or asteroid. As the comet approaches the sun the *nucleus* sometimes appears near the center of the coma, like a star shining through the fog. In large comets the *tail* begins to form when they are about twice the earth's distance from the sun; and at least in one case the tail has attained a length exceeding this distance.

The mass of a comet is small. This is shown by the fact that whenever a comet has passed near a planet or satellite the only perceptible effect is the change in the motion of the comet. Thus the average density of a comet must be very small. This does not mean that a comet's head is entirely gaseous; an aggregation of solid pieces can have small average density if the pieces are far apart compared with their diameters. The observation that stars behind the head of a comet are practically undimmed indicates the wide dispersal of the solid material.

FIG. 9·9. Comet 1941c. In addition to the comet, near the center of the picture, the photograph also shows the zodiacal light extending toward Jupiter and Saturn in the upper right corner. (*Photograph by the Texas Observers, Fort Worth*)

9·9. The Nature of a Comet. A comet appears to be a swarm of relatively small and widely separated solid bodies held together loosely by mutual attractions. As the comet approaches the sun, gas issues explosively from the solid pieces and spreads by diffusion into the coma together with fine dust. The gas glows partly by reflected sunlight, but for the most part by fluorescence stimulated by the sunlight, and it is swept away by pressure of the sun's radiation to form the tail. The activity increases up to some time after perihelion passage, and then declines until the gas and dust have mostly streamed away.

The comet departs as it approaches us—an assemblage of small solid bodies, but with somewhat diminished mass, because the material that formed the tail is not retrieved.

9·10. Formations of Comets' Tails. The material of which a comet's tail is composed has three distinct motions: (1) It is expelled from the

FIG. 9·10. Tail of a Comet Directed Away from the Sun. The tail is usually curved and is longest and brightest near perihelion.

nucleus, sometimes as fast as several miles a second, as indicated by the jets and expanding envelopes. (2) It is repelled from the sun's direction; the material is driven away from the comet's head to form the tail. Since the first motion is still in progress, the tail increases in breadth as the distance from the head increases, often taking the form of a hollow cone, or horn. (3) It is revolving meanwhile around the sun. By the law of areas, the material revolves less rapidly as it moves outward through the tail, falling more and more behind the nucleus, so that the tail is curved.

It is well known that radiation exerts pressure on anything that obstructs it. For large bodies the pressure of the sun's radiation is insignificant in comparison with its powerful attraction. For very small bodies radiation pressure becomes important, since the area on which the light falls decreases as the square of the radius, while the mass to be moved decreases as its cube. The pressure on a dust particle 1/100,000 inch in diameter equals the sun's gravitational attraction; and upon a molecule of gas which absorbs the radiation the pressure may exceed the attraction as much as 150 times.

9·11. The Spectrum of a Comet (Fig. 9·11) is characterized by bright bands produced by the fluorescence of its gases as they are stimulated by the ultraviolet radiation of the sun. The identified bright bands are caused by gases containing carbon, nitrogen, hydrogen, and oxygen.

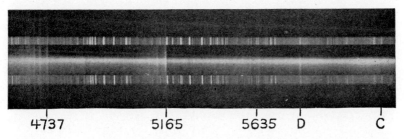

4737   5165   5635   D   C

FIG. 9·11. Spectrum of Halley's Comet. The bright-line spectrum shows the carbon bands, indicated by their wave lengths, and the D line of sodium which lasted only a few days. In the spectrum of sunlight reflected by the comet's head the dark Fraunhofer lines C and F are prominent. A comparison spectrum appears above and below. (*Photographed by V. M. Slipher, Lowell Observatory*)

The actual molecules identified are chiefly carbon (C_2), nitrogen hydride (NH), cyanogen (CN), methyne (CH), and hydroxyl (OH). It is pointed out by Swings at Yerkes Observatory that the last three molecules named are not chemically stable where molecular collisions are frequent; they must result from photo-dissociation of more complex molecules of nature unknown which issued from the solid material.

In addition to the bright bands the spectrum contains a faint replica of the dark-line solar spectrum, showing that the comet shines partly by reflected sunlight. Bright lines of sodium become prominent and lines of iron and other metallic elements appear when a comet is sufficiently heated by close approach to the sun.

METEORS AND METEOR STREAMS

Meteors are small, solid celestial bodies which are invisible, except those that enter the earth's atmosphere and are heated to incandescence by impact of the air molecules. Then they appear momentarily as the streaks of light across the night sky that have long been known as *shoot-*

ing stars. Unusually brilliant ones are called *fireballs*. *Meteorites* are those that partly survive the flight through the air and fall to the ground.

The word "meteor" is derived from the Greek word pertaining to anything in the air. Meteorology, the science of atmospheric phenomena, is not concerned with meteors.

9·12. The Number of Meteors visible to the unaided eye at any one place is usually rather small. The average for a single observer under the best conditions is ten an hour throughout the year. But the ob-

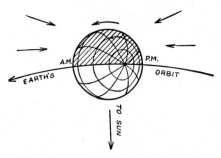

FIG. 9·12. Meteors More Numerous After Midnight. In the morning we are on the forward side of the earth.

server's field of view is limited to a hundred thousandth of the earth's atmospheric shell. Over all the earth's surface, therefore, meteors visible to the unaided eye fall at the rate of a million an hour. The rate is far greater when the smaller meteors are included.

The frequency of the meteors increases through the night, until before dawn four times as many can be seen as after dusk. The reason is that in the evening we are on the following side of the earth with respect to its revolution and are protected except for meteors that overtake us. In the morning we are on the forward side fully exposed to the bombardment.

9·13. The Trails of Meteors begin at heights of from sixty to seventy miles and most of them end more than forty miles from the ground. The brightness of the trail depends chiefly on the kinetic energy of the meteor, that is, on its mass and the square of its velocity. As for the mass, a body no larger than the head of a common pin can account for the majority of the trails.

The velocities relative to the revolving earth increase greatly from dusk to dawn. Suppose that the meteors are moving at the rate of

26 miles a second—parabolic speed (7·25)—when they encounter the earth. Then their speeds relative to the earth vary from 26 *minus* 18½, or 7½ miles a second for those that overtake us, to 26 *plus* 18½, or 44½ miles for the head-on collisions, with the addition of 3 miles and ½ mile a second respectively for the earth's attraction. Thus the

FIG. 9·13. Trail of a Brilliant Meteor. The meteor was brighter than the planet Venus. (*Photographed at the Oak Ridge Station of Harvard Observatory*)

meteors we see in the evening are relatively slow moving and reddish, while those in the morning are swift and have bluer trails.

Photographs of meteor trails have been made in such a way that the trails are interrupted every twentieth of a second. The study of such photographs by Whipple at Harvard Observatory shows that three bright meteors reached us with considerably less than parabolic speed; these three were moving in orbits much like those of close-approaching asteroids or of comets of very short period. Photographs of fainter trails are not yet available, and the visual determinations of the velocities of meteors have not seemed reliable. But it would not be surprising if all meteors investigated should prove to have less than parabolic velocity and therefore, like the comets, to be moving in elliptic orbits around the sun.

9·14. The Nature of Meteors. Meteors, then, are for the most part tiny, solid, swiftly moving bodies which are fused and mostly consumed in their flight through the upper atmosphere. While their trails have very short duration, the bright meteors leave *trains*—hollow cylinders

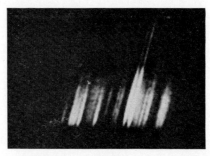

FIG. 9·14. Spectrum of a Meteor Trail. The two conspicuous lines near the middle are the Fraunhofer H and K lines of calcium. (*Photographed by Millman, David Dunlap Observatory, Toronto*)

of phosphorescent expanding gases—along their paths. These remain visible from a few seconds to as much as half an hour and are often twisted by the air currents. The great number of meteors that encounter the earth suggests that their number in the solar system must be very great indeed.

Of the meteors that land on the earth's surface, some are stony and others are metallic, as we shall presently notice. Spectrum analysis of meteor trails (Fig. 9·14), especially by Millman at Toronto, suggests that the meteors that are consumed in the air are similarly divided in their constitutions. The *sporadic meteors,* which appear to be independent travelers, seem to be divided between stony and metallic, while the meteors assembled in swarms and streams seem to be entirely stony. A description of these assemblages and the showers of meteors they produce is now in order.

9·15. Meteoric Showers. Whenever the earth encounters a swarm of meteors, a *meteoric shower* ensues. Since the meteors in the swarm are all moving in parallel paths, the luminous trails of these meteors through the air are parallel, or nearly so. Just as the rails of a track seem to diverge from a point in the distance, so the parallel trails appear to diverge from one point, or small area in the sky. The *radiant* of a meteoric shower is the vanishing point in the perspective of the parallel trails. It is located by extending the trails backward until they meet. Meteoric showers and the swarms that produce them are

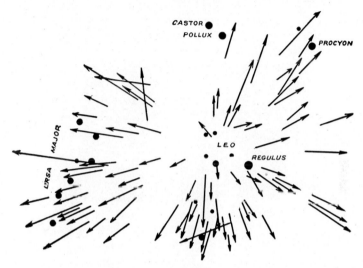

FIG. 9·15. A Shower of Leonid Meteors. The trails were observed at Brown University November 15, 1901, during a watch of five hours. With three or four exceptions the trails apparently diverged from the radiant in Leo.

named from the positions of the radiants among the constellations. The Perseids and Leonids are examples.

A meteoric shower can occur only when the orbit of the swarm crosses the earth's orbit and when swarm and earth arrive together at the crossing point. The place of this point on the earth's orbit of course determines the date of the shower. If the swarm is condensed, the interval between showers depends on the period of revolution of the swarm around the sun. Swarms extended in *streams* may spend more than a year in crossing the earth's orbit, or may be so scattered around their orbits that we encounter some of their members every year.

Disturbing effects of the planets frequently alter the meteoric orbits. Some swarms which formerly produced remarkable showers no longer do so. Other swarms now unknown to us may some day be brought to collision with the earth. A conspicuous meteoric shower, like a brilliant comet, may come unheralded at any time.

9·16. Some Meteoric Showers. The Perseids, or August meteors, furnish the most conspicuous and dependable of the annual showers. They are visible through two or three weeks, with the maximum display about August 12. Their orbit is nearly perpendicular to the earth's orbit and passes near no other planet. Next in order of annual reliability and numbers are the Orionids, whose maximum occurs on October 22, and the Geminids, on December 10.

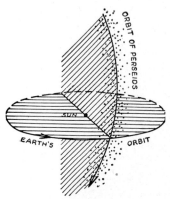

The Leonids (November 16), revolving around the sun in a period of about 33 years, produced in 1833 and 1866 the most brilliant showers of modern times. The showers around 1900 and 1933 were not spectacular. The Bielids (November 24), having their radiant in Andromeda, gave fine displays in 1872 and 1885. They have practically disappeared.

FIG. 9·16. Intersecting Orbits of the Perseids and the Earth.

9·17. Association of Comets and Meteor Streams. Several instances are now established (Table 9·I) in which a comet and a meteor swarm have nearly identical orbits. A particularly interesting case is the association of Halley's comet with what might seem at first to be two separate swarms, the Eta Aquarids and the Orionids. Apparently it is the same stream which we encounter twice—both before and after its perihelion passage.

TABLE 9·I. METEOR SHOWERS AND ASSOCIATED COMETS

Meteor Shower	Date of Maximum	Associated Comet	Comet's Period
Lyrids	April 21	1861 I	400
Eta Aquarids	May 4	Halley	76
Perseids	August 11	1862 III	122
Giacobinids	October 9	1933 III	6½
Orionids	October 19	Halley	76
Taurids	November 9	Encke	3⅓
Leonids	November 15	1866 I	33
Andromedes	November 20	Biela	6½

Another well-known case is that of Biela's comet, a member of Jupiter's family having a period of 6½ years. At its return in 1846 the comet divided into two, which returned in 1852 with wider separation, and have not since been seen. Traveling in the orbit of the lost comet the Bielid meteors produced several brilliant showers, until they vanished as well.

FIG. 9·18. The Zodiacal Light. (*From a painting by E. L. Trouvelot*)

9·18. The Zodiacal Light. The faint glow of the *zodiacal light* is best seen, in northern latitudes, in the west after nightfall in the spring, and in the east before dawn in the autumn, in a clear, moonless sky. It is broadest and brightest near the horizon, and tapers upward, following the course of the ecliptic to a distance of about 90° from the sun; it reaches a greater altitude and is therefore easier to observe when the ecliptic is most nearly perpendicular to the horizon (1·19). In the tropics the zodiacal light is visible throughout the year, both morning and evening, and in especially clear skies it has been traced as a narrow *zodiacal band* completely around the ecliptic.

Opposite the sun this band widens into the elliptical spot, visually some ten degrees in diameter, known as *the counterglow*. These extensions are ordinarily not easy to see. Elvey's photoelectric studies of the counterglow at Yerkes Observatory indicated a brightening of the sky opposite the sun over an area extending some $30°$ in celestial longitude and less in celestial latitude.

This glow along the zodiac is chiefly sunlight reflected by meteoric material which has a strong preference for the ecliptic plane and is more concentrated within the earth's orbit than outside it. The zodiacal light itself can be accounted for if the space within the earth's orbit contains particles a twenty-fifth of an inch in diameter and five miles apart. It is only because of its great volume that this light is visible at all.

Meteorites and Meteor Craters

When a meteor is too large to be entirely consumed in its flight through the air, what remains falls to the ground. During and after its fall it is called a *meteorite*. The fall is frequently accompanied by bright flashes of light and by explosive and roaring sounds—effects that may well be magnified in the reports of startled observers. Most meteorites are found at or only a little way below the surface, having done practically no damage. A few very large ones have blasted out the great pits known as *meteor craters*.

9·19. The Fall of Meteorites. While meteorites often fall singly, it is not uncommon for many to land at the same time and place. Either they entered the atmosphere in a compact swarm, or they entered as a single body which was shattered by the shock of the sudden reduction in speed, as effectively as if it had been struck with a great hammer. When a group of meteorites falls, the individuals are likely to be distributed over an elliptical area whose major axis, perhaps several miles long, is in the direction of the flight.

Whenever meteorites have been picked up almost as soon as they have landed, they have varied from moderately warm to slightly too hot to handle, and have quickly become cold. The heating was only superficial, and the melted material was continually swept away into the train.

Individuals from about 1500 falls have been recovered, and new ones are being found at the rate of twenty-five a year. Many of these were not seen to fall, but their celestial origin is definitely established. Meteorites are usually designated by the locality in which they were found, for example, the Willamette meteorite. Collections of meteorites are displayed in many museums in various parts of the world, for example in the Chicago Museum of Natural History.

FIG. 9·19. The Paragould (Arkansas) Meteorite. The largest single stony meteorite whose fall was observed. It weighs 750 pounds. (*Courtesy of Chicago Museum of Natural History*)

9·20. External Appearance of Meteorites. Characteristic of most meteorites is the thin, glassy, and usually dark crust. It is formed from the fused material that was not swept away, which hardened quickly near the end of the flight through the air. The surface is often irregular, having depressions where softer materials melted away faster than the others.

If the meteorite was shattered shortly before reaching the ground, the fragments are of irregular shape. If the individual had a longer flight through the air, it was shaped by the rush of hot air. Some meteorites turned over and over as they fell. Others kept the same orientation and became cone shaped, a common form.

9·21. Structure and Composition. Meteorites are of two kinds, the irons and stones. There are gradations between the two.

Iron meteorites are silvery under their blackened exteriors; they are

composed mainly of alloys of nickel and iron, especially the alloys kama-
cite and taenite. When a section of one of these meteorites is polished
and treated with dilute acid, an etching of intersecting crystal bands
parallel to the faces of an octahedron (Fig. 9·21) usually appears.

Stony meteorites often appear grayish beneath their crusts, and
usually have a granular structure. The rounded granules are crystals,

FIG. 9·21. Etched Section of the Knowles (Oklahoma) Meteorite. The
pattern of bands is characteristic of the iron meteorites. (*By courtesy of the
American Museum of Natural History, New York*)

chiefly a variety of silicates, of which the most common are magnesium-
iron silicates, such as olivine and enstatite. Quartz is not a constituent.
The peculiar structure of stony meteorites and their possession of specks
of nickel-iron distinguish them from terrestrial rocks.

9·22. Large Meteorites. Something like a dozen known meteorites
weigh more than a ton; they are all masses of nickel-iron. The largest
one, the Hoba West meteorite, lies where it fell in the Grootfontein
district, South West Africa. It weighs fifty or sixty tons; the rec-
tangular upper surface measures 9 by 10 feet and the greatest thickness
is almost 4 feet.

Next in order is one of the group of four that the explorer Peary
found in 1895, near Cape York, Greenland; he brought three of them

FIG. 9·22. Great Meteorite, Grootfontein, South Africa. The largest known meteorite, weighing more than 50 tons. The exposed surface measures about 9 by 10 feet. (*By courtesy of Harvard Observatory*)

FIG. 9·22A. "Ahnighito" Meteorite in the Hayden Planetarium. The largest known meteorite in America; it is a mass of nickel-iron weighing 36½ tons. (*By courtesy of the American Museum of Natural History, New York*)

to New York. The largest Cape York meteorite, the "Ahnighito," weighs 36 tons; it is 11 feet long, 5 feet wide, and 7 feet high. The Willamette meteorite is a cone weighing 15 tons. Large cavities in its base were formed by weathering after the fall of the meteorite, while it remained base uppermost exposed to the moisture of an Oregon forest. Both meteorites are in the Hayden Planetarium, New York.

Three other iron meteorites, each weighing more than ten tons, were found in Mexico, namely, the Bacubirito (27 tons), the Chupaderos (26 tons, in two pieces that fit together), and the El Morito (11 tons). Six other iron meteorites weigh between one and ten tons. None of these was seen to fall. The largest observed fall of iron occurred at Boguslava, 140 miles north of Vladivostok, in 1916. Two individuals weigh 440 and 125 pounds.

Stony meteorites do not have the large dimensions of the irons, evidently because they offer less resistance to fracture and erosion. The largest stone meteorite is the Long Island (Kansas) meteorite, which weighs, all together, more than half a ton; it was broken by the fall. The largest unbroken stone meteorite (Fig. 9·19), now in the Chicago Museum of Natural History, fell at Paragould, Arkansas, on February 17, 1930. It weighs 750 pounds.

9·23. The Siberian Meteorite. The most destructive of known meteorites fell on June 30, 1908, in a densely forested region of north central Siberia. According to the report of an expedition sent out to this region by the Russian Academy of Sciences, an area twenty or thirty miles in radius is completely devastated. The trees, without bark or branches, lie with their tops pointing away from the center of the area. Many craters were found near the center of the region, the largest one 150 feet in diameter.

In the settlement of Vanovara, fifty miles south of the place of the fall, a very hot wave of air had hurled a man several feet from the steps of his house, which was badly damaged by the wave. The air wave was felt and a roaring was heard 400 miles from the place of the fall. This is the only known case of a fall of meteorites which caused serious destruction.

9·24. Meteor Crater in Arizona. Near Canyon Diablo in northeast Arizona there is a circular depression in the desert 4200 feet in diameter and 570 feet in depth, measured from the rim which is 130 feet above the surrounding country. Several tons of meteoric iron, generally in small pieces, have been picked up within a radius of six miles around the crater. The largest individual, weighing half a ton, is preserved in the Chicago Museum of Natural History.

The rocks below the crater floor are crushed to a depth of several hundred feet, and give evidence of having been highly heated. Millions of tons of rock—limestone and sandstone—were displaced outward,

FIG. 9·24. Meteor Crater, Arizona. A great hole in the desert twenty miles west of Winslow, Arizona. (*Photographed by the United States Army Air Corps*)

forming the wall of the crater, while loose blocks of rock lie around the rim, the largest weighing 7000 tons. The weathering of the rocks indicates that the meteorite fell not more than 5000 years ago; the fall was certainly not less than 700 years ago, because cedar trees of this age are growing on the rim.

When a large meteorite, or perhaps a small asteroid, weighing thousands of tons falls to the earth, there is little reduction of its speed in the air. When it collides with the ground, the outer parts of the meteorite and the ground in contact are intensely heated and fused. The gases expand explosively, scattering what is left of the meteorite over the surrounding country and blasting out the crater.

Ten craters or groups of craters in various parts of the world are recognized as of meteoric origin. Meteorites have been found in the vicinities of all of them, varying from rather large individuals in some cases to tiny fragments in others. No other crater approaches the size of the one in Arizona; the second in size is 650 feet across.

THE PROBLEM OF THE ORIGIN OF THE SYSTEM

Speculations as to the development of the solar system have aroused much scientific and popular interest. As hypotheses, to be confronted with the available data and to be discarded if they fail in the test, they have been stimulating. Too often, however, they have been accepted so enthusiastically that their failure has brought disappointment. In a few Sections that follow, we look at the problem of the origin of the solar system and at two hypotheses which have received considerable attention.

9·25. The Problem Stated. A hypothesis of the origin of the solar system starts with an earlier configuration which presumably contains enough material and energy to go around in the end product. It intends to conform to accepted physical principles, and hopes that the product will not fail to agree in any important way with the present solar system.

We have seen that the more massive members of the planetary system exhibit regularities in their movements. The orbits of the larger planets are not far from circles which are nearly in the same plane, and the directions of the revolutions around the sun are from west to east. Many of the larger satellites show the same regularities in the revolutions around their primaries. The less massive members of the system— the smaller satellites, the asteroids, and the comets and meteor swarms— often depart markedly from these regularities. These are some of the features that the hypothetical development must produce. The characteristics of the individual members and of their atmospheres must also be faithfully represented.

One physical principle that has plagued all the hypotheses is the tendency of gases to disperse. Another is the constant quantity of angular momentum in an isolated system. It is in order to examine the second principle.

9·26. Constancy of Angular Momentum. The *angular momentum* of a revolving body, such as a planet revolving around the sun or a particle of a rotating globe of gas, is the product of the mass, the square of the radius, and the rate of the angular motion. The principle of *the conservation of angular momentum* asserts that the total angular momentum (the sum of all these products) of an isolated system is always the same.

Consider a rotating globe of gas. The total angular momentum is found by summing the products of mass, square of distance from axis of rotation, and angular velocity for all the molecules of the gas. Suppose now that the globe of gas shrinks. The mass remains the same. Since the distances of the molecules from the axis are diminished, the angular velocities must increase to maintain the same total angular momentum. Thus the shrinking of a rotating globe causes it to rotate at a faster rate.

In comparing a hypothesis of development with the present state of the solar system we must also notice the distribution of the angular momentum in the system. Jupiter alone has sixty per cent of the total. The four giant planets between them carry ninety-eight per cent.

Three processes have been chiefly invoked in the hypotheses of planetary development:

(1) *Rotational instability*. The material for the formation of the planets was abandoned by a shrinking rotating globe of gas.

(2) *Tidal action*. The material was removed from the sun in excessive tides raised by a passing star.

(3) *Collision*. The passing star collided with a former companion of the sun. Part of the debris remained to form the planets.

9·27. The Nebular Hypothesis of Laplace, proposed in 1796, is an example of the rotational process. It was suggested by the regularities of motions in the solar system and undertook to account for them. This hypothesis is noteworthy for its simplicity and for the confidence it inspired, despite the apology with which it was presented; it was offered "with that diffidence which ought always to attach to whatever is not the result of observation or of calculation."

The account begins with a great globe of hot gas in slow rotation from west to east. As this globe cooled, it contracted and therefore (9·26) rotated faster. The increased speed of rotation caused greater bulging at the equator, until a critical stage was reached at which the centrifugal effect at the equator became equal to the gravitational attraction toward the center. The equatorial ring of gas was then abandoned, and the remainder went on contracting, leaving behind other rings whenever the critical stage was repeated. Each ring gradually assembled into a gaseous globe whose orbit around the sun was the same as the ring from which it was formed, and whose rotation was also from west to east. Most of these lesser globes, before they condensed into planets, developed satellites by the same process. The rings of Saturn seemed to have remained to support the account.

9·28. Criticism of the Nebular Hypothesis. Some of the steps outlined in this hypothesis could not have occurred because of the tendency of gas to disperse. The gaseous rings, for example, could not have assembled into planets.

Overlooking the operational difficulties, the hypothetical solar system would not have conformed to the actual one in the amount and distribution of angular momentum. Calculations have shown that in order to have abandoned the ring from which Neptune was formed the system must have possessed a total angular momentum two hundred times as great as the present total. In addition, the hypothesis requires that the greater part of the present angular momentum should be carried by the sun, where only two per cent of the total is actually found.

The organization of the solar system is more complex than was known in the time of Laplace. Many exceptions have since been discovered, as we have seen, to the regularities that his hypothesis tried to represent.

9·29. The Tidal Hypothesis. Cosmic evolution, formerly presented as an orderly procedure, has in some of the more recent speculations acquired an accompaniment of catastrophe. Around 1900, Chamberlin and Moulton of the University of Chicago proposed a different hypothesis of the origin of the solar system, in which tidal action became the prominent feature.

In this account, a passing star raised tides of such great height in the sun that great quantities of gas broke loose from the sun and streamed away. Much of the gas solidified into small solid pieces which from the start were crowded together in places to form the nuclei of future planets and satellites. The nuclei grew as they swept up more small pieces.

All this material was now revolving around the sun in the same direction the passing star had taken and in something like the plane of its orbit. The individual pieces had orbits of various inclinations to this plane and also of different eccentricities. A large planet or satellite, resulting from the sweeping up of great numbers of small pieces, would be likely to have an orbit of small eccentricity and inclination. A small body, resulting from fewer collisions, might have an orbit of considerable eccentricity and inclination, and would not conform to the regularities.

9·30. Criticism of the Tidal Hypothesis.

Any tidal hypothesis seems to have difficulty with the diffusion of gas and the conservation of angular momentum. Spitzer of Yale Observatory has concluded that extremely hot gas brought out in great quantity from the sun, where it is kept under control by the high pressure, would diffuse explosively instead of condensing to form planets. Russell, at Princeton, has stated the mechanical difficulty. If the disturbing star passed close enough to the sun to cause important tidal disruption, it could scarcely have introduced into the solar system anything like the total angular momentum it now has. On the other hand, if the star passed far enough from the sun to produce the required angular momentum, the tides it raised in the sun would have been inconsiderable.

To meet this objection, it has been supposed that the sun originally had a companion star at the present distance of Jupiter, and that the disturbing star collided with the companion, carrying away most of the wreckage and leaving enough behind to form the planetary system. This alternative has not seemed attractive. It might be a good way to start a tremendous explosion, but not to start a planetary system.

In his authoritative and very readable book entitled *Earth, Moon and Planets,* Whipple of Harvard Observatory remarks: "There appear to be damning arguments against every theory so far proposed for the origin of the planets." But the attempts to solve this important problem are continuing. Some current hypotheses have sought to avoid the pitfalls that beset the earlier ones.

REVIEW QUESTIONS

1. Supply the name of the comet to which each of the following characteristics applies:

    (a) The comet that "travels like a planet."
    (b) The comet having the shortest period of revolution.
    (c) The first periodic comet to become known.
    (d) The comet that broke in two and subsequently disappeared.
    (e) The comet that is expected to return as four comets.

2. What is characteristic of the orbits (a) of Jupiter's family of comets? (b) of a group of comets?

3. How is it possible to determine whether a newly discovered comet is really a new addition to the list or the return of a comet previously seen?

4. Notice in Fig. 9·5A that Halley's comet spends about half its time in the small part of its orbit that lies beyond the orbit of Neptune. Explain.

5. Show that the members of a comet group may seem to have identical orbits in the sun's vicinity, and yet have widely different periods of revolution.

6. Explain the following features of comets' tails:

(a) Source of the material.
(b) Their direction.
(c) Their frequent shape of a hollow cone.
(d) Their curvature.

7. What is the spectroscopic evidence that comets shine partly by their own light and partly by reflected sunlight?

8. More meteors are likely to be visible before sunrise than after sunset. Those seen in the morning differ in appearance from the evening meteors. Explain.

9. Explain the radiant of a meteoric shower. What is the method of naming meteoric showers? Give an example.

10. The speeds of large meteorites are less reduced by air resistance than are those of small ones. Explain.

11. State the characteristics of stony and of iron meteorites.

12. Was Meteor Crater in Arizona caused by a large meteor, a comet, or a small asteroid?

13. On the basis of the principle of the conservation of angular momentum, explain the effect of a contraction of the earth on the length of the day.

14. Outline the nebular hypothesis of Laplace. Mention some features of the solar system that are inconsistent with this hypothesis.

15. Outline and criticize the tidal hypothesis of the origin of the solar system.

The David Dunlap Observatory of the University of Toronto, Richmond Hill, Ontario.

CHAPTER X

THE SUN

THE SUN'S RADIATION AND TEMPERATURE — THE SUN'S VISIBLE SUR-
FACE; SUNSPOTS — THE CHROMOSPHERE AND CORONA

We have dealt at considerable length with the characteristics of the solar system because this system occupies the foreground in our picture of the physical universe. As the dominant member and the power plant of the system the sun has a prominent part in the picture. Viewed from another part of the stellar system, however, the sun would appear as only one of many stars. From the viewpoint of astronomy the sun is important because it is the only star near enough to be observed in detail. No other star shows more than a point of light through the largest telescope. In the study of the sun we are learning about a star.

10·1. The Sun's Constitution. The sun is a globe of hot gas, whose visible surface is 864,000 miles in diameter. In volume it is one and a third million times as large as the earth; in mass it is a third of a million times as great, so that its average density is one fourth the earth's mean density, or 1.4 times the density of water.

The interior of the sun, below the visible surface, is known to us only indirectly from theoretical researches. Its temperature increases from 6000° K at the lowest visible level to many million degrees at the center.

The photosphere, or "light sphere," is the visible surface; it is mottled by brighter granulations and faculae, and is marked by darker sunspots. The gases above the photosphere constitute the sun's *atmosphere.*

The reversing layer extends immediately above the photosphere to the height of a few hundred miles. It is the stratum in which the majority of the dark lines of the solar spectrum originate.

The chromosphere, or "color sphere," is so named because of its scarlet color which is caused by the glow of hydrogen. It is several thousand miles in height and from it the red prominences rise at times to heights of hundreds of thousand miles; they are visible during total

solar eclipses and with special apparatus at other times. The reversing
layer may be regarded as the lowest part of the chromosphere.

The corona, the outermost solar envelope, appears at the time of
total eclipse as a filmy, pearly halo of intricate structure. Its inner part
can also be observed with special apparatus at other times.

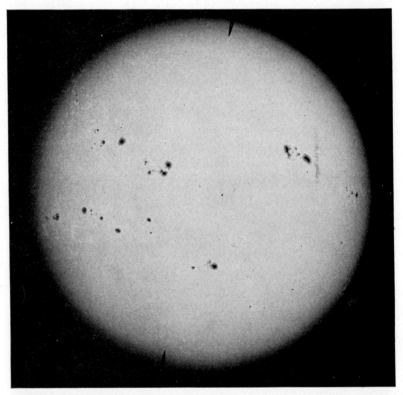

Fig. 10·1. The Sun, July 11, 1937. Sunspots are numerous. Faculae are
visible near the edge where the photosphere is less bright. (*Photographed at
Mount Wilson Observatory*)

10·2. The Sun's Rotation. The gradual movement of sunspots across
the disk of the sun is a well known effect of the sun's rotation from west
to east. A spot now near the center of the disk will disappear at the
edge in about a week. Two weeks later the spot will appear at the
opposite edge if it lasts that long, and after a week more it will again
be near the center of the disk. This apparent period of four weeks is
made about two days more than the actual rotation period by the earth's

revolution around the sun. It has long been known that the period of
the sun's rotation increases from around 25 days at the equator to 27

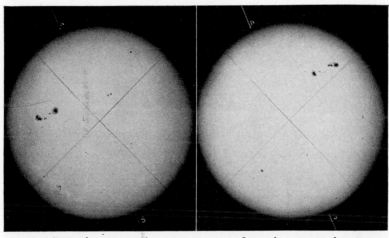

September 17, 1926   September 22, 1926

FIG. 10·2. The Sun's Rotation Shown by Movements of Sunspots. The large
group is displaced to the right by the sun's rotation. (*Photographed at the Royal
Observatory, Greenwich*)

days in latitude 35°, beyond which spots rarely appear. This increase
toward the poles is verified by spectroscopic observations.

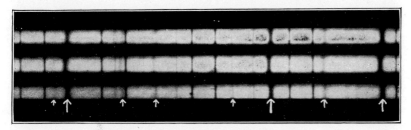

FIG. 10·2A. Effect of the Sun's Rotation on Its Spectrum. In the upper and
lower spectra, of the sun's west limb, the solar lines are displaced to the right
(red). In the middle spectrum, of the east limb, the lines are displaced to the
left (violet). Solar lines are indicated by the arrows. Telluric lines, which
are not marked, are not affected by the sun's rotation. Only a small part of the
spectrum is shown. (*Photographed at Mount Wilson Observatory*)

The speed of the sun's rotation in any latitude can be determined
by photographing on the same plate the spectra of the east (approach-

ing) and west (receding) edges, and comparing the two (Fig. 10·2A). The lines in the first spectrum are displaced toward the violet by the Doppler effect; in the second spectrum they are displaced toward the red. Half the difference denotes the apparent speed of the rotation in that latitude, and from it the actual period can be derived. The period of the sun's rotation as determined from the spectra increases progressively from less than 25 days at the equator to as much as 35 days in latitude 80°.

The Sun's Radiation and Temperature

10·3. Intensity of the Sun's Radiation; the Solar Constant. In order to measure the rate at which we receive energy from the sun it is necessary to employ a device that is sensitive to all wave lengths. Neither the eye nor the photographic plate serves this purpose, for they are sensitive to only very limited ranges of wave length. All radiation, when it is absorbed, produces heat. Thus the heating effect of the sun's radiation is a measure of its intensity. The *pyrheliometer* is an instrument designed for observations of this kind; it contains a thermometer for measuring the rate at which the sun's radiation raises the temperature of a small quantity of water or mercury, or of a metallic disk. Instruments of this type are in continuous use at the stations of the Astrophysical Observatory of the Smithsonian Institution.

The *solar constant* is a measure of the rate at which energy is received by a surface exposed at right angles to the sun's radiation just outside the atmosphere, when the earth is at its mean distance from the sun. It is expressed in terms of the heat produced at this surface by complete absorption of the radiation. The average value of the solar constant is 1.94 calories a minute per square centimeter. A *calorie* is the quantity of heat required to increase by 1° C the temperature of one gram of water (at 15° C). This "constant" seems to be subject to slight variations.

10·4. Energy Radiated by the Sun. The value of the solar constant, 1.94 calories per square centimeter per minute, may be expressed in units more convenient for calculation; it equals 1.35×10^6 ergs per square centimeter per second. Multiplying this by the number of square centimeters in the surface of a sphere whose radius is the earth's mean distance from the sun we have a measure of the sun's total radiation. Since the space between the sun and the earth is practically transparent, the total energy intercepted by the sphere is identical with that which leaves the sun's surface. It is equal to 3.8×10^{33} ergs per second (about 5×10^{23} horsepower). This enormous output of energy suggests that the sun must be very hot. Dividing this total radiation by the number of square centimeters in the sun's surface we find that the rate of the sun's radiation is 6.25×10^{10} ergs per square centimeter per second (about 70,000 horsepower per square yard).

10·5. Laws of Radiation. When a piece of metal is heated to incandescence, it first has a dull red glow. The glow brightens as the metal is heated further, and changes to bluish white. The relations between the temperature of a body and the quantity or quality, or both, of the radiation it emits are expressed by the *laws of radiation*. Strictly, these laws apply to a hypothetical standard, a *perfect radiator* which has the greatest possible efficiency as a radiator at any temperature, but they seem to serve reasonably well for the sun and stars.

Stefan's law states that the total energy, E ergs, emitted in one second by a square centimeter of the radiator is directly proportional to the fourth power of its absolute temperature. The relation is: $E = aT^4$, where the value of the constant, $a = 5.73 \times 10^{-5}$, is known from laboratory experiments. Thus, if the temperature of a body is doubled, its total radiation becomes sixteen times as intense as before.

Wien's law states that the wave length, λ_{max} in centimeters, for which the radiation is the most intense, is inversely proportional to the absolute temperature. The relation is: $\lambda_{max} = 0.288/T$. Thus if the temperature is $4000°$ K, the brightest part of the spectrum has a wave length of 7200×10^{-8} cm, or 7200 angstroms, in the red; if the temperature is raised to $8000°$ K, the greatest intensity is shifted to 3600 angstroms, in the ultraviolet.

Planck's law, derived from theoretical considerations, is the most general of the radiation laws. By means of this rather complex formula, which may be found in treatises on physics, it is possible to calculate for a perfect radiator at any assigned temperature the relative intensities of its radiation in various wave lengths.

10·6. The Spectral Energy Curve, calculated from the general law for a particular temperature (Fig. 10·6) shows how the intensity of the radiation varies throughout the spectrum. For a higher temperature the curve is higher at all points; but the increase is greater for the shorter wave lengths, so that the peak of the curve is shifted toward the violet end of the spectrum.

Stefan's law and Wien's law refer to special features of the spectral energy curve. The former relates to the area under the curve, which represents the total amount of energy radiated at a particular temperature; the latter gives the wave length of the most intense radiation at that temperature.

By combination of the data of observation with these radiation laws the sun's effective temperature can be determined, that is to say, the

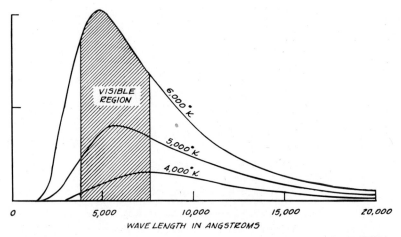

FIG. 10·6. Energy Curves of a Perfect Radiator. The heights are proportional to the intensity of the radiation. As the temperature is increased, the total radiation, represented by the area under the curve, increases (Stefan's law), and the peak of the curve is shifted to shorter wave lengths (Wien's law). The shape of the curve for each temperature is calculated by Planck's formula. The shaded area represents the radiation to which the eye is sensitive.

temperature that the sun's surface must have, if it is a perfect radiator, in order to radiate as it does.

10·7. The Sun's Temperature. The effective temperature of the sun is 5750° K. This value is obtained by substituting the rate of the sun's radiation (6.25×10^{10} ergs per square centimeter per second) in the formula of Stefan's law. Since the rate is determined from the solar constant, which is derived from radiation from all parts of the disk, this effective temperature is the average for the whole disk; it is the value to be used when the temperatures of the sun and stars are compared. It will be noticed later that the sun's disk is less luminous near the edge than at the center.

The effective temperature *at the center of the sun's disk* is about 6000° K, as determined:

(1) *By Stefan's law.* The rate of radiation in all wave lengths is calculated from the value of the solar constant increased by 16 per cent. The resulting temperature is 5960° K.

(2) *By Wien's law.* The wave length of the most intense radiation is found by measurements in the solar spectrum, with allowance for selective absorption in the earth's atmosphere. The resulting temperature is 6150° K.

(3) *By Planck's formula.* The observed intensities of the solar spectrum in the various wave lengths are compared with curves calculated by the formula for different temperatures until the best fit is found. The spectral energy curve for the temperature of 6000° K is in fair agreement with the observed intensities.

10·8. Temperatures in Different Parts of the Sun. The sun's effective temperature of 5750° K is the average for all parts of the disk. The temperature near the middle of the disk is somewhat higher, while near the edge it is not much about 5000°. The temperature of sunspots is reduced to 4800°, or even less.

Below the photosphere the temperature rises so rapidly with increasing depth that most of the sun's interior is above a million degrees. The temperature of the lower chromosphere is around 4500°, and even in the outer corona it is as much as 3000°. These are temperatures that a perfect radiator would have in these regions. Throughout the sun the heat is sufficient to keep all the materials in the gaseous state.

10·9. Problems of the Sun's Radiation. The enormous outflow of energy from the sun has continued at about the present rate for hundreds of million years, according to geological records. It is interesting to inquire where all this energy comes from, and how much longer the supply will last to keep the sun shining.

There is a vast supply of energy in the nuclei of atoms, but it is generally pretty well sealed up. "Atom-smashers," such as the cyclotron, release atomic energy on a small scale, and atomic bombs do so in startling amounts. But the automatic release of this energy on a great scale can perhaps be accomplished at the high temperature of the sun's interior. The particular process currently favored is the combination of hydrogen atoms to form helium, with accompanying liberation of energy. There is enough hydrogen in the sun to supply material for such a process almost indefinitely. This problem will be further considered in connection with the radiations of the stars in general.

Another problem relates to the lavish expenditure of the sun's radiation. Of all the energy that pours forth from the sun, less than one part in two hundred million is intercepted by the planets and their satellites. The remainder spreads through space with little chance of interruption. It would seem that nature is squandering its resources of energy so prodigally that it must ultimately end in bankruptcy. But we may have a very imperfect view of the situation.

THE SUN'S VISIBLE SURFACE; SUNSPOTS

10·10. Observing the Sun's Surface. It is unsafe to look very long at the sun on a clear day even without the telescope; to look at it *with* the telescope, without special precaution, invites immediate and serious injury to the eye, for the objective acts as a burning-glass. The most convenient way to observe the sun with the telescope is to hold a sheet of smooth white cardboard back of the eyepiece, racking the eyepiece out beyond the usual position of focus until the sun's image is sharply defined on the card. In this way many can observe at once. For studying the finer details of the solar surface the direct view is better. Special solar eyepieces admit to the eye only enough light to form a clear image of the sun.

Photographs of the sun have been made on every clear day for many years at a number of observatories. These provide an accurate and permanent record of the appearance of the sun's surface.

10·11. The Tower Telescope. Fixed telescopes are of great value in solar investigations. They permit the use of long-focus objectives that are needed to form large images of the sun, with the minimum of mechanical construction. The largest of the fixed telescopes is the 150-foot tower telescope of the Mount Wilson Observatory.

The tower telescope has at its summit a little dome which contains a coelostat, a plane mirror equatorially mounted and driven by clockwork. This and a second fixed mirror beside it reflect the sunlight downward to a 12-inch objective of 150-foot focus just below them, which forms an image of the sun 17 inches in diameter in the laboratory at the base of the tower. Under the laboratory is a well 80 feet deep, into which the sunlight can be directed upon a grating which returns it to the laboratory dispersed into spectra.

There are two other fixed solar telescopes on Mount Wilson, a tower 60 feet in height and the Snow telescope which is horizontal. The 50-foot tower telescope (Fig. 10·28A) of the McMath-Hulbert

Observatory at Lake Angelus, Michigan, has been remarkably effective in the study of the solar prominences.

FIG. 10·11. Tower Telescopes of Mount Wilson Observatory.

10·12. The Photosphere. While the photosphere, or visible surface of the sun, seems as sharply defined as the surface of a ball, it is only an apparent surface. The gas is still very tenuous at this depth, producing a pressure not more than a hundredth of our atmospheric pressure at sea level. But with the rapidly increasing temperature at this depth the gas has become highly ionized. By their absorption of the light from below, the multitudes of ions produce an opaque haze. The photosphere is as far into the sun as we can see.

Moreover, the photosphere is not perfectly spherical; it is higher near the edge of the disk than near its center. The evidence is that the sun's disk is less luminous and redder near the edge. The reddening is noticeable in the unusual color of the sunlight when the sun is almost totally eclipsed. This fading at the edge is conspicuous on the original photographs with ordinary blue-sensitive plates, though it is often compensated when prints are made for illustrations. The generally accepted explanation of the darkening at the sun's edge is that the light coming to us from the edge has to penetrate a greater thickness of the over-

lying gases. The light that succeeds in reaching us comes from a higher
and cooler level, so that it is less bright and redder than the light from
the lower levels near the center of the disk.

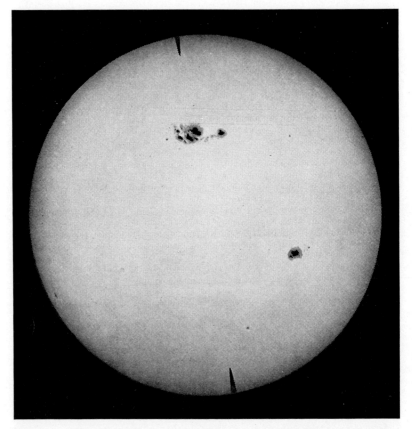

FIG. 10·12. The Photosphere. An extremely large group of sunspots is shown.
(Photographed at Mount Wilson Observatory)

10·13. Granulations of the Photosphere. Through the telescope the
photosphere presents a mottled appearance which is resolved under good
conditions into bright *granules* scattered on the less luminous and by contrast grayish background. The granules average 700 miles in diameter
and cover a third of the photosphere. These are hot spots, hotter by a
hundred degrees or more than the rest of the surface. A single granule
lasts only a few minutes. What we see is a seething surface where
hotter gases come from below and quickly cool.

Near the edge of the sun the granules are not distinct.   Here the larger bright areas of the *faculae* (little torches) at somewhat higher levels are often seen against the less luminous background.   But the dark spots of the photosphere have proved more interesting than the bright ones.

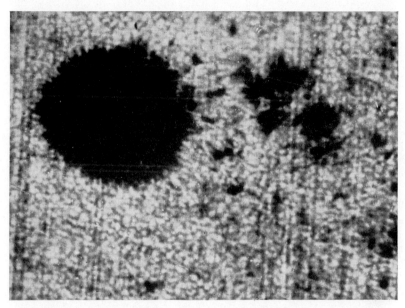

Fig. 10·13.   Granulations of the Photosphere.   In the vicinity of a spot group. (*Photographed at Yerkes Observatory*)

10·14. Sunspots.   A sunspot consists of two distinct parts: the *umbra,* the more or less central dark part, and the *penumbra,* the lighter border which is three fourths as bright as the photosphere.   Sunspots are dark by contrast with their brighter surroundings; they are hotter and brighter than most artificial sources of light.

Individual spots vary in size from specks that are scarcely distinguishable from the inter-granular spaces to the great spots, as much as 50,000 miles in diameter, which are visible to the unaided eye—through a dark glass or in a hazy sky.   They come and go, lasting from a few days to usually not more than a few weeks.   With the sun's rotation from west to east they move across the disk from east to west relative to positions in the sky; and they move independently as well.   Sunspots always occur in groups.   When a single spot is seen, it is the survivor of a group.

10·15. The Life of a Spot Group. Rapid development and slower decline characterize the life history of the normal group, as Nicholson at Mount Wilson Observatory describes it.

In its very early stages the group consists of several small spots strung out in nearly the same latitude. As the group develops, a large compact *preceding spot* dominates the part that is going ahead in the direction of

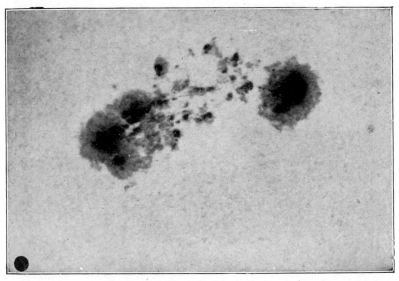

FIG. 10·15. A Large Sunspot Group. The group is extended in the direction of the sun's rotation, which is toward the right. The follower spot is breaking up. The black disk in the corner represents the relative size of the earth. (*Photographed at Mount Wilson Observatory*)

the sun's rotation, while a somewhat less large and compact *following spot* is conspicuous in the part that is moving behind. The following spot is usually a little farther from the equator than the preceding spot. Meanwhile these principal spots draw apart to a difference of ten degrees or more in longitude. At the end of a week the group attains its maximum area and the decline sets in.

The following spot breaks up into smaller spots which diminish in size and vanish, along with the originally small spots. Finally the preceding spot remains alone, a single umbra at the center of a nearly circular penumbra. It may last several weeks, or even months; the record for observed duration is held by a spot that lasted eighteen months. It usually disappears by becoming smaller and smaller, not by breaking up as the following spot generally does. This is the average behavior of a spot group. Sometimes the following spot is the larger and surviving member.

10·16. The Sunspot Cycle. In some years sunspots are so numerous that many spots may be seen whenever the sun is observed, while in other years the sun may remain spotless for several days. The variation in the number of spot groups is roughly periodic, as Fig. 10·16 shows.

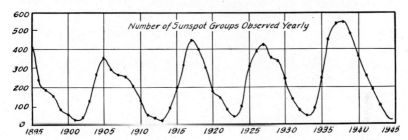

FIG. 10·16. The Sunspot Number Cycle. The point for each year represents the number of spot groups observed during that year. The curve shows the roughly periodic variation in the numbers. (*From data by S. B. Nicholson*)

The average interval between the times when the greatest number of spot groups appear is 11.3 years; the interval has varied from 7 to 14 years. The rise from minimum to maximum spottedness is more rapid than the decline. Not only is the period of the sunspot cycle variable, but the number of spot groups observed yearly varies from one maximum to another. It is accordingly possible to predict only approximately the date of a future maximum and the magnitude of the display of spots. The latest maximum occurred in 1938, and the following minimum was reached in 1944.

10·17. The Shifting of Sunspot Zones. The sunspot cycle is also characterized by the shifting equatorward of the two rather narrow zones in which the spots appear at a particular time. The beginning of each new cycle is announced about a year in advance by the breaking out of small spots in the neighborhoods of heliographic latitudes 30°, north and south. As these spots vanish and others appear, the disturbance closes in toward the sun's equator. At the time of sunspot maximum the zones of activity are around latitudes 10°; and when minimum is reached the fading disturbance is marked by a few spots about 5° from the equator. Meanwhile the early members of the new cycle have made their appearance in the higher latitudes.

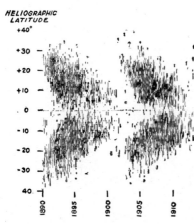

FIG. 10·17. Shifting of Sunspot Zones. The disturbed areas gradually draw in toward the sun's equator. As the disturbance dies out near the equator, a new cycle of spots begins at higher latitudes. (*From a diagram by E. W. Maunder*)

The explanation of this one-way shifting of the spot zones, like that of the number cycle itself, is unknown. Nor is it understood why the spots are restricted, for the most part, to the regions between latitudes 5° and 30°, and why none is found beyond 45°.

10·18. The Sunspot Spectrum.

The spectrum of a sunspot gives decisive evidence as to two characteristics of the spots:

(1) *Lower temperature of sunspots.* As compared with the normal solar spectrum: (a) The continuous background of the spot spectrum is weakened progressively from red to violet. (b) Certain of the dark lines are strengthened; they are lines that are conspicuous in laboratory spectra of sources at lower temperature. (c) Other dark lines are weakened; these are lines of ionized atoms which are weaker at lower temperatures, when other conditions are unaltered. (d) Dark bands appear in the spot spectrum, which are absent in the normal spectrum. These are produced by chemical compounds, in particular, titanium oxide and the hydrides of calcium and magnesium, which cannot form at the higher temperature above the undisturbed surface of the sun. Estimates of the temperature of the spot umbra, based on these and other considerations, range from 4800° to as low as 4300° K.

(2) *Magnetic fields in sunspots.* Many lines in the sunspot spectrum are widened, and some are plainly split. This effect had been known for some time before Hale, at Mount Wilson Observatory in 1908, demonstrated its association with the magnetism of sunspots.

10·19. Sunspots as Magnets. *The Zeeman effect,* known by the name of the physicist who discovered it, is the splitting of the lines in the spectrum when the source is in a strong magnetic field. The effect is complex. We notice here what occurs only when the light under observation comes out in the direction of the line joining the poles of the magnet. The lines in its spectrum are divided into pairs, if they can be seen separately. The amount of their separation depends on the strength of the field. The two components of a pair are circularly polarized in opposite directions. With an appropriate analyzer it is possible to deter-

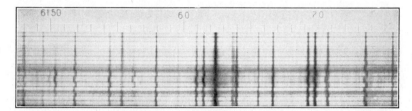

FIG. 10·19. Zeeman Effect in the Sunspot Spectrum. A small part of the Mount Wilson photographic map of the sunspot spectrum. A Nicol prism and compound quarter-wave plate over the slit of the spectroscope divides the spectrum lengthwise into several strips in which the violet and red components of a line are alternately suppressed. Thus the lines widened by the Zeeman effect have a zigzag appearance.

mine the polarity of the magnet, that is to say, whether its positive or negative pole is toward the observer.

In the spectrum of a spot near the center of the sun's disk the lines are so divided into pairs. The conclusion is that sunspots are magnets. In the largest spots the field is 200,000 times as strong as the earth's magnetic field. The analyzer can show the polarity of each spot, whether the positive or negative pole is on top. A daily polarity record of sunspots is kept at Mount Wilson Observatory.

10·20. The Polarities of Sunspots. Most spot groups are *bipolar.* If the leading members of the group have positive polarity, the following members have negative polarity. If the group we are considering is in the sun's northern hemisphere, the statement applies to all other bipolar groups in this hemisphere at that time. But for all such groups in the southern hemisphere the situation is reversed; the leading members have negative polarity and the following members positive. Not all spot groups are bipolar. In some the polarities of the individual spots are so confused that a dividing line cannot be drawn to separate the polarities. These exceptional cases are often large active groups associated with terrestrial magnetic storms.

A remarkable feature of sunspot magnetism is the *reversal of polarity with the beginning of each new cycle*. When the groups of the new cycle appear in the higher latitudes the parts that had positive polarity by the rule of the old cycle now have negative polarity and vice versa.

In addition to these localized magnetic effects, the sun has a *general magnetic field* with opposite poles in the northern and southern hemispheres. The strength of this field is so low that its observation is difficult. It seems to be established that the polarity of the general field is not reversed with the beginning of a new spot cycle.

10·21. The Nature of Sunspots is not yet completely understood. But the clues we have already examined, and others that will be examined later, seem significant enough to lead to the eventual solution of the problem.

We have noticed that sunspots are cooler areas of the solar surface. They are restricted to latitudes within 45° of the sun's equator. They come in cycles; the disturbance appears in the higher latitudes and shifts toward the equator, until it disappears and is replaced by a new cycle in the higher latitudes. Sunspots have magnetic fields. They occur in groups whose preceding and following parts usually have opposite polarities. The polarities in the two hemispheres are opposite. All polarities are reversed with the beginning of each new cycle.

The most plausible interpretation of spot magnetism is that a sunspot is a vortex. Thus the whirling of electrified material in the vortex causes the spot to be an electromagnet, and the direction of the whirl determines the polarity of the spot. Aside from the magnetism of the spot itself, there is no observational evidence to support this interpretation.

A working hypothesis of long standing, which has not proved entirely satisfactory, pictures the spot as the top of a column of hot gas ascending from below the sun's surface. As fast as it reaches the photosphere, where the surrounding pressure is greatly reduced, the gas expands rapidly and is therefore cooled, causing the dark sunspot.

THE CHROMOSPHERE AND CORONA

It is the custom to speak of the photosphere as the surface of the sun, and of the more nearly transparent gases above it as constituting the sun's atmosphere. But all these parts of the sun are gaseous, and they merge one into another. The photosphere, as it has already been noted, is the region from which most of the sunlight emerges, and below which we cannot see. The thickness of the photosphere is estimated in tens of miles. The reversing layer is most effective in producing the dark lines in the solar spectrum. Immediately above the photosphere and having a thickness of several hundred miles, it may be regarded either as a separate layer, or else as the lowest and densest part of the chromosphere. The thickness of the chromosphere is measured in thousands of miles; above it the prominences rise to heights of many tens of thousand miles. The corona, above all, is hundreds of thousand miles in depth. The mass of the sun's atmosphere is one fifty-billionth part of the sun's whole mass.

10·22. The Flash Spectrum. Since the dark lines of the solar spectrum, with the exception of the telluric lines (4·23), are produced by

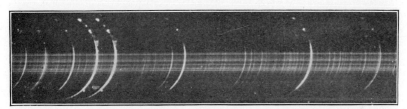

FIG. 10·22. The Flash Spectrum. Photographed by J. A. Anderson near the end of the total eclipse of January 24, 1925. The pair of long crescents at the left are the H and K lines of calcium. Projections to the right of these lines are prominences. Breaks in the crescents are caused by irregularities in the moon's surface. (*By courtesy of the Mount Wilson Observatory*)

absorption of light from the photosphere by the gases which lie above it, these gases alone should give a bright-line spectrum; and this spectrum should match approximately the dark-line pattern of the ordinary solar spectrum. The bright-line spectrum of the chromosphere is known as the *flash spectrum,* because it flashes into view in the spectroscope near the beginning of total solar eclipse and disappears soon after the end of totality.

When the slitless spectroscope is employed (Fig. 10·22), the bright lines are images of the thin crescent of the chromosphere left uncovered by the moon. The thickest crescent images, produced by calcium and hydrogen, rise some eight thousand miles above the photosphere. The strong red line of hydrogen is responsible for the scarlet hue of the chromosphere.

With some exceptions the bright crescents match in position, though not always in relative intensity, the dark lines of the solar spectrum. The most conspicuous differences are found in the hydrogen and helium lines. All the hydrogen lines of the Balmer series are present in the flash spectrum, but only the first four are noticed in the dark-line spectrum. Helium lines, which are prominent in the spectra of the chromosphere and prominences, are almost entirely absent in the dark-line spectrum of the sun. The element helium was discovered in the spectrum of the prominences.

10·23. Chemical Elements in the Sun. Sixty-six of the 96 chemical elements are recognized in the sun's atmosphere by comparisons of lines in the solar spectrum with the spectra of the elements in the laboratory. Of the 30 elements not listed by Miss Moore at Princeton as recognized, about half have their strongest lines in the far ultraviolet part of the spectrum which is cut out by absorption in the earth's atmosphere. Most of the others are either so radioactive that their abundance must be low, or else their spectra have not yet been adequately determined in the laboratory.

It seems probable that all the chemical elements are present in the sun, and that their relative abundance in the sun's atmosphere and the earth's crust are similar, with some important exceptions. Hydrogen and helium, in particular, are far more abundant in the sun.

10·24. Spectroheliograms are photographs of the chromosphere taken in the light of a single chemical element. These revealing photographs show how the gases of this element are distributed above the sun's surface. They are taken with the *spectroheliograph,* a special adaptation of the spectroscope. The operation of this instrument, which employs two slits, is as follows:

The image of the sun is focused by the telescope objective on the first slit which admits the light from a narrow strip of the sun's disk to the grating. The spectrum produced by the grating falls on a screen containing the second slit parallel to the first. This slit allows the light from only a limited region of the spectrum to pass through to the photographic plate. By a slight rotation of the grating any part of the spectrum can be brought upon the second slit, for example, the dark K line of calcium. It will be understood that the dark lines of the solar spectrum are not devoid of light; their light is fainter because it comes from the cooler gas above the photosphere.

The operation so far described would give a photograph of only a narrow strip of the sun's disk in calcium light. If the first slit is moved completely across the sun's disk and the second slit corresponding over

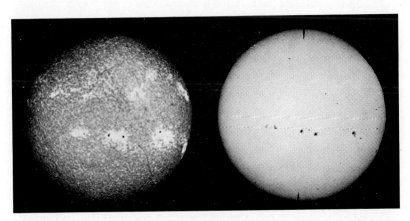

Fig. 10·24. Direct Photograph and Spectroheliogram of the Sun. The spectroheliogram is taken with the K line of calcium. Calcium flocculi are conspicuous in the sunspot zones and especially near the spots. (*Photographed at Mount Wilson Observatory*)

the photographic plate while the plate is being exposed, the result is a spectroheliogram of the entire disk.

The spectrohelioscope accomplishes the small result for visual observations. The two slits are made to oscillate rapidly enough to give a persistent image of a part of the sun's disk in the light of a spectrum line.

10·25. The Flocculi of the Chromosphere. The lines of the solar spectrum most used for the spectroheliograms are the Fraunhofer K line of calcium in the violet and the C line of hydrogen (the Hα line in the red). The centers of these lines give views at the highest levels, the C line higher than the K line. If a portion of the continuous spectrum is set on the second slit, the photosphere is shown as in the direct photograph.

As it appears in the spectroheliograms, the chromosphere is mottled with bright and dark patches known as *flocculi;* they are masses of gas which are hotter or cooler respectively than those around them in the photographs. Calcium flocculi are generally bright; they appear especially in the vicinity of spot groups and are sometimes so closely bunched

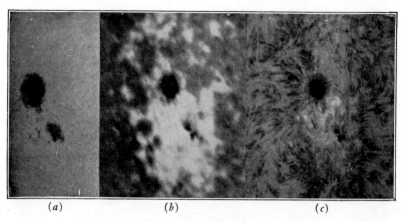

(a)   (b)   (c)

FIG. 10·25. A Sunspot Region at Three Levels. (a) Direct photograph. (b) Spectroheliogram, with the edge of the K line of calcium. (c) Spectroheliogram in hydrogen light. (*Photographed at Mount Wilson Observatory*)

that they conceal the spots below. Hydrogen flocculi are both bright and dark, and are frequently drawn out in filaments.

10·26. The Solar Flares are spectacular features of the chromosphere, also known as active flocculi and solar eruptions. They are usually, but not always, associated with sunspots, and particularly with the earlier stages of the large and active spot groups which are connected with terrestrial magnetic storms. The solar flares appear nearly the same in the calcium and hydrogen spectroheliograms. They are intensely bright and very short lived; they rise in a few minutes to maximum intensity and remain abnormally bright for a few hours.

A solar flare is accompanied by outbursts of ultraviolet radiation which cause much ionization of the earth's upper atmosphere, and a consequent fading of high frequency radio reception at the instant the flare is seen. It also seems to be accompanied by an outflow of a corpuscular stream which reaches us about a day later, producing a second disturbance of the earth's atmosphere.

FIG. 10·26. A Solar Flare. A very bright solar eruption photographed with the center of the Hα line. (*Photographed at the Astrophysical Observatory, Meudon, France*)

FIG. 10·27. Vortices Above Sunspots North and South of the Sun's Equator. A portion of the sun photographed in the light of the Hα line. The regions above the two spots are whirling in opposite directions. (*Photographed at Mount Wilson Observatory*)

10·27. Vortices in the Chromosphere. In the vicinity of spot groups the hydrogen flocculi are drawn into curved filaments as they are whirled in vortices several thousand miles above the spot level. The great majority of these vortices turn counterclockwise in the sun's northern hemisphere and clockwise in the southern hemisphere, like cyclones in the earth's atmosphere (2·8). They are evidently produced by the deflection of inflowing gas by the sun's rotation. These upper vortices do not reverse direction at sunspot minimum; nor would they be expected to do so if the explanation is correct.

One other feature of the hydrogen spectroheliograms should be noticed. Large elongated dark patches, roughly parallel to the sun's equator, are frequently seen in these photographs. Whenever the patches are carried past the edge of the disk by the sun's rotation, they appear bright against the background of the sky. These are the solar prominences.

10·28. The Solar Prominences are best observed at the edge of the sun when they are silhouetted against the sky. Their color is scarlet like

FIG. 10·28. Active Prominence Observed at the Total Eclipse of May 29, 1919. At this eclipse the displacement of stars near the edge of the sun predicted by Einstein was observed (6·8). (*Photographed by Eddington*)

that of the upper chromosphere, owing to the predominance of the red Hα line of hydrogen. They make their appearance as great clouds high above the surface of the sun and usually rain down into the chromosphere. Their vivid color, contrasting with the pearly glow of the corona, contributes to the splendor of the total eclipse of the sun. But the investigation of the prominences is carried on almost entirely at other times than eclipses by means of the spectroheliograph and other special devices.

A very effective study of the behavior of the prominences is being made at the McMath-Hulbert Observatory. Successions of photographs

FIG. 10·28A. The 50-foot Tower Telescope of the McMath-Hulbert Observatory of the University of Michigan. (*From a drawing by Russell W. Porter*)

are taken on motion picture films. The projection of these films gives a dramatic and highly illuminating portrayal of these activities above the chromosphere.

10·29. Forms and Motions of Prominences. The solar prominences exhibit much variety and complexity of form and movement. Pettit at Mount Wilson Observatory divides the prominences into six classes and these again into subclasses. His six principal classes are as follows:

(1) *Active prominences* are the most common. They are structures

of interlacing filaments that pour their streamers down to the chromosphere.

(2) *Eruptive prominences* are among the rarer types. They *rise* from active material above the chromosphere, attaining great speeds and

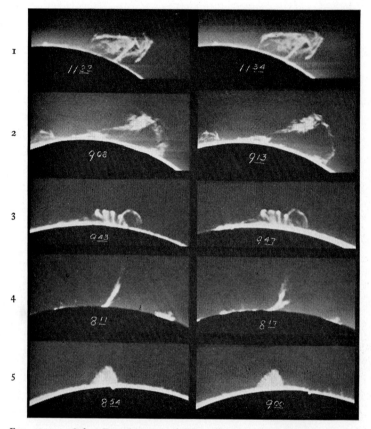

FIG. 10·29. Solar Prominences of Five Classes. The classes from top to bottom are: (1) active; (2) eruptive; (3) sunspot; (4) tornado; (5) quiescent. Two views of each are shown, separated by intervals of a few minutes. (*Photographed by Edison Pettit, Mount Wilson Observatory*)

heights before they fade away. The eruptive prominence of March 20, 1938, had a speed of 450 miles a second and a height of nearly a million miles above the sun's surface when it disappeared. This and some other types appear to move with uniform speed, except that at intervals the speed abruptly changes.

(3) *Sunspot prominences* are associated with sunspots. They have a variety of forms. Some of them are like fountains.

(4) *Tornado prominences* are twisted columns.

(5) *Quiescent prominences* have the least activity and therefore the longest lives. The most common form is the "haystack."

(6) *Coronal prominences* last only a few minutes. They are long streams coming down from the region of the corona.

10·30. The Corona can be seen ordinarily only during total solar eclipse, when its total light is found to be not more than half as bright

FIG. 10·30. Photograph of the Corona, August 31, 1932. Near the time of sunspot minimum. Short, curved polar streamers and long equatorial extensions characterize the corona at this phase of the sunspot cycle. (*Photographed by Paul A. McNally, Georgetown College Observatory*)

as the full moon. The light falls off so rapidly with increasing height that it is difficult to photograph the whole corona satisfactorily with a single exposure. Half the light comes from within 3', or less than 100,000 miles, of the sun's surface. This is the *inner corona,* whose color is yellowish. The *outer corona* is pearly white and is characterized by the delicate streamers and petals that contribute to the beauty of the total solar eclipse; these appear superposed on a nearly circular glow around the sun.

At other times than total eclipse the corona is ordinarily invisible; the sunlight scattered by our atmosphere makes the sky immediately out-side the edge of the sun thousands of times brighter than inner corona. Yet the brightest parts of the corona and the prominences around the edge of the uneclipsed sun can be observed with a special type of tele-scope, the *coronagraph,* which reduces to a minimum the effect of the atmospheric glare around the edge of the sun. Telescopes of this type are in use on the Pic du Midi in the French Pyrenees and at the Har-vard Observatory Solar Station at Climax, Colorado.

The spectrum of the corona is a replica of the solar spectrum on which are superposed bright lines of the coronal light itself. Lines at these wave lengths have not been observed elsewhere, with the single exception of the variable star RS Ophiuchi. They are doubtless unusual lines of familiar elements. Edler ascribes the coronal lines to transi-tions in from nine to thirteen times ionized iron atoms and similarly ionized calcium and titanium atoms.

10·31. Changing Appearance of Coronal Streamers.

The details of the outer corona exhibit a cycle of changes in the eleven-year period of the sunspots. Near the times of the greatest numbers of sunspots the corona has been likened to a dahlia, because petal-like streamers extend out to something like the same distance in various directions. Near sunspot minimum, short, curved streamers appear around the poles and long streamers extend from the equatorial regions.

10·32. Associated Solar and Terrestrial Disturbances.

Sunspots are the most obvious manifestations of solar disturbances whose influence extends to all levels of the sun that come under observation. When sunspots are most numerous, the calcium flocculi and the prominences of the class that gather above the spot groups are accordingly most numerous, while the coronal streamers take on the appearance associated with spot maximum. Disturbances of the earth's magnetic field and dis-plays of aurora are more frequent around the times of sunspot maxima. Violent magnetic disturbances, known as *magnetic storms,* are likewise most numerous when there are many sunspots.

A magnetic storm is indicated by very erratic variations of the com-pass needle. It is accompanied by strong earth currents which seriously interfere with telegraph and telephone communication, and by effects in

FIG. 10·31. Photograph of the Corona, June 8, 1937. Approaching the time of sunspot maximum. At this phase the corona has been likened to a dahlia because of the petal-like streamers in various directions. (*Photographed by Fernando de Romaña at Huangra, Peru, for Harvard Observatory*)

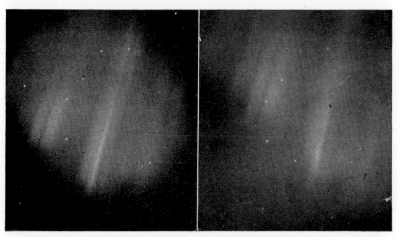

FIG. 10·32. Auroral Streamers. Photographed Simultaneously at Two Stations. The difference in direction of the streamers can be seen with reference to the stars of the Dipper. (*By courtesy of Carl Störmer, Oslo, Norway*)

the atmosphere which disrupt short-wave radio communication and cause brilliant auroras. Such a violent disturbance is likely to be associated with a large and active group of sunspots near the center of the sun's disk and especially when a solar flare (10·26) appears in the group.

The most spectacular feature of the magnetic disturbance is the display of the *aurora,* or "northern lights," as they are often known to people of the northern hemisphere. Characteristic of many displays is the luminous arch in the northern sky, having its apex in the direction of the magnetic pole. Rays like searchlike beams spread upward from the arch, while bright patches, streamers, and draperies sometimes extend to all parts of the sky. The color is pale green, often varied with red and yellow. Auroras are more frequent in the higher latitudes of both hemispheres. The light is presumably caused by the recombination of atoms of the upper atmosphere after their disruption by electrified particles emitted by the sun.

Review Questions

1. Associate each of the following characteristics with the region of the sun (photosphere, reversing layer, chromosphere, corona) to which it applies:

(a) Scarlet color.
(b) Would produce continuous spectrum if seen separately.
(c) Source of most dark lines of solar spectrum.
(d) Ordinarily observed only during total solar eclipse.
(e) Region of sunspots.
(f) Appears in spectroheliograms.

2. If the temperature of a body is raised, what is the effect on (a) its total radiation? (b) the wave length of its maximum radiation?

3. Why does the sun's photosphere appear as a sharply defined disk? Why does the brightness of the disk diminish toward the edge?

4. Trace the growth and decline of a normal spot group.

5. In what respects does the sun's rotation differ from the earth's rotation?

6. Show by means of a diagram that the apparent period of the sun's rotation as determined by observations of a sunspot is longer than the true period in that latitude owing to the earth's revolution.

7. Sunspots move across the sun's disk with the solar rotation in the direction of the sun's daily motion across the sky, namely, from east to west. Yet the sun rotates from west to east. Explain.

8. Describe and correlate the 11-year variations in the numbers and latitudes of sunspots.

9. What features of sunspot spectra show that the spots are cooler than the surrounding surface of the sun?

10. Discuss the polarities of bipolar spot groups in the northern and southern hemispheres and their changes with succeeding cycles.

11. What is the evidence that regions above the sunspots are vortices? Does the direction of the spin differ (a) between the two hemispheres? (b) from one cycle to the next?

12. "Direct photographs" of the sun are frequently made with the spectro-heliograph by setting the first slit on a continuous part of the solar spectrum. Explain.

13. How are the chemical elements in the sun identified? Assign possible reasons for the failure to recognize some of the known elements.

14. What occurrences on the earth are definitely associated with disturbances on the sun?

PROBLEMS

1. Calculate the effective temperature of the sun by substituting the rate of the sun's radiation (6.25×10^{10} ergs per square centimeter per second) in the formula of Stefan's law.

Answer: $T^4 = 6.25 \times 10^{10}/5.73 \times 10^{-5}$; $T = 5750°$ K.

2. Assuming that sunspots are electromagnets and using the left hand rule, determine the direction of spin of a spot whose positive (north) pole is on top.

Answer: Grasp the axis of the spot with the left hand with thumb extended toward the positive pole. The charged particles in the spot are moving in the direction the fingers point. The spot is spinning in the clockwise direction.

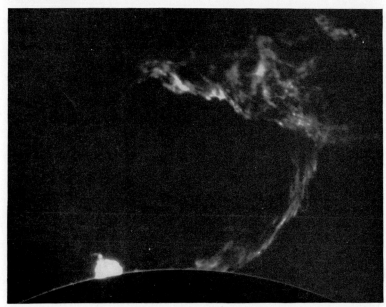

Solar Prominence.   (*Photographed at Fremont Pass Station of Harvard Observatory at Climax, Colorado*)

CHAPTER XI

THE STARS

DISTANCES OF THE STARS — MOTIONS OF THE STARS — STELLAR SPECTRA — MAGNITUDES OF THE STARS — LUMINOSITIES OF THE STARS

DISTANCES OF THE STARS

For our study of the stars we require first of all an understanding of the basic data of observation, how these are determined and in what terms it is the custom to express them. These are the distances of the stars, their motions relative to the sun, the character of their spectra, and their relative brightness.

11·1. The Parallax of a Star. In consequence of the earth's revolution around the sun, a nearer star seems to describe a little orbit an-

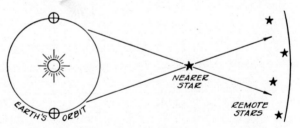

FIG. 11·1. The Parallax of a Star. Owing to the earth's revolution the nearer star appears to oscillate relative to remote stars.

nually with respect to more distant stars. This apparent orbit has almost the same form as the aberration orbit (2·15); it varies from nearly a circle for a star at the ecliptic pole to a straight line on the ecliptic. It is much smaller, however, even for the nearer stars, and shrinks to imperceptible size for the more distant ones.

The *heliocentric parallax* of a star is half the major axis of its parallax orbit, with a slight correction for the eccentricity of the earth's orbit. It is otherwise the maximum difference between the directions of the star as seen from the earth and sun during the year. We shall refer to it as the *parallax* of the star.

After Copernicus had proposed the heliocentric theory of the planetary motions, the inability of astronomers to detect the parallax displacements of the stars meant either that the earth was stationary after all or that the stars were enormously more remote than they were supposed to be at that time. When the earth's revolution was decisively demonstrated by the discovery of the aberration of starlight, the search for perceptible parallaxes was renewed as a promising means of determining the distances of stars. It was not until 1838, however, that the many attempts to observe this effect finally met with success; in that year, Bessel at Königsberg measured the parallax of the star 61 Cygni. The parallaxes of other stars were thereafter gradually detected. But the earlier visual methods were not accurate enough to deal with any except the larger parallaxes.

11·2. Measurements of Parallax. Beginning in 1903, with the 40-inch telescope of Yerkes Observatory, Frank Schlesinger laid the foundations on which the modern photographic determinations of stellar parallaxes are based. The methods of observation and reduction which he developed gave such greatly increased accuracy that many astronomers were encouraged to enter this important and exacting field. As a consequence of this concerted effort, direct parallaxes of several thousand stars are already measured.

The parallax of a star is determined by observing its change of position relative to stars which are apparently close to it, but are really so much farther away from us that they are not greatly affected by the earth's revolution. The procedure is to obtain sets of photographs of the region at intervals of about six months when the star under investigation is near the extremities of its tiny parallax orbit. Two sets are not enough, because the star also has a motion of its own in a straight line with respect to the more distant stars; in combination with the parallax effect it accordingly advances among them in a series of loops. At least five sets of photographs are usually required to extricate the parallax accurately.

It will be noted that the result obtained is the *relative parallax;* for the comparison stars themselves are shifted slightly in the same directions as the parallax star. The *absolute parallax* is obtained by adding a correction not exceeding a few thousandths of a second of arc, which depends on the brightness of the comparison stars, and which can be reliably estimated. Even after the correction is made, the parallax of a distant star occasionally comes out negative, indicating that the unavoidable errors of observation are larger in this case than the parallax itself, and happen to take this direction, or that the mean distance of the comparison stars is less than that of the parallax star.

FIG. 11·2. Eye End of the 40-inch Telescope of Yerkes Observatory Arranged for Photography. Instead of the eyepiece the double-slide plate holder is attached; it carries a small eyepiece (at the upper edge) containing cross wires with which the observer guides on a star near the edge of the field while the exposure is in progress.

11·3. Units of Distance: the Parsec and the Light Year.

When the star's parallax, p, has been measured, its distance is found by the relation (Fig. 11·3):

$$\text{Distance (in astronomical units)} = 206{,}265''/p''.$$

Since one astronomical unit, the earth's mean distance from the sun, equals 149,500,000 km, or 92,900,000 miles, we have the star's distance:

Distance (in kilometers) $= 206,265''/p'' \times 1.495 \times 10^8$.

Distance (in miles) $= 206,265''/p'' \times 9.290 \times 10^7$.

But the distance of a star expressed in miles, or even in astronomical units, is an inconveniently large number. It is better to use larger units, either the parsec or the light year.

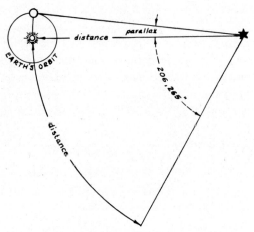

FIG. 11·3. Relation Between Parallax and Distance. The radius of a circle laid off around the circumference subtends an angle (the radian) equal to 206,265". From the two sectors we have the proportion: distance of the star is to the radius of the earth's orbit as 206,265" is to the star's parallax.

The *parsec* is the distance at which a star would have a *parallax* of one *sec*ond of arc. This distance, by the above relations, is 206,265 astronomical units, or 3.08×10^{13} km, or 1.92×10^{13} miles. The advantage of the parsec is its simple relation to the parallax:

$$\text{Distance (in parsecs)} = 1''/p''.$$

The *light year* is the distance traversed by light in one year; it is equal to the speed of light, 2.998×10^5 km/sec, multiplied by 3.156×10^7, the number of seconds in a year. The light year is therefore 9.46×10^{12} km, or 5.88×10^{12} miles (nearly six million million miles). One parsec equals 3.258 light years. Thus:

$$\text{Distance (in light years)} = 3''.258/p''.$$

As an example, consider the brightest star, Sirius, also one of the nearest, whose parallax is 0″.381. The distance of Sirius in astronomical units is 206,265″/0″.381, or a little more than half a million astronomical units, which amounts to about 50 million million miles. The distance in parsecs is 1/0.381, or 2.6 parsecs. The distance in light years is 3.258/0.381, or 8.6 light years.

11·4. The Nearest Stars. Seventeen stars are known, counting a double star as one system, within the distance of 12 light years from the sun. Data concerning these, kindly furnished by van de Kamp of Sproul Observatory, are listed in Table 11·I. While three of the very brightest stars are included, the majority of the nearest stars are invisible without the telescope, for their magnitudes are numbers greater than six; and it is probable that other very faint stars will eventually be added to the list. It is to be noticed in passing that the annual proper motions of the nearest stars exceed their parallaxes, and also that many of these stars are double.

The distinction of being the sun's nearest known neighbor is held by

TABLE 11·I. THE NEAREST STARS

Name	Right Ascension	Declination	Apparent Visual Magnitude	Absolute Parallax	Distance in Light Years	Annual Proper Motion
* Alpha Centauri	14$^{\rm h}$ 33$^{\rm m}$	−60°.4	† 0.3, 1.7	0″.761	4.3	3″.68
Barnard's star	17 53	+ 4 .4	9.7	.530	6.1	10 .30
Lalande 21185	10 58	+36 .6	7.6	.411	7.9	4 .78
Wolf 359	10 52	+ 7 .6	13.5	.408	8.0	4 .84
* Sirius	6 41	−16 .6	−1.6, 7.1	.381	8.6	1 .32
Ross 154	18 44	−24 .0	11	.350	9.3	0 .67
Ross 248	23 37	+43 .7	12.2	.317	10.3	1 .58
Luyten 789-6	22 33	−15 .9	12.3	.315	10.3	3 .27
Epsilon Eridani	3 28	− 9 .8	3.8	.305	10.7	0 .97
* Procyon	7 34	+ 5 .5	0.5, 10.8	.295	11.0	1 .25
* 61 Cygni	21 2	+38 .2	5.6, 6.3	.294	11.1	5 .22
Ross 128	11 42	+ 1 .4	11.1	.292	11.2	1 .40
Epsilon Indi	21 56	−57 .2	4.7	.291	11.2	4 .67
Tau Ceti	1 39	−16 .4	3.6	.290	11.2	1 .92
* Struve 2398	18 42	+59 .5	8.9, 9.7	.287	11.3	2 .29
BD −12° 4523	16 25	−12 .4	9.7	.281	11.6	1 .24
* Groombridge 34	0 13	+43 .4	8.1, 10.9	.278	11.7	2 .91

* Visual double stars.
† A second companion of magnitude 11.

the bright double star Alpha Centauri. A star of the eleventh magnitude, sometimes called "Proxima," is a member of this system; it is situated a little more than two degrees from the two bright stars.

11·5. Limitations of the Direct Method. The *direct,* or *trigonometric,* method of determining stellar parallaxes diminishes in accuracy as more distant stars are observed. The probable error of the best parallaxes, in which several independent determinations are averaged, is of the order of 0".005. For the very nearest stars the error is less than one per cent of the parallax. The percentage of error increases as the parallax decreases; it is ten per cent for a parallax of 0".05. If the parallax is as small as 0".01 ± 0".005, it follows from the definition of the probable error that the chance is one half that the true value lies between 0".015 and 0".005, and that the star's distance is between 67 and 200 parsecs. It is equally probable that the true value is outside these limits. Thus the percentage of error in measuring the distances of the stars by the direct method increases with the distance, and becomes very large for distances exceeding 100 parsecs, or around 300 light years.

Since the success of many investigations of the stars depends on the knowledge of their distances, astronomers have sought for and have discovered indirect ways of determining parallaxes. These will be considered in appropriate places as we proceed.

Motions of the Stars

We have thus far been concerned with apparent motions of the stars caused by movements of the earth, motions such as their rising and setting which do not affect the forms of the constellations. It is now in order to consider the motions of the stars themselves and how they are investigated. While their motions relative to one another and to the sun are often swift, they seem very slow because of the great distances of the stars.

Halley, in 1718, was the first to demonstrate that the stars are not "fixed." He showed that several bright stars had moved from the places assigned them in Ptolemy's ancient catalog by something like the moon's apparent diameter. It was later established that the sun itself is in motion relative to the stars around it.

11·6. Two Projections of a Star's Motion. (1) *Proper motion* is the rate of change in the star's direction, or apparent place on the celestial sphere; this *angular* rate decreases, in general, as the star's distance increases. (2) *Radial velocity* is the star's speed of approach or recession; this *linear* rate is independent of the star's distance, and is accordingly often the only projection that can be measured. The observed

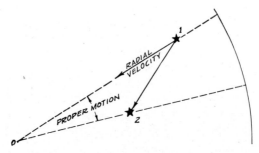

FIG. 11·6. Proper Motion and Radial Velocity. As the star moves from *I* to *2*, its proper motion is the rate of its change in direction as viewed from *O;* its radial velocity is the rate of its approach or recession.

motion is referred to the sun by correcting it for the effects of the earth's rotation, revolution, and precessional motion.

Proper motions, radial velocities, and distances of the stars constitute the principal data in the studies of stellar motions.

11·7. Proper Motions of the Stars.

With the accumulation of accurate catalogs of star positions, separated by considerable intervals of time, the proper motions of all the lucid stars have become known, and of many telescopic stars as well. The procedure is to compare the right ascension and declination of each star, which have been accurately measured on two occasions as widely separated as possible. After allowance has been made for the star's displacement in the meantime due to precession and other motions of the earth, the remaining difference represents the proper motion of the star.

Many thousand proper motions are being detected and measured by the direct comparison of two photographs of a region. Indeed, the largest proper motions have been found in this way. The comparison is simple because precession, aberration, and other apparent displacements of the stars, with the exception of parallax, are nearly the same over a small area of the sky.

The method of "blinking" is effective for the detection of any differences between two photographs that are being compared. The two plates are so arranged under the blink microscope that corresponding star images appear superposed. By mechanical means the plates are alternately hidden several times a second. If all the stars in the region have not moved appreciably between the exposures, the appearance is the same as before the blinking began. If a star is displaced on one plate relative to the other, the result is a jumping effect which at once attracts the observer's attention.

11·8. Stars with Large Proper Motions. The largest known proper motion is that of a telescopic star known as "Barnard's star," after the

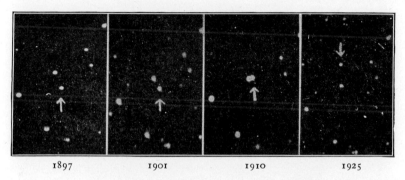

| 1897 | 1901 | 1910 | 1925 |

FIG. 11·8. Proper Motion of "Proxima" Centauri. This faint associate of Alpha Centauri is marked by an arrow on each photograph. Its motion is shown relative to the apparently neighboring but much more distant stars. (*Photographed at the southern station of Harvard Observatory*)

name of the discoverer. This star is moving with respect to its neighbors at the rate of 10″.25 a year, so that in 180 years it moves through an angle equal to the moon's apparent diameter. If all the stars were moving as fast as this and at random, the forms of the constellations would be altered appreciably in the course of a lifetime. But this is exceptional. The proper motions of only two hundred stars exceed 1″ a year, and the average for all naked-eye stars is not greater than 0″.1 a year.

It is to be noticed that the proper motion is angular. A star having a large proper motion may be actually in rapid motion, or it may be nearer than most stars, or both, which is true of Barnard's star. It is also to be noticed that the proper motion relates only to that part of the star's motion that is transverse to the line of sight.

11·9. Radial Velocities. The motion of a star in the line of sight, or its radial velocity, is determined from measurements of the positions of

FIG. 11·9. Single-Prism Spectrograph. Attached to the 37-inch reflecting telescope of the Observatory, University of Michigan. The case is removed to show the prism.

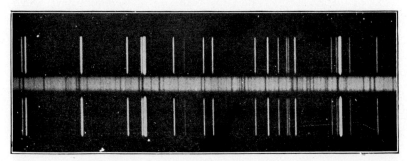

FIG. 11·9A. Doppler Shift in the Spectrum of Procyon. The dark lines in the star's spectrum are displaced to the violet (left) with respect to corresponding bright lines in the comparison spectrum of iron and vanadium, above and below. At the time the spectrogram was taken, this star and the earth were approaching at the rate of 30 km/sec. (*Photographed at Lowell Observatory*)

lines in the star's spectrum. By the Doppler principle (4·24), if the star is approaching us, the lines of its spectrum are displaced toward the violet; if the star is receding, the lines are displaced toward the red end of the spectrum; and the amount of the displacement is proportional to the speed of approach or recession. For a line of a particular wave length, the relation is:

$$\text{Radial velocity} = \frac{\text{change of wave length}}{\text{wave length}} \times \text{velocity of light.}$$

If, for example, a line whose wave length is 4000 angstroms is displaced one angstrom toward the violet, the star is approaching us with the speed of 1/4000 of 186,300 miles a second, or 46.6 miles a second.

The ordinary procedure is to photograph on the same plate the spectrum of the star and of a laboratory source, often luminous iron or titanium vapor, near the slit of the spectroscope which is attached at the eye end of the telescope (Fig. 11·9). The photograph, or *spectrogram* (Fig. 11·9A), is then observed under a microscope, and the positions of the star lines are measured micrometrically with respect to the *comparison lines* of the laboratory source, which have no Doppler displacement. The radial velocities of most of the lucid stars and of many telescopic stars as well are known. Velocities up to 20 miles a second (32 km/sec) are common; those exceeding 100 km/sec are rare.

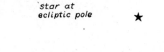

11·10. Annual Variation in the Radial Velocities of the Stars.

As a consequence of the earth's revolution around the sun, the observed radial velocities of the stars, with the exception of stars near the

FIG. 11·10. Annual Variation in the Radial Velocity of a Star. Owing to the earth's revolution the lines in the spectrum of a star oscillate in a period of a year. The effect is greatest for stars at the ecliptic, and diminishes to zero at the ecliptic poles.

ecliptic poles, exhibit annual fluctuations. When the earth is approaching a star, the lines in the star's spectrum are displaced to the violet; and when it is receding, the lines are displaced toward the red end of the spectrum. In practice the observed radial velocity of the star is *reduced to the sun* by correcting for this effect, and for the slight daily fluctuation due to the earth's rotation.

This annually periodic effect on the radial velocities of the stars

constitutes an additional proof of the earth's revolution around the sun.
It also affords a precise means of determining the earth's distance from
the sun. As the simplest case, consider a star on the ecliptic and at rest
with respect to the sun. Once during the year the earth is moving
directly toward the star; six months later it is moving directly away.
On each occasion the radial velocity of the star is numerically equal to
the speed of the earth's revolution. A simple calculation then gives the
earth's distance from the sun. Calculations based on the observed radial
velocities of many stars have given a result in close agreement with the
distance derived in other ways.

11·11. Space Velocities. When the annual proper motion, μ, of a star
and its parallax, p, are known, the tangential velocity, T, can be cal-

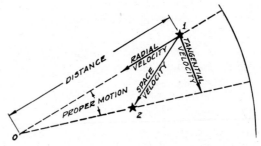

FIG. 11·11.   Relation Between Space Velocity, Tangential Velocity, Radial
Velocity, Proper Motion, and Distance of a Star.

culated. The *tangential velocity* is the star's velocity with respect to
the sun at right angles to the line of sight; it equals $4.74\mu/p$ km/sec.

When the star's radial velocity, V, is known as well, in kilometers
a second, the *space velocity*, v, which is the star's velocity with respect
to the sun, is the diagonal of the right triangle given by the relation:
$v^2 = V^2 + T^2$; and the direction of motion relative to the line of sight
is denoted by the angle it makes with that line.

The space velocities of the stars are generally of the same order as
the velocities of the planets in their revolutions around the sun; the
majority are between five and twenty miles a second. Among the
brightest stars, Arcturus has the highest space velocity, 135 km or 84
miles a second.

11·12. The Sun's Motion. The space velocities of the stars are referred to the sun. But the sun is only one of the stars and is moving
among them. It is therefore important to determine how the sun is

moving and to correct the space velocities of the stars for the effects of this motion.

If the sun with its planetary system is moving in a particular direction among the stars and if the stars have random motions, these stars should seem to be passing by in the opposite direction. The stars ahead of us should seem to be opening out from the *apex* of the sun's way, the point of the celestial sphere toward which the sun's motion is directed. The stars behind us should seem to be closing in toward the opposite *antapex*. So reasoned William Herschel, English astronomer and pioneer in the study of sidereal astronomy. Although the proper motions of only thirteen stars were then available, he determined, in 1783, the position of the apex within 10° of the place now assigned to the "standard apex."

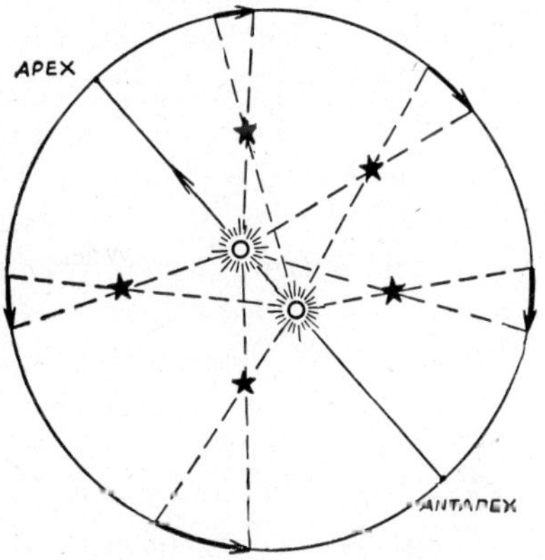

FIG. 11·12. Apparent Motions of the Stars Produced by the Solar Motion. The stars are apparently drifting away from the point on the celestial sphere toward which the sun is moving.

11·13. The "Standard Apex" of the Sun's Way is referred to the average of the stars visible to the naked eye. It is situated approximately in right ascension 18^h 0^m and declination +30°, in the constellation Hercules about 10° southwest of the bright star Vega. With respect to these stars the solar system is moving in this direction at the rate of 20 km/sec, or about 12 miles a second. In the course of a year we progress through the local field of stars four times as far as the distance from the earth to the sun. The corresponding antapex is in the constellation Columba, about 30° south of Orion's belt.

The recent determinations are based on the proper motions and also the radial velocities of thousands of stars. When the radial velocities are employed, the apex is evidently the point in the heavens around which the stars have the greatest average velocity of approach, while around the antapex they have the greatest velocity of recession; and this average is the speed of the sun's motion relative to these particular stars. The positions of the apex from the proper motions and radial velocities nearly agree, as they should, since the reference stars are in both cases, in general, in the sun's neighborhood.

When the sun's motion is referred to fainter stars, and especially to stars having higher space velocities, the apex is displaced toward the northeast. Thus from their analyses of the proper motions of 18,000 of the brighter telescopic stars, van de Kamp and Vyssotsky locate the apex in right ascension 19^h.0 and declination $+36°$.

11·14. Stellar Distances from the Sun's Motion. We have noticed that the direct parallax method is limited to the nearer stars. For the more distant ones the diameter of the earth's orbit is too short to serve as an adequate base line. At first sight it might seem that the sun's motion could provide the ideal base line for measuring stellar parallaxes. In one year it takes us a distance twice as great as the diameter of the earth's orbit. If this longer base line is still too short to produce appreciable parallax of the distant stars, we could wait two years, or perhaps a hundred, until the base line would become long enough.

Since the stars have motions of their own, it is impossible to say what part of a star's proper motion is parallactic and what part is peculiar to the star itself. Thus the longer base line provided by the sun's motion cannot be used to determine the distances of individual stars, though it has produced reliable mean parallaxes.

STELLAR SPECTRA

11·15. Photographs of Stellar Spectra are made in two different ways. One method employs a complete spectroscope, containing one or more prisms or a grating with its slit at the focus of the telescope objective (Fig. 11·9). By means of reflecting prisms over parts of the slit, the light of a laboratory source is introduced on either side of the beam of starlight, and the spectrum of this source appears as bright comparison lines adjacent to the star's spectrum. The comparison lines permit the determinations of radial velocity and the wave lengths of lines in the star's spectrum.

A second method is preferred when the spectra of many stars are to be examined, as in the classification of stellar spectra. A large prism, usually of small angle, is placed in front of the objective of a photographic telescope (Fig. 11·15), so that the whole apparatus becomes a spectroscope without slit or collimator. In order to give the spectra width enough to bring out the lines clearly, the prism is so placed that the spectra extend north and south on the plates; the spectra can be given suitable breadth by setting the driving mechanism to run a little fast or slow, causing the star to drift slightly during the exposure. The

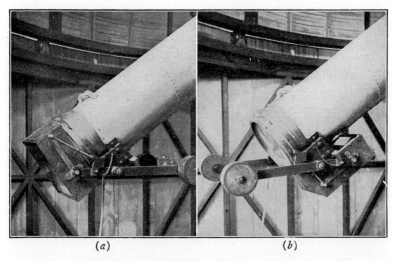

(a)   (b)

FIG. 11·15. Objective Prism Attached to the 11-inch Telescope, Harvard Observatory. (a) The prism in its case in position before the objective. (b) The prism swung out of the way when the telescope is employed for other purposes.

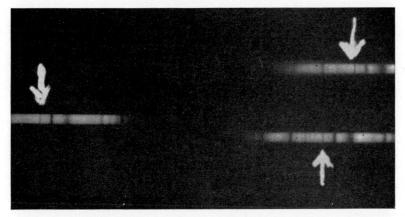

FIG. 11·15A. Objective Prism Spectra of Stars with Comparison Line. The absorption line of neodymium chloride is indicated by the arrows. (*Photographed by B. J. Bok and S. W. McCuskey, Harvard Observatory*)

photograph with the objective prism shows the spectra of all stars of sufficient brightness in the field of view.

Photographs with the objective prism cannot have arrays of comparison lines as with the slit spectroscope. It is possible, however, to provide the spectrum of each star with a standard of rest by introducing before the photographic plate a cell of neodymium chloride; this absorbs a fairly narrow line (Fig. 11·15A) in the blue region of each spectrum.

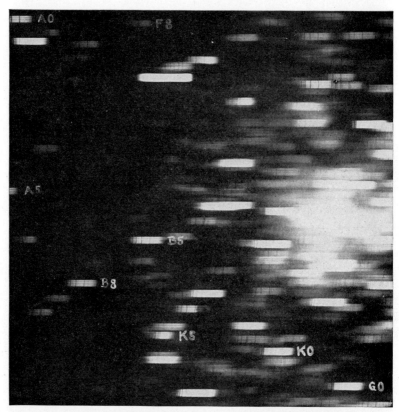

FIG. 11·16. Objective Prism Spectra of Stars. (*From a portion of a photograph at Harvard Observatory*)

11·16. "The Henry Draper Catalogue." Pickering, in 1885, inaugurated the photographic study of stellar spectra with the objective prism, a great work which has been carried on ever since by Harvard Observatory. Many thousands of plates have been secured of all regions of the heavens, and the spectra of more than a quarter of a million stars have been studied, for many years under the immediate direction of Miss Cannon. *The Henry Draper Catalogue,* in nine volumes completed in 1924, gives the approximate positions, magnitudes, and spectral classes of 225,300 stars; this catalog is a memorial to the astronomer who was the first in America to study stellar spectra. Extensions are being published, particularly to the fainter stars in the Milky Way.

11·17. The Classification of Stellar Spectra. One of the outstanding results of the program above mentioned was the discovery that the patterns of the great majority of stellar spectra can be arranged in a single continuous sequence. This regular gradation of the spectra is the basis of the *Draper Classification,* for which Miss Cannon was chiefly responsible. Various stages in the sequence are denoted by the seven classes O, B, A, F, G, K, M, which are subdivided on the decimal system. Thus a star of class G5 is about halfway between G0 and K0; B2 is nearer to B0 than to A0. Fully 99 per cent of the stars are included in the classes B to M. Three other classes complete the Draper Classification of ordinary stellar spectra; these are R, N, and S which form side branches near the red end of the sequence.

Other classifications have been made on the scale of the Draper Classification, but based on different or additional criteria. For our present purpose it will be sufficient to notice the chief characteristics of the seven classes which comprise the main part of this classification, as they appear in the region of the spectrum ordinarily photographed.

11·18. The Sequence of Stellar Spectra. The sequence is characterized particularly by the rise and decline in the intensity of the hydrogen lines which occur throughout its extent. Other elements in different states become prominent at different stages of the sequence, while bands produced by chemical compounds appear toward the end. In general, the colors of the stars become redder along the sequence. The principal classes are:

Class O. Lines of ionized helium, oxygen, and nitrogen, as well as the hydrogen lines, characterize the spectra of these extremely hot stars. Bright lines are frequent.

Class B. Lines of neutral *helium* attain their greatest intensity at B2 and then fade, until at B9 they have practically disappeared. Hydrogen lines increase in intensity through the subdivisions. Examples are Rigel and Spica.

Class A. *Hydrogen lines* attain maximum intensity at A0. Examples are Sirius and Vega. Stars of classes B and A are blue.

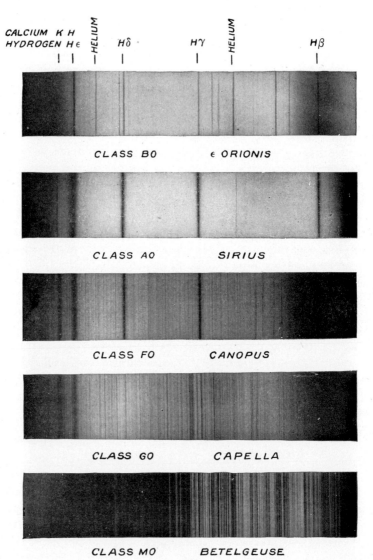

FIG. 11·18. Representative Stellar Spectra. Typical spectra of the principal classes, with the exception of class K which is intermediate between G and M. (*Photographed at Harvard Observatory*)

Class F. Hydrogen lines are declining, while lines of the metals are increasing in intensity, notably the Fraunhofer *H and K lines of calcium.* Canopus and Procyon are examples.

Class G. Lines of the metals in great numbers are prominent. These stars are yellow. The sun and Capella are examples.

Class K. Lines of the metals now surpass the hydrogen lines in strength. The H and K lines of calcium reach their greatest intensity. Bands begin to appear near the end of the class. These stars are reddish. Examples are Arcturus and Aldebaran.

Class M. Bands of the titanium oxide spectrum are prominent. The violet end of the spectrum is much weakened. The stars of this class are red. Betelgeuse and Antares are examples.

11·19. Significance of the Spectral Sequence. The classification of stellar spectra that we have now examined is based on gradations in the patterns of the lines. It is independent of theoretical considerations relative to the physical conditions of the stars. The account of the physical significance of the sequence, given in Chapter 14, may be briefly anticipated here.

It is remarkable that almost all of the vast number of stars whose spectra have been examined can be arranged in a single continuous sequence. This linear arrangement means that the variety in the spectral patterns is caused chiefly by the variation of a single physical condition, namely, temperature. Indeed, this is indicated by the increasing redness of the stars along the sequence. Density of the star, as we shall see, is an important contributing factor. This factor enters in the more recent two-dimensional classification of stellar spectra at Yerkes Observatory.

MAGNITUDES OF THE STARS

11·20. Scale of Magnitudes. The grading of the naked-eye stars in early times into six magnitudes (1·25) was intended primarily to assist in identifying them. There is no evidence that the choice of six groups, rather than some other number, was governed by any definite idea of numerical relations between the groups. For many centuries afterward, the magnitudes of the stars were accepted as they appeared in Ptolemy's catalog. It was not until the comparatively recent times of the Herschels that stellar magnitudes began to enter as important factors into astronomical investigations, for example, in statistical studies of the organization of the stellar system.

About 1830, John Herschel reached the conclusion that a geometrical progression in the apparent brightness of the stars is associated with the arithmetical progression of their magnitudes. The problem was then to ascertain the constant ratio of brightness corresponding to a difference of one magnitude, which would best represent the magnitudes already assigned to the naked-eye stars. Pogson at Radcliffe, in 1856, proposed the adoption of the ratio whose logarithm is 0.4, a convenient value differing only a little from the average ratio derived from his own observations and those of other astronomers. He adjusted the zero of this fixed scale so as to secure as good agreement as possible with the early catalog at the sixth magnitude. The scale is now generally accepted.

Pogson's rule is a special case of a general psycho-physical relation established, in 1834, by the physiologist Weber, and given a more precise phrasing by Fechner, in 1859. By Fechner's law, $S = c \log R$, where S is the intensity of a sensation, R is the stimulus producing it, and c is a constant factor of proportionality. Pogson had evaluated the constant in the corresponding relation: $m - n = c \log (l_n/l_m)$, where l_m and l_n are the apparent brightnesses of two stars whose magnitudes are m and n respectively. The constant is 2.5, or 1/0.4, or 1/log 2.512. If the difference, $m - n$, is one magnitude, $l_n/l_m = 2.512$.

The logarithm of a number to the base 10 is the power to which 10 must be raised in order to obtain the number. Thus the logarithm of 100 is 2; the logarithm of 2.512 is 0.4.

11·21. Relation Between Brightness and Magnitude. We have seen that the ratio of brightness between two stars which differ by exactly one magnitude is the number whose logarithm is 0.4, which is about 2.512. A few values of the ratio of brightness where the magnitude difference is a whole number are as follows:

Magnitude difference	Ratio of brightness
1.0 magnitude	2.512
2.0 magnitudes	6.31
3.0 magnitudes	15.85
4.0 magnitudes	39.8
5.0 magnitudes	100.0

In general, the ratio of apparent brightness, l_n/l_m, of two stars or other sources of light whose magnitudes are m and n can be derived by the formula:

$$\log (l_n/l_m) = 0.4(m - n).$$

It is to be noted that the number which expresses the magnitude diminishes algebraically as the brightness increases, and that the choice of the zero point makes the magnitudes of the very brightest celestial objects negative. The magnitude of the brightest star, Sirius, is -1.6. The magnitude of the planet Venus at greatest brilliancy is -4.4, while that of the full moon is -12.6, and of the sun -26.6. Stars of the twenty-first magnitude can be photographed with the 100-inch telescope on Mount Wilson.

The following examples illustrate some of the uses of the relation between apparent brightness and magnitude:

(1) How much brighter is Sirius (magnitude -1.6) than a star whose magnitude is 21.0?

$$\log (l_n/l_m) = 0.4 \times 22.6 = 9.04$$
$$l_n/l_m = \text{about } 1100 \text{ million times.}$$

(2) Nova Aquilae, in the course of two or three days in June, 1918, increased in brightness about 45,000 times. How many magnitudes did it rise?

$$\log (l_n/l_m) = \log 45{,}000 = 4.65 = 0.4(m - n)$$
$$m - n = 4.65/0.4 = \text{about } 11.6 \text{ magnitudes.}$$

(3) The bright star Castor, which appears single to the naked eye, is resolved by the telescope into two stars whose magnitudes are 1.99 and 2.85. What is the magnitude of the two combined?

$$\log (l_n/l_m) = 0.4 \times 0.86 = 0.344$$
$$l_n/l_m = 2.21; \ (l_m + l_n)/l_m = l_x/l_m = 3.21$$
$$\log (l_x/l_m) = 0.507 = 0.4(m - x)$$
$$m - x = 0.507/0.4 = 1.27$$
$$x = 2.85 - 1.27 = 1.58, \text{ the combined magnitude.}$$

11·22. Visual and Photovisual Magnitudes.

The *apparent magnitude* of a star refers to its observed brightness. Its value for a particular star depends on the part of the spectrum to which the receiver of the light is specially sensitive. If the receiver is the eye alone or the eye at the telescope, it is the apparent *visual magnitude* that is determined.

Visual methods of determining the visual magnitudes of stars are now largely replaced by the more convenient and reliable photographic method. By use of a specially stained plate and a suitable color filter in front of the plate it is possible to determine the *photovisual magnitude* of a star in very close agreement with the visual scale.

11·23. The Brightest Stars.

The twenty stars in Table 11·II are brighter than visual magnitude 1.5. The first and second columns give the designation of each star according to the Bayer system, and its proper name, if the star has one. In the seven cases where the star can be resolved with the telescope into a close double, the magnitude is that of the two combined, but the spectral class is that of the brighter component. Classes from B to M are here represented; evidently the bluest of the brightest stars are Beta Centauri and Alpha Crucis, while the reddest ones are Betelgeuse and Antares.

The fifth and sixth columns, which give the parallax and distance of each star as published by van de Kamp, show that the brightest stars vary greatly in their distances from us. While Alpha Centauri, Sirius, and Procyon are among the nearest stars (11·4), Rigel and Deneb are so remote that they must be stars of very high luminosity to shine so bright in our skies. The significance of the last column will be explained later in this Chapter.

TABLE 11·II. THE BRIGHTEST STARS

Name		Apparent Visual Magnitude	Spectrum	Parallax	Distance in Light Years	Absolute Visual Magnitude
α Canis Majoris	Sirius	−1.58 ^{d}	Ao	o″.381	8.6	+1.3
* α Carinae	Canopus	−0.86	Fo	.033	100	−3.2
* α Centauri		+0.06 ^{d}	Go	.761	4.3	+4.7
α Lyrae	Vega	0.14	Ao	.123	26	+0.5
α Aurigae	Capella	0.21	Go	.077	42	−0.4
α Boötis	Arcturus	0.24	Ko	.098	33	+0.2
β Orionis	Rigel	0.34 ^{d}	B8	.006	540	−5.8
α Canis Minoris	Procyon	0.48 ^{d} ·	F3	.295	11.1	+2.9
* α Eridani	Achernar	0.60	B5	.045	70	−1.1
* β Centauri		0.86	B1	.017	190	−2.9
α Aquilae	Altair	0.89	A5	.208	15.7	+2.5
α Orionis	Betelgeuse	0.92 ^{v}	M2	.011	300	−3.9
* α Crucis		1.05 ^{d}	B1	.015	220	−2.7
α Tauri	Aldebaran	1.06 ^{d}	K5	.062	53	+0.1
β Geminorum	Pollux	1.21	Ko	.114	29	+1.5
α Virginis	Spica	1.21	B2	.027	120	−1.6
α Scorpii	Antares	1.22 ^{d}	M1	.013	250	−3.2
α Piscis Austrini	Fomalhaut	1.29	A3	.139	23	+2.0
α Cygni	Deneb	1.33	A2	.008	400	−4.2
α Leonis	Regulus	1.34	B8	.049	67	−0.3

* Not visible in latitude 40° N.

^{d} Double star with the telescope. The combined magnitude is given.

^{v} Light varies irregularly through a range of about a magnitude.

All but five of the brightest stars are visible at some time in the year throughout the United States. Those five become visible south of the following north latitudes: Canopus, 38°; Achernar, 33°; Alpha and Beta Centauri, 30°; Alpha Crucis, 28°.

11·24. Photographic Magnitudes.

The *photographic magnitude* of a star is the magnitude as determined by the ordinary blue-sensitive photographic plate. The most effective way of doing this depends on the relation between the brightness of the star and the diameter of its round

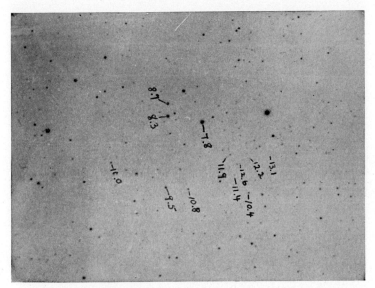

FIG. 11·24. A Magnitude Sequence. A negative of a region of the sky, with a magnitude sequence by Leon Campbell, Harvard Observatory.

image in the photograph; a brighter star has a larger image than a fainter one.

A frequent procedure is to place the original negative glass side up on a viewing frame and to mark a sequence of stars of known magnitudes grading by small steps from the brightest to the faintest magnitudes to be determined. These are used as standards for estimating the magnitudes of other stars on the photograph. Another procedure is advantageous where many magnitudes are to be determined on a plate. The negative is placed film side up on a movable frame. A graduated scale of star images on a small section cut from a plate is fixed under the microscope, film down and almost in contact with the film of the plate itself. The scale is calibrated by comparison with the images of stars of known magnitude on the plate and can then be used for estimating the magnitudes of other stars on that plate.

Photographic magnitudes of stars determined with considerable accuracy are available in many areas of the heavens. The master magnitude sequence, both photographic and photovisual, is established near the north celestial pole by Seares of Mount Wilson Observatory.

FIG. 11·24A. Movable Frame for Determining Magnitudes. A "counting machine" of University of Illinois Observatory.

11·25. Color Index. Since the ordinary photographic plate is less sensitive than the eye to red light, and more sensitive to blue light, red stars are fainter photographically than they are visually as compared with blue stars.

The *color index* of a star is the photographic magnitude minus the visual magnitude. The photographic scale is adjusted so that the color index is zero for stars of spectral class Ao, such as Sirius. For the bluest stars the color index is negative, amounting to as much as $-0^m.3$; it is positive for red stars, ordinarily reaching a value of two magnitudes for stars such as Betelgeuse. In practice, color index is often derived from comparisons at other wave lengths. The recent greatly increased speed and quality of red-sensitive plates makes them very suitable for this purpose when exposed behind a red filter.

Color index is a measure of the star's color, and therefore gives evidence as to its temperature and spectral class if nothing intervenes between the star and observer to redden the light. If the spectral class is also known and if the measured index is greater than would normally be expected for a star of that class, the excess reveals the presence and

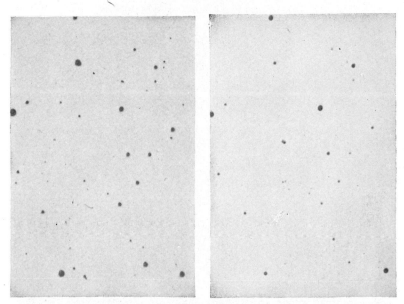

FIG. 11·25. Comparison of Blue and Red-Sensitive Photographs. (Left) A region of the sky photographed with a blue-sensitive plate. (Right) The same region with red-sensitive plate and red filter. (*Photographed with Ross-Fecker camera, University of Illinois Observatory*)

extent of the intervening absorbing medium. This information, as we shall see, is of value in the study of the Milky Way.

11·26. Photoelectric Magnitudes. Stebbins and Kunz at the University of Illinois, beginning in 1914, were pioneers in the successful use of the photoelectric cell in celestial photometry, employing a type of cell that is remarkably sensitive and almost without dark current. When a beam of starlight is admitted through the clear window of the cell, the inner surface, coated with the hydride of an alkaline metal, becomes electrically charged at a rate which depends directly on the apparent brightness of the star. Its effectiveness increased by the use of amplifiers and in connection with large telescopes, the photoelectric photometer can now be employed in observations of extremely faint stars

Fig. 11·26. Photoelectric Photometer Attached to the 15-inch Refracting Telescope of Washburn Observatory, University of Wisconsin. The photoelectric cell and amplifying tube are withdrawn from their places in the vacuum chamber above.

and other celestial objects. With filters of different colors it permits the determinations of color index having a relative error less than one per cent.

LUMINOSITIES OF THE STARS

11·27. Absolute Magnitudes. The apparent magnitude of a star relates to its brightness as we observe it; this depends on the star's luminosity, or brightness at a specified distance, and on its actual distance. One star may appear brighter than another only because it is the nearer; thus the sun appears brighter than Capella. In order to rank the stars fairly with respect to luminosity, it is necessary to place them all at the same distance away or, what amounts to the same thing, to calculate how bright they would appear if they were placed at the same distance. By agreement the standard distance is ten parsecs.

The *absolute magnitude* of a star is the apparent magnitude it would have at the distance of 10 parsecs (parallax 0″.1).

When the parallax, p'', is known and the apparent magnitude, m, has been determined by observation, the absolute magnitude, M, can be calculated by the formula:

$$M = m + 5 + 5 \log p, \text{ or}$$

$$M = m + 5 - 5 \log r,$$

where r is the distance in parsecs. This important formula is derived from the relation between brightness and magnitude (11·21) and the fact that the brightness of a point source of light varies inversely as the square of its distance. The absolute magnitude is of the same sort as the apparent magnitude employed in its calculation; it may be visual, photographic, or some other kind.

When the absolute magnitudes, M_1 and M_2, of any two stars are known, the ratio of their luminosities, L_2 and L_1, is given by the formula:

$$\log (L_2/L_1) = 0.4(M_1 - M_2).$$

11·28. Relative Luminosities. It is the custom to express the luminosity of a star in terms of the sun's luminosity, that is to say, as the number of times the star would outshine the sun if both were at the same distance. This ratio can be obtained by substituting the absolute magnitudes of the sun and star in the preceding formula.

The sun's apparent visual magnitude, m, is -26.6; its parallax, p, on the same basis as those of the stars, must be taken as the radian, 206,265″, whose logarithm is 5.314. By the first formula of the preceding Section, the sun's absolute visual magnitude is $-26.6 + 5 + 26.6$, or $+5.0$. *At the standard distance of 10 parsecs the sun would appear as a star of the fifth magnitude.* The expression for the star's relative visual luminosity becomes:

$$\log (\text{luminosity}) = 0.4(5.0 - \text{absolute magnitude}).$$

Since the majority of the brightest stars are more remote than 10 parsecs, they must be more luminous than the sun. Indeed, this is true of all the stars of Table 11·II, as is shown by their absolute magnitudes. Rigel and Deneb are of the order of ten thousand times as luminous as the sun. At the same time we have noticed, in Table 11·I, that many stars much nearer than the standard distance are visible only with the telescope, so that they must be considerably less luminous than the sun. The conclusion is that the stars differ very greatly in luminosity.

The above formula is employed in the following examples:

(1) Compare the luminosities of Sirius and the sun. From Table 11·II we find for Sirius $M = +1.3$.

$\log L = 0.4(5.0 - 1.3) = 1.4$. Thus the luminosity of Sirius is 30 times the sun's luminosity.

(2) Compare the luminosities of Barnard's star (absolute visual magnitude $+ 13.3$) and the sun.

$\log L = 0.4(5.0 - 13.3) = -3.3 = 6.7 - 10$. The luminosity of Barnard's star is .0005 times the sun's luminosity.

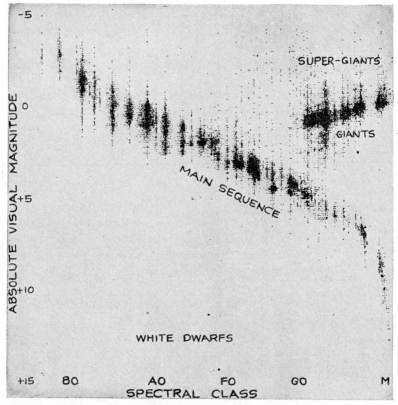

Fig. 11·29. Spectrum-Luminosity Diagram. The points represent 6700 stars. (*Diagram by W. Gyllenberg, Lund Observatory*)

11·29. Stars of the Main Sequence. When the absolute magnitudes of the stars are plotted against the spectral classes, as in Fig. 11·29, it is found that the majority of the points are arranged in a narrow band running diagonally across the diagram. More than half of the points in the band are within one magnitude of the curve which they define. The mean curve drops steadily along the spectral sequence, from absolute magnitude −2.5 for stars of class Bo to +10 for class Mo. This is known as the *main sequence*.

The sun (class Go, absolute magnitude +5.0) is close to the mean curve, occupying a fairly central position along the main sequence. It is about a hundred times fainter than the average class A star, and the same amount brighter than the average class M star of the main sequence. Inasmuch as the sun if it were placed at the relatively small distance of 10 parsecs would be an inconspicuous star to the naked eye, the red stars of the sequence ought generally to be telescopic objects. Indeed, this is true of many of the nearest red stars, such as Barnard's star.

On the other hand, the red stars Betelgeuse and Antares are among the apparently brightest stars in the sky; they are more distant than 10 parsecs, and are accordingly much more luminous than the sun. These and many other stars are represented by points in the diagram which fall systematically above those of the main sequence.

11·30. Giant and Dwarf Stars. Since its introduction by Russell at Princeton, in 1913, the spectrum-luminosity diagram has played a leading part in directing the studies of the stars. The Danish astronomer Hertzsprung had previously drawn attention to the sharp distinction between the red stars of high and low luminosity, and had named them giant stars and dwarf stars respectively. The original "dwarfs" are those we have called "stars of the main sequence."

Giant stars are stars, such as Capella and Arcturus, that are decidedly more luminous than stars of the main sequence. *Supergiant stars* are extraordinarily luminous giants; examples are Rigel, Antares, and Betelgeuse. They are sometimes distinguished by prefixing the letter "c" to the usual spectral designation; thus Rigel is of class cB8. Spectroscopically the supergiants are characterized by the exceptional sharpness of the lines in their spectra.

The points in the diagram that appear far below the main sequence represent the *white dwarf stars,* small and very dense stars of which an example is the companion of Sirius.

11·31. Relative Frequencies of Stars of Different Luminosities. The relative numbers of stars of different absolute magnitudes in a selected volume of space is shown in Table 11·III. The formula by which these values are expressed is known as the luminosity function; it varies with the different investigators and is least reliable at the faint end. Within sixteen light years of the sun the stars around absolute magnitude +15 seems to be the most numerous.

TABLE 11·III. RELATIVE NUMBERS OF STARS OF DIFFERENT VISUAL LUMINOSITIES

Absolute Magnitude	Luminosity	Relative Number
— 5.0	10,000	1
— 2.5	1,000	50
0.0	100	2,000
+ 2.5	10	10,000
+ 5.0	1	40,000
+ 7.5	0.1	50,000
+ 10.0	0.01	100,000
+ 12.5	0.001	200,000

For every supergiant of absolute magnitude — 5, there are forty thousand stars of magnitude +5 like the sun, and a quarter of a million stars of magnitude +15. *In a selected volume of space,* stars of low luminosity are in the great majority. But *as seen with the naked eye,* the stars of high luminosity are the more numerous. It is because the less luminous stars that are visible to the naked eye occupy a smaller volume of space around us, a volume that shrinks as we progress down the main sequence until even the nearest stars at the red end of this sequence are invisible without the telescope.

REVIEW QUESTIONS

1. State the term associated with each of the following definitions:

(a) Difference in direction of a star as viewed from the earth and sun.
(b) Distance of a star whose parallax is one second of arc.
(c) Change in the direction of a star relative to its neighbors.
(d) Motion of a star determined by the Doppler effect in its spectrum.
(e) Difference between photographic and visual magnitude of a star.
(f) Apparent magnitude of a star at the distance of ten parsecs.

2. Explain the method of determining (a) the parallax of a star; (b) the proper motion; (c) the radial velocity. Which of these are determined less reliably as the distance of the star is greater?

3. The parallax of Arcturus is nearly 0".1. Using this value, calculate the distance of the star in astronomical units, miles, parsecs, and light years.

4. The annual variation in the radial velocities of the stars affords a precise means of determining the earth's distance from the sun. Explain. (Simplify the explanation by taking a star at rest in the ecliptic and assuming that the earth's orbit is circular.)

5. How can the apex of the sun's way be located by (a) the proper motions of the stars? (b) their radial velocities?

6. State the spectral class or classes of stars whose spectra are characterized as follows:

(a) Hydrogen lines are most intense.
(b) Bands of titanium oxide are prominent.
(c) Lines of metals are prominent.
(d) Lines of ionized helium, oxygen, and nitrogen appear.
(e) Lines of neutral helium are most intense.

7. A certain blue star and a red star appear equally bright to the unaided eye. How do they compare in brightness as (a) viewed with the telescope? (b) photographed with a blue-sensitive plate? (c) yellow-sensitive plate? (d) red-sensitive plate?

8. Of the apparently brightest stars (Table 11·II) name (a) the brightest of all; (b) the reddest; (c) the bluest; (d) the star having the greatest luminosity; (e) the nearest to us.

9. What is gained by comparing the absolute magnitudes of stars rather than their apparent magnitudes?

10. The apparent magnitude of a star can be easily determined. Explain (a) that the absolute magnitude can then be calculated if the distance is known, or (b) that the distance of the star can be calculated if the absolute magnitude is independently known.

11. Distinguish between main-sequence, giant, supergiant, and dwarf stars.

12. Account for the greater brightness of a giant star as compared with a main-sequence star of the same spectral class.

Problems

1. The parallax of Alpha Centauri is 0".761. Calculate its maximum change in position on photographs taken with the 26-inch Yale telescope at Johannesburg. The scale of these plates is 18".28 to the millimeter.

Answer: 0.083 mm, or about three thousandths of an inch.

2. The parallax of Vega is 0".123. Calculate its distance in parsecs and light years.

Answer: 8.1 parsecs; 26 light years.

3. Show that the tangential velocity of a star, T, equals $4.74\mu''/p''$ km/sec, where μ is the annual proper motion, p the parallax, and d the distance in astronomical units.

Answer: $T = \mu/206,265 \times d$; $d = 206,265/p$. Convert from astronomical units/year to km/sec.

4. Calculate the ratio of apparent visual brightness of the sun and Sirius.

Answer: The sun is 10,000 million times as bright as Sirius.

5. Calculate the ratio of the visual luminosity of Capella and the sun.

Answer: Capella is 145 times as luminous as the sun.

6. Derive the relation: $M = m - 5 \log r$, where M would be the magnitude of a star if it were distant 10 parsecs, and m is the magnitude at its actual distance, r.

Answer: By the formula of 11·21: $0.4 (M - m) = \log (l_m/l_M)$. Since the brightness of a star varies inversely as the square of its distance, the right side of the equation becomes $2 - 2 \log r$.

The Milky Way in Cepheus. (*Photographed by F. E. Ross, Yerkes Observatory*)

CHAPTER XII

VARIABLE STARS

Variable stars are stars that vary in brightness, and frequently in other respects as well. These variations are fluctuations and not progressive changes, so that they do not permanently alter the configurations of the constellations. Variable stars fall chiefly into three classes with respect to the cause of their variability: (1) *Pulsating stars,* comprising Cepheid, long-period, and irregular variables; (2) *novae,* supernovae, and also nova-like stars; (3) *eclipsing stars* which vary in light owing to periodic eclipses of mutually revolving stars.

Pulsating and exploding stars are considered in this Chapter, and also planetary nebulae which are consequences of the explosions. The account of eclipsing stars, which are associated with the binary stars, is left for the following Chapter.

12·1. The Light Curve of a star is the curve which shows how the star's magnitude varies with time. It is the curve which best fits an array of points where the observed magnitudes are plotted against the times of the observations. If the variation is periodic, the times of successive maximum or minimum brightness can presently be derived, and from these the *elements of the light variation.* These are the *epoch,* or time of a chosen maximum or minimum, and the *period* of the variation. The *mean light curve* is then obtained by plotting all the observed magnitudes with respect to *phase,* or interval of time since the maximum or minimum preceding each observation.

As an example, the elements of the variable star Eta Aquilae are: Maximum brightness $= 2414827.15 + 7^{d}.1767.E$, where the first number is the epoch, expressed in Julian days (2·30), and the second is the period in days. In order to predict the times of future maxima we have simply to multiply the period by $E = 1, 2, \ldots$, and to add the results successively to the epoch. The mean light curve of this star is shown in Fig. 12·1.

Variable stars are designated according to a plan that started simple enough, but became complicated when the discoveries of these stars ran into many thousands. Unless the star already has a letter in the Bayer system (1·24), it is assigned a capital letter, or two, in the order in which its variability is recognized, which is followed by the possessive of the name of its constellation. For each constellation the letters are used in the order: R, S, . . . Z; RR, RS, . . . RZ; SS, . . . SZ; and so on, until ZZ is reached. Subsequent variables are AA, AB, . . . AZ; BB, . . . BZ; etc. By the time QZ is reached (the letter J is not employed) 334 variable stars

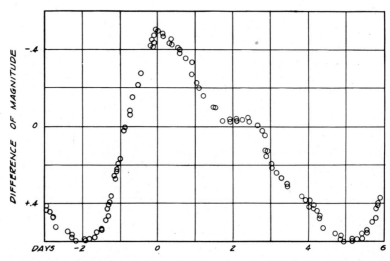

FIG. 12·1. Light Curve of Eta Aquilae. A typical Cepheid variable having a period of about seven days. (*Light curve by C. C. Wylie from his photoelectric observations at the University of Illinois*)

are so designated in the constellation. Examples are R Leonis, SZ Herculis, and AC Cygni. After the lettering of the variables has reached QZ the subsequent designations are V335, V336, etc.; an example is V335 Sagittarii.

PULSATING STARS

12·2. Cepheid Variable Stars. All periodic physical (not eclipsing) variable stars having periods up to 45 days are known as *Cepheid variable stars.* The name comes from one of the earliest recognized examples, Delta Cephei. The majority are of two kinds: typical Cepheids and short-period, or cluster-type, Cepheids.

Typical Cepheids have periods from more than a day to 45 days, and most commonly around five days. They are generally very steady, both in period and form of light curve. The increase in brightness is more rapid than the decline, and the range of the variation is about fifty per cent greater photographically than visually; the visual range is not far from one magnitude. The shape of the light curve is somewhat different for variations of different periods; thus for periods around eight days there is often a hump (Fig. 12·1) in the declining branch of the curve.

These stars are yellow supergiants (spectral classes F and G), and are very rare. Their high luminosity, however, raises them to apparent prominence out of proportion to their actual number. About a dozen typical Cepheids are visible to the naked eye; the brightest are Delta Cephei, Eta Aquilae, Zeta Geminorum, and Beta Doradus. Polaris is included among the Cepheids, but its visual range is only 0.08 magnitude.

12·3. Short-Period Cepheids are also called *cluster type Cepheids* because they were first observed in the globular star clusters, though they

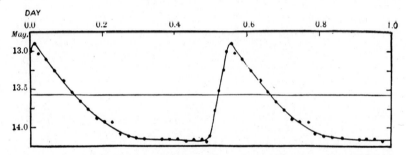

FIG. 12·3. Light Curve of a Short-Period Cepheid Variable. The extremely rapid rise to maximum light is characteristic of many short-period Cepheids. (From *Harvard College Observatory Circular* 315)

are now recognized in greater numbers outside the clusters. Their periods are around half a day, ranging from an hour and a half to about one day, and are likely to be slightly unsteady. Their light curves generally resemble those of typical Cepheids; their variation around maximum light is extremely rapid and their stay around minimum is relatively prolonged.

These stars are of spectral class A, having less luminosity than the supergiant typical Cepheids, so that they cannot be seen as far away. Not one of them is bright enough to be visible to the naked eye; RR Lyrae and R Muscae are of the seventh magnitude. The fact that they are recognized in greater numbers shows that in any selected volume of space they must far outnumber the typical Cepheids.

12·4. The Spectra of Cepheid Variables show two features that are especially significant for the physical interpretation of these stars. In addition to the variability of the light of a Cepheid:

(1) *The spectral class is variable.* From maximum to minimum light the spectral class advances about a whole class. In the case of Delta Cephei, for example, the change is from F4 to G6, which means a drop of nearly 1000° C in surface temperature. Thus the Cepheid stars are hotter at maximum brightness and cooler at minimum.

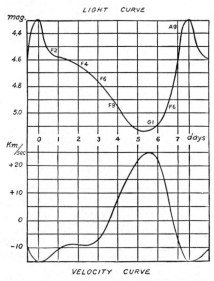

FIG. 12·4. Light and Velocity Curves of W Sagittarii. Maximum brightness coincides with greatest velocity of approach; minimum light with greatest velocity of recession. From maximum to minimum light the spectrum changes by more than a whole class. (*Diagram by Curtiss; spectral classes by Shapley*)

(2) *The spectrum lines oscillate* in the period of the light variation. The curve representing the variation of the radial velocity with time is the mirror image of the light curve (Fig. 12·4). At maximum brightness of the star the lines are displaced farthest toward the violet, and at minimum brightness they are displaced farthest toward the red end of the spectrum. It is now generally supposed that this is a Doppler displacement owing to the motion in the line of sight of the part of the star's surface turned toward us. At maximum light these gases are approaching us, and at minimum light they are receding from us.

As the most reasonable construction of the evidence, Harlow Shapley, in 1914, proposed the pulsation theory.

12·5. Pulsating Stars. A normal star appears to maintain a nice balance between the inward urge of gravity on the one hand and the outward pressure of the hot gases and of the star's radiation on the other. Suppose that the balance is upset and that the star expands. By expansion it is finally overcooled and gravity gets control. The star then contracts and is thereby heated, until pressure again predominates and expansion begins again. Thus the star rhythmically expands and contracts.

As the gases surge outward and inward we have the Doppler oscillation of the spectrum lines. When the star is most expanded, it is cooler, and therefore fainter and of redder spectral class. When it is most contracted, it is hotter, and therefore brighter and of bluer spectral class, according to the theory in its simplest form. But at maximum light, as we have seen, the layers of the star under spectroscopic scrutiny are not at highest compression; instead they are moving outward at the greatest speed.

This is the most noticeable discrepancy between the theory and what is observed. It has been suggested that the interior of the Cepheid variable may pulsate as the theory requires, and that the outer layers may oscillate in different phase with compressional waves coming up to the surface. In addition, it might be supposed that frictional damping of the pulsation could be detected over the time the Cepheids have been under observation. But the question of the maintenance of the pulsation is associated with the problem of its cause, which awaits solution.

12·6. The Period-Luminosity Relation. The more luminous a typical Cepheid variable is, the longer is the period of its variation. The relation is illustrated by the curve of Fig. 12·6 which shows how the logarithm of the period increases as the median absolute photographic magnitude becomes brighter. First established in its useful form by Shapley, in 1918, this relation has given the Cepheid stars a very important place in astronomical inquiry. Wherever a Cepheid is found, its distance can be determined by use of this relation. The procedure is as follows:

When the period of the variation has been determined by observation, the corresponding median absolute magnitude, M, is read from the curve. The *median* magnitude is the average between the magnitudes at maximum and minimum brightness. If the median apparent magnitude, m, has also been observed, the distance of the star, d, in parsecs, can be calculated by the formula:

$$\log d = (m - M + 5)/5.$$

Cepheid variables have added importance because of their high luminosity and therefore the great distances at which they can be observed. Here is a way of measuring the distances of stars far beyond the limits for the direct parallax measurements. If an intervening dusty medium dims the starlight, appropriate allowance must be made. The presence and effect of dust in space will be considered at a later time.

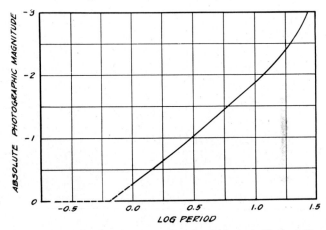

FIG. 12·6. Period-Luminosity Curve for Typical Cepheid Variables. From this curve the absolute median photographic magnitude of the variable star can be read when the period of its light variation is known. The magnitudes of all short-period Cepheids are not far from zero.

Short-period Cepheids do not share the period-luminosity relation, but they do show a uniformity that is equally valuable. The median absolute photographic magnitude is not far from zero for all of them. Whenever a short-period Cepheid is found, its distance can be calculated by the above formula, in which $M = 0$. Examples of the calculation of the distances of Cepheid variables follow:

(1) The Cepheid variable SY Aurigae has a period of 10 days. Its photographic magnitude varies from 9.8 to 11.0. Required its distance, supposing that no dust intervenes.

The median photographic magnitude is 10.4. The logarithm of the period is 1.0, and the corresponding absolute magnitude, from the curve, is −1.8. Thus $\log d = (10.4 + 1.8 + 5.0)/5 = 3.44$.

The distance is 2800 parsecs.

(2) Required the distance of the short-period Cepheid variable RX Eridani, whose period is 0.6 days and median photographic magnitude 9.2. We again suppose no intervening dust.

The absolute photographic magnitude of a short-period Cepheid is taken as 0.0. Thus $\log d = (9.2 - 0.0 + 5.0)/5 = 2.84$.

The distance is 690 parsecs.

12·7. Semi-Regular Variables Related to Cepheids.

Among the small groups of variable stars which do not conform to the principal patterns, we notice in passing a group of 25 stars that forms a sort of connecting link between the Cepheids and the red variables. It is

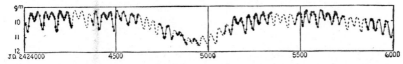

FIG. 12·7. Light Curve of RV Tauri. (From Campbell and Jacchia's *The Story of Variable Stars*, by courtesy of The Blakiston Company)

known after its prototype as the RV Tauri group. The spectra are of class K, and the stars are redder at minimum, like the Cepheids.

RV Tauri itself can serve as an example, though the pattern is not the same throughout the group. The light curve (Fig. 12·7) shows a semi-regular variation of about a magnitude in a period of 79 days; this comprises two maxima of nearly equal brightness, and two unequal minima. There is also a superimposed variation in a period of 1300 days. The complex variations of RV Tauri stars and other semi-regular variables may arise from combinations of pulsations whose separation is left for future inquiries.

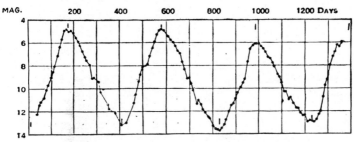

FIG. 12·8. Light Curve of the Long-Period Variable Chi Cygni. (*From observations by the American Association of Variable Star Observers*)

12·8. Long-Period Variables.

This type of variability is restricted to red giant and supergiant stars. Most of these stars are of spectral class M, though classes R, N, and S are also represented. The periods range from a few months to two years, and are the most frequent around 275 days. The light variations range from four to nearly ten visual magnitudes, in the case of Chi Cygni. In periodicity, range of brightness, and form of light curve, the long-period variable stars exhibit an approach to regularity analogous to the sunspot numbers. Departure from regularity is particularly noticeable in the brightness at maximum light; as an example, the maxima of Chi Cygni range in a random way from visual magnitude 3.6, when the star is easily visible to the naked eye, to magnitude 6.8, when it is invisible without the telescope.

While there is wide variation among these variables, many of their light curves show the following changes. With increasing period, they have flatter minima, steeper increase to maxima, and increasing range of the light variation.

12·9. The Spectra of Long-Period Variables contain the dark lines and bands characteristic of the spectra of red stars, and also bright lines,

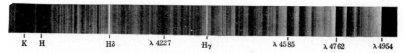

K   H   Hδ   λ 4227   Hγ   λ 4585   λ 4762   λ 4954

FIG. 12·9. Spectrum of Mira. Titanium oxide bands are prominent at the right. Hydrogen lines are bright. (*Photographed by W. C. Rufus, University of Michigan*)

particularly the hydrogen lines. The bright lines make their appearance about midway between minimum and maximum light, attain greatest strength after maximum, and disappear before minimum is reached. The variation in intensity of the bright lines lags about a sixth of the period behind the light variation. While the cause of the bright lines is not understood, it seems certain that these lines are produced at lower levels than the dark lines, because the bright lines are weakened wherever the dark lines overlap them.

The dark lines oscillate slightly in the period of the light variation; but they show that the greatest velocity of recession at their level occurs at maximum brightness of the star, which is the reverse of the rule of the Cepheid variables (12·5). The bright lines also oscillate in the same period. At their level the greatest velocity of approach occurs at maximum brightness of the lines themselves (one sixth of the period after the maximum brightness of the star), which resembles the rule of the Cepheids. It would seem that long-period variables are pulsating stars and that they pulsate in different phase at different levels.

As with the Cepheids, the spectra of the long-period variables shift toward the red end of the sequence from maximum to minimum light with diminishing temperatures of the stars. But the temperature drop

is only about half that of the Cepheids, while the decrease in brightness is much greater. We can best consider the problem by referring to
a particular star.

12·10. Mira ("The Wonderful"). The best known, and at times the
brightest, of the long-period variables is Omicron Ceti, or Mira, whose
light variations have been observed for more than three centuries. Its
maxima range from the second to the fifth visual magnitude, and its

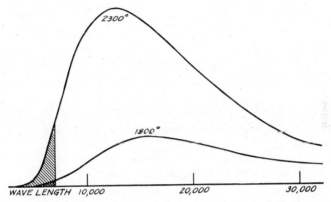

FIG. 12·10. Variation of Mira in Light and in Total Radiation. Energy
curves at maximum and minimum. At maximum light the total radiation, represented by the area under the curve, has increased only two or three times.
The visible radiation, represented by the shaded area, has increased many times.
(*Diagram by A. H. Joy in Contributions from the Mount Wilson Observatory*)

minima from the eighth to the tenth. The average period of its light
variation is 330 days.

From minimum to maximum light the spectrum of Mira changes
from M9 to M6, and the temperature from 1900° to 2600° C., an increase by the factor 1.37. By Stefan's law (10·5) the rate of the star's
radiation increases as the fourth power of this quantity, or by the factor
3.5. Yet the light increases five magnitudes, or by the factor 100. The
difference between the two numbers arises partly from the fact (Fig.
12·10) that the change in the visible radiation between the two temperatures is greater than the change in the total radiation. In addition,
a whole magnitude of the visual variation of Mira can be accounted
for by the changing intensity of the titanium oxide dark bands which
leave gaps in the part of the spectrum to which the eye is especially
sensitive. Even so, the light variation seems greater than would be
expected. Merrill at Mount Wilson Observatory suggests that the

excess may be owing to a liquid veil that is drawn around the star's atmosphere at its coolest temperature.

12·11. Irregular Variable Stars. Red stars fall into three groups with respect to the variability of their light: (1) Red stars of the main sequence are not intrinsically variable; (2) giant and supergiant red stars whose spectra contain bright lines are long-period variables; (3) giant and supergiant red stars whose spectra have very weak bright lines or more often none at all are likely to be irregular or semi-regular variables. The light variations of the third class are likely to be less than a magnitude and are often so small that they can be detected only by precision apparatus, such as the photoelectric photometer. Irregular variables may well exhibit such complex surface pulsations that the underlying periodicities are difficult to determine.

Betelgeuse is the brightest of the irregular, or semi-regular variables. Its range in visual light is from magnitude 0.2 to 1.2. A semi-regular variation of 150 to 300 days is superposed on a fluctuation in a period of six years.

12·12. The Period-Spectrum Relation. All spectral classes from B to the reddest ones are represented successively among the pulsating giant and supergiant stars arrayed with respect to the periods of their fluctuations. Some unstable Cepheids of very short period are of class B. Short-period Cepheids are mostly of class A at maximum light. Typical Cepheids show a preference for classes F and G. The RV Tauri stars are mostly of class K. Long-period variables belong to classes M, N, R, and S. The relation can frequently be seen within the different types of variable stars. Altogether the relation is so impressive that this array has been called "the great sequence" by the Gaposchkins at Harvard Observatory.

Since these stars diminish in density with increasing redness, as we shall notice later, we have here an inverse relation between period and density. Eddington at the University of Cambridge reached the theoretical conclusion for all Cepheid variables that the product of the period and square root of the density must be nearly constant. And the conclusion seems to hold for long-period variables as well.

Novae

Novae are stars that rise rapidly from comparative obscurity and then gradually subside to something like their former faintness. They are "new stars" only in the sense of their temporary grandeur. They are designated by the word "Nova" followed by the possessive of the constellation name and the year of the outburst; Nova Puppis 1942 is an example. Some of them are also designated by letters along with ordinary variable stars. The present account is concerned with the novae in the galactic system. Novae in the extragalactic systems, including the even more spectacular supernovae, are described in Chapter XVIII.

12·13. The Brightest Novae. About a hundred novae have been discovered in the galactic system. At the present rate the number is in-

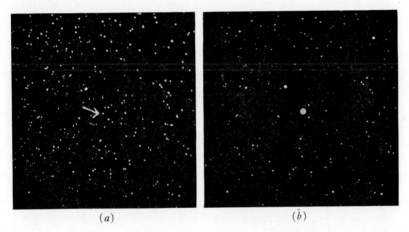

(a)   (b̄)

FIG. 12·13. Nova Aquilae 1918, Before and After the Outburst. (a) In 1905, as an apparently invariable star of the eleventh magnitude. (b) On July 12, 1918, more than a month after the outburst. (*Photographed at Yerkes Observatory*)

creased by an average of two a year, but many more escape detection. Seven of the recorded novae rose to the first magnitude, or brighter.

The brightest nova on record appeared in Cassiopeia in November, 1572, and was observed by Tycho Brahe. This star became as bright as Venus at greatest brilliancy, and could be seen in full daylight; thereafter it gradually faded and finally disappeared from view (there were then no telescopes) in the spring of 1574. Next in order of brightness was "Kepler's star" in Ophiuchus in 1604, which rivaled Jupiter in brightness and remained visible to the naked eye for eighteen months. It is interesting that the remaining five of the seven brightest novae on record appeared in the present century.

Nova Persei 1901 rose to magnitude 0.1, or slightly brighter than Capella. Nova Aquilae 1918 reached magnitude −1.4, almost as bright as Sirius. Nova Pictoris 1925, magnitude 1.2, was as bright as Spica. Nova Herculis 1934, magnitude 1.5, was not much inferior to Deneb. Nova Puppis 1942, discovered on November 12 of that year, was of magnitude 0.35, as bright as Rigel.

12·14. Light Variations of Novae. Characteristic of light curves of novae is their abrupt rise to maximum, a rise averaging thirteen magnitudes, which is an increase of 160,000 times in brightness. The out-

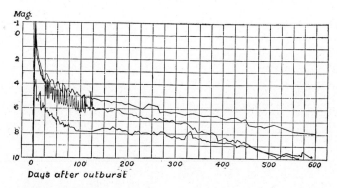

FIG. 12·14. Light Curves of Nova Aquilae 1918, Nova Persei 1901, and Nova Geminorum 1912. They are designated in order of decreasing height. (From *Harvard College Observatory Annals*)

bursts occur without warning; Nova Aquilae 1918, for example, had shown no evidence of variability during the previous thirty years in which the photographic records are available.

Almost immediately after maximum the decline begins; it is likely to proceed rapidly at first, and then more slowly with occasional partial recoveries. But this pattern is not without exceptions. Nova Herculis 1934 declined so slowly after its maximum on December 22 that it remained visible to the unaided eye until early in April, 1935; then it fell rapidly to magnitude 13 at the end of the month. There it rebounded almost to naked-eye visibility, where it remained practically invariable until a new decline set in early in 1936.

Novae have returned eventually to very nearly the same faint magnitudes they had before the outbursts occurred, which suggests that the effect on the stars is only superficial. From a dozen to nearly forty years have elapsed before they have settled down to stability again. As late as 1936, Nova Persei 1901 was still varying through nearly two magnitudes.

The succession of changes in the spectra of novae will be easier to follow if we look first at the current physical interpretation of their behavior.

12·15. The Nature of Novae. Previous to its outburst a nova is a white star considerably denser than corresponding stars of the main sequence. The sudden liberation of an excessive amount of energy in

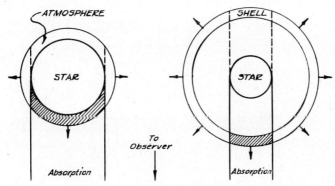

FIG. 12·15. Schematic Picture of an Exploding Star. Before the explosion (left) the star's atmosphere produces a dark-line spectrum. Soon after the explosion (right) the expanding gaseous shell emits much light, adding bright bands to the spectrum.

the star's interior causes the photosphere to expand rapidly in the attempt to radiate the energy, so that the star becomes much brighter. When the effort to restore equilibrium fails, the star explodes; the radiating surface then begins to contract, and the star becomes fainter. The gases released by the explosion form a rapidly expanding luminous envelope around the star. This envelope may become large enough to be visible through the telescope. If the explosion is of sufficiently large scale, the envelope may remain visible for thousands of years as a planetary nebula.

Eventually the nebula becomes so diluted by expansion that it disappears, and only the star remains, apparently not much the worse for its experience. The star is then white, but is smaller and denser than the white stars of the main sequence. For example, Nova Aquilae 1918 now has a quarter the diameter of the sun and is seventy times as dense as the sun.

12·16. Spectral Changes of Novae. The spectra of all normal novae undergo about the same succession of changes. While the star is swelling and its brightness is accordingly increasing, the spectrum is continuous and crossed by dark lines in the pattern of a class A star. These absorption lines are produced in the part of the star's atmosphere that lies between us and the main body of the star. As the star expands, these gases are rushing toward us, so that the dark lines are displaced toward

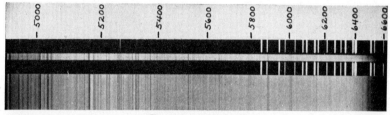

December 23, 1934

January 12, 1935

FIG. 12·16. Spectrum of Nova Herculis 1934 at Two Stages. The unwidened spectrum of the nova between lines of the comparison spectrum is shown above and the widened spectrum below in each case. (*Photographed at Lick Observatory*)

the violet. The amount of the displacement corresponds to a speed of expansion of the order of 1000 km/sec, or more than two million miles an hour. The dark-line pattern remains at the maximum brightness of the star, showing that the photosphere is still intact at that phase.

Bright bands, whose centers are not appreciably displaced, make their appearance soon after maximum. They represent the light from all parts of the gaseous shell (Fig. 12·15), which has broken loose and is rapidly expanding. The light comes from all parts of the shell, some parts approaching us and others receding, so that the bright lines are broadened into bands by the Doppler effect. The bright bands are bordered at their violet edges by dark lines absorbed by the small part of the shell that is in front of the star and is approaching with the highest speed. The dark lines have several components. Evidently there are several explosions of varying effectiveness; speeds of expansion as high as 3400 km/sec have been observed.

The subsequent changes in the spectrum are about what would be expected as the brightness of the star diminishes and the envelope of gas is rendered more and more tenuous by its expansion. Since some of these features involve processes we have not yet considered, they will be only briefly noted at this time.

The continuous spectrum and the dark lines gradually fade, while the bright bands become more conspicuous. The pattern of lines and bands changes as the gases of the shell are more tenuous and more highly ionized. When the star has declined about four magnitudes from the maximum brightness, the lines that characterize the bright-line spectrum of the gaseous nebulae appear and eventually are the dominating feature. After several years, the nebular lines fade and the spectrum resembles that of a Wolf-Rayet star. Finally, when the star has returned to about its original brightness, the spectrum is continuous with no prominent features.

Meanwhile the color of the nova changes. It is white until the maximum brightness is attained. Then it turns red, like the sun's chromosphere, with the dominance of the red hydrogen line. It presently changes to the green of nebular light, and finally returns to white.

12·17. Recurrent Novae and Nova-Like Stars.

It seems improbable that every star, including the sun, is likely to explode at some time; novae before and after the outbursts appear to belong to a special category of stars. It may be that these stars explode repeatedly. At any rate, there are nova-like stars that do so. The star RS Ophiuchi, normally around the twelfth magnitude, rose abruptly to the fourth magnitude in 1898 and again in 1933. The star T Pyxidis rose rapidly from its normal magnitude thirteen to nearly naked-eye visibility in 1890, 1902, and 1920. In addition, the star U Scorpii has three recorded explosions, the latest in 1936.

Variable stars of the U Geminorum group resemble novae in a number of respects. An example is SS Cygni (Fig. 12·17). Normally faint, around magnitude 15, they suddenly increase in brightness five magnitudes or less at irregular intervals and decline somewhat more slowly. Their spectra at minimum contain wide bright lines which practically fade away at maximum. While the intervals between the outbursts of these stars are irregular, the average interval for any one of them over ten-year periods is about the same. The average intervals range from several months to two or three weeks, and the range of the light variation diminishes with diminishing interval.

There is some indication that the variation in magnitude for all nova-like stars varies directly as the logarithm of the average interval between

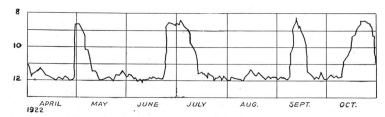

FIG. 12·17.   Light Curve of SS Cygni.

the outbursts.   If the relation holds for normal novae as well, the intervals between their outbursts are several thousand years.

12·18. Expanding Envelopes of Novae. The spectroscopic evidence of gaseous shells expanding around exploded stars is verified by the sub-

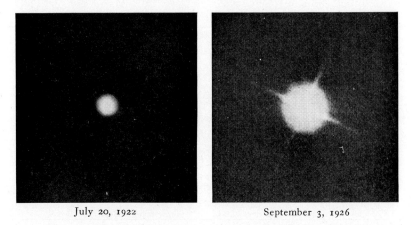

July 20, 1922   September 3, 1926

FIG. 12·18.   Expanding Envelope Around Nova Aquilae 1918. (*Photographed at Mount Wilson Observatory*)

sequent observations of the shells with the telescope, when they have grown large enough to become visible. Some instances are Nova Persei 1901, Nova Aquilae 1918, and Nova Herculis 1934. While the envelope around Nova Aquilae is spherical, those around other novae, including the other two mentioned, were observed to be irregular in shape.

The envelope around Nova Aquilae began to be visible through the telescope about four months after the explosion occurred. Since then it has increased in radius about $1''$ a year. The radial velocity of the expansion, as determined from the strongly displaced dark lines in the spectrum or from half the widths of the bright bands, is 1700 km/sec. Since the tangential velocity of expansion, T, is presumably the same as the radial velocity, and since the angular velocity, μ, is also known, the distance, D, in parsecs of the nova can be found by the relation $(11 \cdot 11): D = 0.211\,T/\mu$. The distance of Nova Aquilae is accordingly 360 parsecs, or 1200 light years. By the year 1940 the envelope around this star had attained a diameter exceeding ten thousand times the earth's distance from the sun, or a million million miles. This is the diameter of a typical planetary nebula.

Planetary Nebulae

Planetary nebulae are so named because the majority appear through the telescope as elliptical disks, though in their other characteristics they have nothing in common with the planets. With very few exceptions they have stars at their centers. Their resemblance to the expanding envelopes around the novae is in almost every respect so striking that there can be little doubt of close connection between the two.

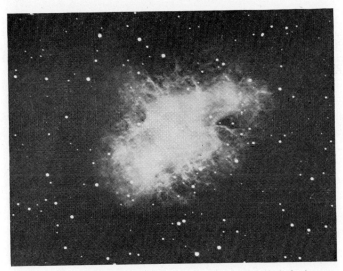

FIG. 12·19.   Crab Nebula, Messier 1, in Taurus. This nebula is expanding, presumably from the site of an explosion. (*Photographed at Mount Wilson Observatory*)

12·19. Expansion of the Crab Nebula. The Crab nebula in Taurus is an example of an envelope that has been expanding for several hundreds instead of a few tens of years, as in instances we have already noticed. It consists of a homogeneous central structure surrounded by an intricate system of filaments. Photographs over an interval of a third of a century show that the semi-major axis of the nebula, whose present value is about 90″, is increasing at the rate of 0″.1 a year. If the rate has been constant all along, the explosion occurred nine hun-

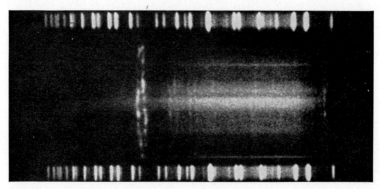

FIG. 12·19A. Spectrum of Crab Nebula, showing doubling of lines. Comparison spectra appear above and below. (*Photographed at Lick Observatory*)

dred years ago. It is supposed that this was the nova reported as having been seen in this part of the sky in the year 1054; one report gave its brightness as equal to that of Jupiter. The star itself has not been certainly identified, but a small patch of nebulosity has been found near the supposed position.

In the spectrum of the light from the middle of the Crab nebula the bright lines are double (Fig. 12·19A). These lines are produced by the filaments that surround the nucleus. The lines from the filaments in front, which are approaching us in the expansion, are displaced to the violet by the Doppler effect; those from the filaments in behind, which are receding from us, are displaced toward the red end of the spectrum. Thus the doubling of the lines. Evidently the nucleus of the nebula is transparent. The amounts of the displacements of the lines show that the rate of the expansion is 1300 km/sec, or 70 million miles a day. The distance of the Crab nebula is 1250 parsecs, or 4100 light years.

12·20. Planetary Nebulae. About 130 planetary nebulae are recognized in the galactic system, and all are too faint to be viewed without

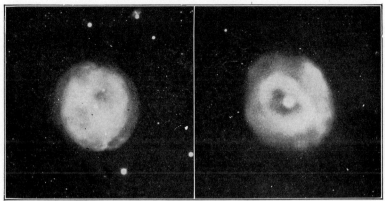

Owl Nebula in Ursa Major.   NGC 7662 in Andromeda.
Diameter 200″   Diameter 30″

Fig. 12·20. Two Planetary Nebulae. (*Photographed at Mount Wilson Observatory*)

the telescope. They appear generally as faintly luminous elliptical disks which are brighter toward the circumference. The outside is enough brighter in some cases so that they look like rings; a well known example is the Ring nebula in Lyra. In some, as in the Dumb-bell nebula in Vulpecula, the light falls off markedly toward the extremities of their

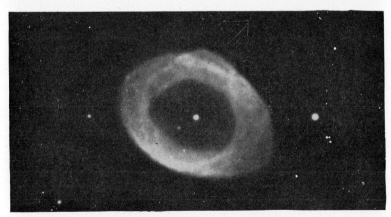

Fig. 12·20A. The Ring Nebula in Lyra. The greatest diameter is 83″. The elliptical disk, the diminished brightness near the extremities of the major axis, the complex structural details, and the central star are features to be noted. A more recent photograph, by Duncan, shows a faint, roughly circular outer ring twice as great as the bright ring. (*Photographed at Mount Wilson Observatory*)

major axes. A Saturn-like nebula in Aquarius is an example of the variety of their forms. Multiple rings, dark patches, and bright filaments contribute to what has been called "the bewildering complexity" of their structure.

These objects are nebulous envelopes around central stars which in the majority of cases are visible in the photographs. Where the central star is not seen, it may well be hidden by dark material. The gases glow with a fluorescence stimulated by the central star. The average planetary nebula has a diameter of the order of a million million miles, or ten thousand times the distance from the earth to the sun.

The central stars resemble the novae at minimum brightness. They are dense stars, and their light is so blue that they are more easily visible in the photographs than to the eye at the telescope.

12·21. The Spectra of Planetary Nebulae show prominently the bright lines produced by glowing gas. When the exposures are sufficiently

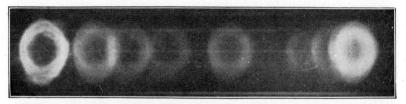

FIG. 12·21. Slitless Spectrogram of the Ring Nebula. A separate image of the nebula is formed by each wave length emitted. The brightest images correspond to the two pairs of "nebular lines" in the ultraviolet (left) and in the green (right). (*Photographed at Lick Observatory*)

long, the continuous spectrum of the light of the central star that is reflected by the gaseous envelope appears as well. The bright lines give evidence that the material of planetary nebulae has about the same chemical composition as the atmospheres of ordinary stars. The slant of the lines, when the slit of the spectroscope is placed along the major axis of the elliptical disks, shows that these nebulae are rotating, which would be inferred from the shapes of the disks themselves. With a slitless spectroscope the bright lines are replaced (Fig. 12·21) by images of the nebulae in the wave lengths of the light they emit. When the slit of the spectroscope is placed centrally across the disks of planetary nebulae, the bright lines appear bow-shaped, as in the spectrum of the Crab nebula (12·19A). Thus these nebulae generally are expanding.

Planetary nebulae and their central stars closely resemble novae and their envelopes with a single puzzling exception. The observed speeds of expansion of the planetaries (except the Crab nebula which is not always included in this category) are around 20 km/sec, while the speeds of the nova envelopes are many hundred kilometers a second. It may be that the speed diminishes as the interval after the explosion runs into centuries, or that a special type of explosion is needed to produce typical planetary nebulae. With the assumption that their rate of expansion is constant, it is estimated that the life of one of these nebulae—from its beginning in the explosion to the time when it is so diluted by expansion as to become invisible—is some 30,000 years. A planetary nebula is relatively only a momentary feature of the star fields.

REVIEW QUESTIONS

1. Draw the characteristic light curve of each of the following classes of stars:

(a) A star that is invariable in brightness.
(b) A pulsating star.
(c) A nova.
(d) An eclipsing star.

2. Enumerate four differences between short-period and typical Cepheid stars.

3. State two differences between the spectrum of a Cepheid variable star at maximum and minimum brightness. Explain that this correlation does not seem consistent with the pulsation theory in its simplest form.

4. Show that the distance of a Cepheid variable star can be determined when the period of its variability is known.

5. Contrast Cepheid and long-period variable stars with respect to the following features:

(a) Spectral class.
(b) Regularity of variation.
(c) Oscillation of spectral lines.
(d) Range of light variation.

6. Account for the following successive features of novae and their spectra:

(a) Increase in brightness before explosion.
(b) Decrease in brightness after explosion.
(c) Bright bands in spectra having dark lines at their violet edges.
(d) Gradual fading of continuous spectrum.
(e) Appearance of bright lines characteristic of gaseous nebulae.
(f) Eventual reappearance of star's spectrum.
(g) Expanding shell around star.

7. What is the evidence (a) that a star may explode repeatedly? (b) that the sun is likely to explode?

8. Explain that the distance of a nova can be determined by observing the rate of its expanding envelope in successive photographs and from the spectrum.

9. Review the evidence that the Crab nebula is the product of a nova.

10. What is the outstanding difference between planetary nebulae and the envelopes expanding around recent novae?

The 72-inch Reflecting Telescope, Dominion Astrophysical Observatory, Victoria.

CHAPTER XIII

BINARY STARS

VISUAL BINARIES — SPECTROSCOPIC BINARIES — ECLIPSING BINARIES —
DIMENSIONS OF THE STARS

Binary stars are pairs of stars whose members are physically connected. The connection is frequently shown by the mutual revolutions of the members of the pairs. Often the periods are so long that the revolutions have not progressed far enough to be detected. In such cases the physical connection is established wherever the components have the same proper motion. *Visual binaries* are those that can be separated with the telescope. *Spectroscopic binaries* appear single through the telescope; their binary character is revealed by periodic oscillations of the lines in their spectra. Many spectroscopic binaries have orbits so nearly edgewise to the earth that the members of the revolving systems undergo mutual eclipses, and are accordingly *eclipsing binaries* as well.

Visual Binaries

13·1. Optical and Physical Doubles. The fact that certain stars which appear single to the unaided eye are resolved with the telescope into double stars was recorded casually by early observers, beginning with the discovery, in 1650, that Mizar in the handle of the Great Dipper is a double star. The members of such pairs were supposed to appear close together only by the accident of their having nearly the same direction, until William Herschel, in 1803, observed that the components of Castor are in mutual revolution. He then made the distinction between "optical double stars" and the binary systems which he called "real double stars," that is to say, two stars close together and united by the bond of their mutual gravitation.

Aitken's *New General Catalogue* lists 17,180 visual double stars within 120° of the north celestial pole. The ideal double star catalog, as Aitken remarks, would contain only physically connected pairs of stars. But sufficient time has not elapsed since the discoveries of many double stars to definitely establish such connection. It is therefore desirable to adopt a limiting separation beyond which the doubles are likely to be accidental. The adopted limit is 200″ for the first magnitude stars, 20″ for the sixth, and 3″ for the tenth.

13·2. Measurements of Visual Binaries

13·2. Measurements of Visual Binaries are made most effectively with the *position micrometer* (Fig. 13·2) attached at the eye end of the

FIG. 13·2. Micrometer of the 36-inch Refractor, Lick Observatory.

telescope. In this form of micrometer the thread is not only moved parallel to itself to measure angular distances, but it can also be rotated to measure directions in the field. The position of the *companion,* or fainter star, of the pair with respect to the *primary star* is obtained by measuring its position angle and distance.

The *position angle* is the angle at the primary star between the directions of the companion and the north celestial pole; it is measured counterclockwise. The *distance* is the angular separation of the two stars. The least separation that can be measured with the 36-inch telescope of Lick Observatory is 0″.1.

Photography can be successfully used in the measurement of double stars of sufficiently wide separation. As an example, Alden measured some three hundred pairs on plates taken with the Yale 26-inch photographic telescope at Johannesburg; the scale of the plates is: 1 mm = 18″.28. The separations of these doubles generally exceeded 2″. The orbits of the separate components, rather than the relative orbit, can be determined by referring them to other stars shown in the photographs.

13·3. The Apparent Ellipse and the True Orbit. The *true orbit* of the companion with respect to the primary star may lie in any plane at all. It follows from the law of gravitation that the true orbit must be a conic, presumably an ellipse, with the primary star at one focus, and that the companion must move in accordance with the law of equal

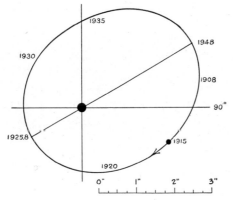

FIG. 13·3. Orbit of Krueger 60. The relative apparent orbit of the fainter star, as determined by Aitken.

areas (7·16). The observed orbit is the projection of the true orbit on the plane at right angles to the line of sight; it must also be an ellipse (the *apparent ellipse*), and the law of areas must be fulfilled by the apparent motion of the companion relative to the primary, but the primary will not be at the focus of the apparent ellipse.

When the measurement of a double star has been continued through a considerable part of a complete revolution, the observed positions of the companion are plotted on a convenient scale. After a number of trials the apparent ellipse is drawn that seems best to fit the plotted points, and from it the true orbit can be calculated by any one of several available methods.

The *elements of the relative orbit* resemble the elements of a planetary orbit (7·26). They are: *a,* the semi-major axis of the orbit, or the mean distance between the stars, expressed in seconds of arc; *T,* the time of *periastron* passage, that is, when the stars are nearest; *e,* the eccentricity; *i,* the inclination of the orbit plane to the plane through the primary star at right angles to the line of sight; Ω, the position angle of the node that lies between 0° and 180°; ω, the angle in the plane of the true orbit between that node and the periastron point, in the direction of motion. P denotes the period of revolution, in years.

When the parallax of the binary is known, the linear scale of the orbit can be found by the relation: a (in astronomical units) = a (in seconds of arc)/parallax. Everything is then known about the orbit, except which end is tipped toward us; it remains to be decided by the spectroscope whether the companion is approaching or receding from us when it passes the node.

13·4. Visual Binaries of Special Interest.

More than two thousand visual binaries have already shown evidence of orbital motion. Only five per cent of these have revolved far enough since their discoveries to

| 1908 | 1915 | 1920 |

FIG. 13·4. The Binary System Krueger 60. Between 1908 and 1920 the binary star, in the upper left corner, completed about a quarter of a revolution. See Fig. 13·3. (*Photographed at Yerkes Observatory*)

permit definitive determinations of their orbits. Some characteristics of a few systems of special interest are shown in Table 13·I. It will be noticed that these orbits are more eccentric than the planetary orbits, and that the combined masses are of the order of twice the sun's mass.

BD − 8°4352. This system has an unusually short period, 1.7 years, for a visual binary. The average separation of the two stars does not greatly exceed the earth's distance from the sun.

Delta Equulei. Also revolving in a very short period, the components of the system have a separation less than Jupiter's distance from the sun. The mass of each one is about equal to the sun's mass.

42 Comae. The true orbit is almost exactly edgewise to the sun, so that the apparent ellipse is practically a straight line.

Krueger 60. This system (Fig. 13·4) is remarkable for its small mass. Each star is only a fifth as massive as the sun.

Alpha Centauri. The nearest binary system, it was also one of the first to be discovered. The separation at periastron is a little more than Saturn's distance from the sun, while at apastron it is midway between the mean distances of Neptune and Pluto from the sun. A faint star, sometimes known as "Proxima," belongs to the system, though it is two degrees away from the bright pair. It is actually ten thousand astronomical units from them, and must require a million years for a single revolution around them.

Castor. This double star was the first to be observed in revolution, though its period exceeds three centuries. The mean separation is twice the mean distance of Pluto from the sun.

TABLE 13·I.   RELATIVE ORBITS OF VISUAL BINARIES

Name	Visual Magnitudes		Period	Semi-Major Axis	Eccentricity	Direct Parallax	Combined Mass
			P	a	e	p	$m_1 + m_2$
			years				
BD −8° 4352	9.9	10.0	1.7	0″.18		0″.148	0.7
Delta Equulei	5.3	5.4	5.7	0 .27	0.39	.066	2.1
42 Comae	5.2	5.2	25.9	0 .66	.52	.058	2.2
Procyon	0.5	13.5	40.2	4 .26	.31	.295	1.9
Krueger 60	9.3	10.8	44.5	2 .36	.41	.257	0.4
Sirius	−1.6	8.4	49.9	7 .62	.59	.381	3.2
Alpha Centauri	0.3	1.7	80.1	17 .66	.52	.761	1.9
Castor	2.0	2.8	340	5 .84	.43	.074	4.2

13·5. Companions of Sirius and Procyon. The discoveries of the faint companions of Sirius and Procyon constitute the first chapter of what has been called "the astronomy of the invisible," namely, the detection of unseen celestial bodies by their gravitational effects on the motions of visible bodies. The discovery of Neptune (8·37) is another famous example. As in the case of Neptune, the companions of both Sirius and Procyon were subsequently observed with the telescope.

As early as 1834, Bessel at Königsberg noticed that Sirius did not have the uniform proper motion that characterizes stars in general, but was pursuing a wavy course. He later suspected a smaller fluctuation in the proper motion of Procyon. Presently he reached the conclusion that both stars are attended by unseen companions and that the mutual revolutions of the pairs cause the waves in the proper motions of the primary stars. Later, the orbits of both systems were calculated, though the companion stars had not yet been detected.

The companion of Sirius was first observed, in 1862, by Clark, a telescope maker who was testing the 18-inch refractor now at the Dearborn Observatory. Despite the brilliance of its primary, the companion is not difficult to see with a large telescope, except near the periastron. We shall refer to this star later as an example of stars having very great density. The companion of Procyon proved to be more elusive; it was finally seen at Lick Observatory, in 1896.

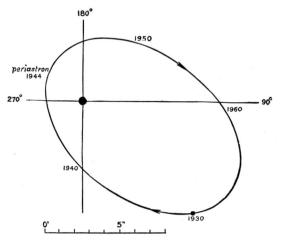

FIG. 13·5. Orbit of Sirius. The relative apparent orbit of the companion as determined by Aitken. The stars were closest in 1944.

13·6. Multiple Stars. The third member of the system of Alpha Centauri is not an uncommon occurrence. It is estimated that five per cent of the visual binaries are at least triple systems. Castor, a moderately separated double, has a faint attendant 73″ distant from the primary. The well-known quadruple system of Epsilon Lyrae consists of two pairs; each pair has a separation of about 3″, and the pairs are 207″ apart. Many visual systems prove to be more complex when they are examined with the spectroscope. Each of the three components of Castor, for example, is a close double, making six stars in all in the system.

Photographic observations of high accuracy give evidence of perturbations in the orbits of several visual binaries caused by unseen members of the systems. An example is the well-known double star 61 Cygni, whose visible members revolve in a period of 700 years. Strand at Sproul Observatory concludes that an invisible star revolves with one of the visible components in a period of about five years. According to his calculations this star has a remarkably small mass, only one sixteenth the mass of the sun, or sixteen times the mass of the planet Jupiter.

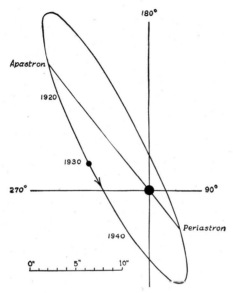

FIG. 13·6. Orbit of Alpha Centauri.

13·7. Masses of Visual Binaries. The mass of a celestial body can be determined whenever its gravitational effect on the motion of another body a known distance away is appreciable. This method fails for single stars which are too far removed from other stars to noticeably affect their motions. It also fails for the majority of visual binary stars which have thus far given no indication of mutual revolution. But the masses can be evaluated for those binary systems whose orbits have been calculated and whose distances are known. This constitutes an important product of the studies of visual binaries.

By the restatement of Kepler's harmonic law ($7·23$) the sum of the masses, m_1 and m_2, of the two components of a binary system, in terms of the sun's mass (the earth's mass is neglected), is given by the relation:

$$m_1 + m_2 = a^3/P^2 p^3,$$

where a is the semi-major axis of the relative orbit in seconds of arc, P is the period of revolution in sidereal years, and p is the parallax in seconds of arc.

The sum of the masses is all that can be determined from the relative orbit. When, however, the revolutions of the two stars have been observed with reference to neighboring stars, or with the spectroscope, the individual masses become known; for the ratio of the masses is in-

versely as the ratio of the distances of the two stars from the common
focus of their orbits.

As an example of the use of the above relation we calculate the sum
of the masses of Sirius and its companion from the data in Table 13·I.
$$m_1 + m_2 = (7.62)^3/(49.9)^2(.381)^3 = 443/138 = 3.2.$$
The combined mass of Sirius and its companion is 3.2 times the sun's
mass.

13·8. The Mass-Luminosity Relation. An important result of the
studies of binary stars is the discovery of a simple relation between their
masses and luminosities. The more massive the star, the greater is its

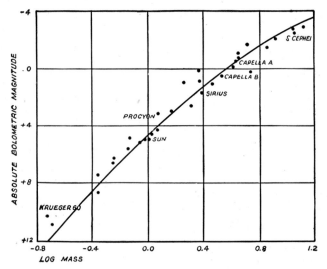

FIG. 13·8. Mass-Luminosity Relation. The dots show how the observed magnitudes of stars are related to the logarithms of their masses.

luminosity. Eddington at the University of Cambridge, in 1924, called
attention to this relation, not only as shown by the observed data but
also as required by a particular model of a star which he employed in a
theoretical study of stellar interiors. While it was later found that a
variety of models can produce about the same theoretical curve, the relation remains as a valuable means of determining the masses of single
stars whose luminosities are known.

In Fig. 13·8, as originally shown by Eddington, the logarithms of
the masses of a number of stars (the sun's mass is taken as unity) are
plotted against their absolute bolometric magnitudes. Bolometric mag-

nitude refers to the radiation in all wave lengths; it can easily be derived from the visual magnitude for a star of known spectral class. Thus, with some exceptions, the mass of any single star can be read from the curve if its absolute magnitude is known. Certain stars, including the companion of Sirius, do not conform to the relation; they are much fainter than their masses would indicate.

13·9. Dynamical Parallaxes. The formula of Section 13·7, in the form

$$p^3 = a^3/P^2(m_1 + m_2)$$

may be employed to determine the parallaxes of binary systems when the combined masses of the components are already known. An approximate value of the sum of the masses can be used, because the parallax is inversely proportional to the cube root of this sum. Parallaxes of systems so determined are known as *dynamical parallaxes*.

Since the combined mass of a binary system is usually not far from twice the sun's mass, a preliminary value of the parallax is found by putting $m_1 + m_2 = 2$ in the preceding formula, when a and P are known. Given the apparent magnitudes of the two stars and their approximate distance from us, their absolute magnitudes are calculated by the usual rule (11·27), and more nearly correct masses are obtained from the curve of Fig. 13·8. The required parallax of the system is finally found by substituting the new masses in the formula.

By a procedure which depends primarily on the mass-luminosity relation, Russell and Miss Moore at Princeton calculated the dynamical parallaxes of more than two thousand visual binary systems. Such parallaxes for systems having well-determined orbits have statistical probable errors of five per cent.

SPECTROSCOPIC BINARIES

Binary systems whose components are so close together that they appear as single stars through the telescope are discovered and studied with the aid of the spectroscope. Unless their orbits are at right angles to the line of sight, the revolving stars alternately approach and recede from the earth. In accordance with the Doppler principle (4·24), the lines in their spectra are displaced to the violet in the first case and to the red in the second, so that they oscillate in the periods of the revolutions. Spectroscopic binaries are not to be confused with pulsating stars (12·4) whose spectrum lines also oscillate.

13·10. Oscillations of Spectrum Lines. It is of interest that the brighter component of Mizar, the first visual double star discovered, was the first spectroscopic binary to become known, in 1889. The lines in the spectrum of this star were found to be double on some objective prism photographs at Harvard Observatory, while they were single on others. Mizar is an example of spectroscopic systems whose components are about equally bright and are of the same spectral class. The spectrum shows two sets of lines whose oscillations are opposite in phase. When one star is approaching us in its revolution, the other star is re-

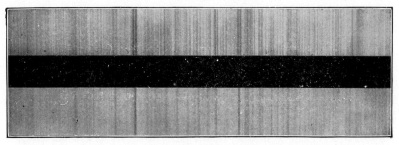

FIG. 13·10. Spectrum of Mizar (Zeta Ursae Majoris). The first known spectroscopic binary. The lines of the two components are separated in the upper spectrogram, and superposed in the lower one. (*Photographed at Yerkes Observatory*)

ceding from us. The lines in the spectrum of the first star are displaced to the violet, while those of the second star are displaced to the red, and the lines appear double. A quarter of the period later, when both stars are moving across the line of sight, the lines of the two spectra have no Doppler displacement and are accordingly superposed.

If one member of the pair is as much as a magnitude brighter than the other, which is true of most of these binaries, only the spectrum of the brighter star is likely to be visible. The periodic oscillation of the lines in the spectrum shows that the star is a binary. Examples of spectroscopic binaries among the bright stars are Capella, Spica, Castor, and Algol.

The *Fourth Catalogue of Spectroscopic Binaries* of the Lick Observatory (1936) lists 1420 known spectroscopic binaries and gives elements of the orbits of 375 systems.

13·11. The Velocity Curve of one of the stars of a spectroscopic binary shows how the velocity of the star in the line of sight varies during a complete revolution. It is a smooth curve drawn to represent the radial

velocities of the star at different phases of its revolution; the radial
velocities are calculated from the displacements of the spectrum lines

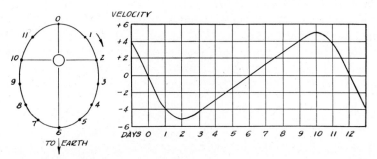

FIG. 13·11. Relation Between the Orbit and Velocity of a Spectroscopic
Binary. The period of this binary is 12 days. Only one spectrum appears.
From 0 to 6 days the star is approaching the earth; from 6 to 12 days it is
receding. The greatest radial velocities occur when the star is crossing the
"plane of the sky," at 2 and 10 days.

measured on photographs taken at the different phases. If the orbit is
circular, the radial velocities are represented by a sine curve. If the

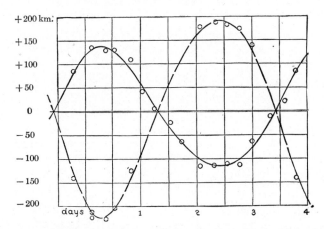

FIG. 13·11A. Velocity Curves of Spica (Alpha Virginis). Both spectra are
visible, but the lines of the fainter, less massive star are clearly seen only near
times of maximum separation of the lines. (From *Publications of the Allegheny
Observatory*)

orbit is elliptical, the form of the velocity curve depends on the eccentricity of the ellipse and also on its orientation when projected on a
plane passing through the line of sight. Fig. 13·11 shows the form of

the velocity curve for an ellipse of moderate eccentricity, whose projected major axis is directed toward the earth and whose apastron point is nearest the earth.

Conversely, when the velocity curve is known, the orbit of the star can be calculated by an appropriate method. Whenever the lines of both spectra are visible in the photographs, it is possible to determine the velocity curves (Fig. 13·11A) and orbits of both components of the binary.

13·12. Orbits of Spectroscopic Binaries. It is the projection of the orbit on a plane through the line of sight that is calculated from the velocity curve. The inclination, i, of the plane of the orbit to the plane of the sky cannot be determined from the spectroscopic observations. Thus the size of the orbit remains unknown; the semi-major axis, a, appears in combination with the inclination in the quantity $a \sin i$. But the eccentricity of the orbit, the position and time of periastron passage, and, of course, the period of revolution are uniquely determined. The eccentricities average 0.17; the periods range from a few hours to several months.

Likewise the sum of the masses of the two stars of a spectroscopic binary is not obtained unless the inclination of the orbit is known independently. Where both spectra are visible, the value of $(m_1 + m_2)$ $\sin^3 i$ can be derived by the formula of Section 13·7. In such cases the ratio of the masses m_1/m_2 is easily evaluated from the velocity curves; it is inversely as the ratio of the velocity ranges of the two stars.

As an example, the velocity range of the brighter component of Spica (Fig. 13·11A) is 252 km/sec, while that of the fainter star is 416 km/sec. The ratio of the masses, m_1/m_2 is 416/252, or 1.6. The calculation of the projected orbits gives $(m_1 + m_2) \sin^3 i = 15.4$ times the sun's mass. If the inclination of the orbit to the plane of the sky is not far from 90°, $m_1 + m_2 = 15.4$; and the mass of the brighter component of Spica is 9.6 times the sun's mass, while the fainter star is 5.8 times as massive as the sun.

13·13. Features of Binary Systems. The attempts to find characteristics of visual and spectroscopic binaries which can provide clues to the origin and development of these systems have not been very successful thus far. We notice three features which may have significance.

(1) *The great number of systems.* It is estimated that a quarter of all the stars are double. The process that develops binary stars is not an unusual one.

(2) *The variety in the separations.* There is a gradation from rapidly revolving pairs almost in contact to doubles whose components are

so widely separated that the only observed connection between them is their common motion through space.

(3) *The correlation between length of period and eccentricity of orbit.* There is a fairly steady increase in the average eccentricity from the nearly circular orbits of binaries having periods up to a few days to eccentricities averaging around 0.7 for pairs whose periods of revolution run into thousands of years.

One theory of the origin of double stars which received considerable attention resembles a theory of the earth-moon system (5·26). It is the account of a single star which became unstable because of the excessive rate of its rotation, and separated to form a spectroscopic binary. The amount of the separation gradually increased owing to tidal friction, until the pair became a visual binary. This theory is not now viewed with much favor.

Eclipsing Binaries

A spectroscopic binary is also an eclipsing binary when its orbit is so nearly edgewise to the earth that the revolving stars undergo mutual eclipses. Since the system appears as a single star through the telescope, what is observed is that the light of the star becomes fainter at regular intervals. Eclipsing binaries are variable stars only because the planes of their orbits happen to pass nearly through the earth's position. To an observer in another part of the stellar system their light would be constant, and another group of spectroscopic binaries, to us invariable in brightness, would exhibit eclipse phenomena.

13·14. Algol, the "Demon Star," is the most familiar of the eclipsing binaries and was the first of this type to become known. The discovery that its light diminishes at intervals of about 2 days and 21 hours was made as early as 1783, and the theory was then proposed that the bright star is partially eclipsed by a faint companion revolving around it in this period. The correctness of this view was established in 1889, when a spectroscopic study of Algol showed that it is a binary and that the radial velocity of the bright star changes from recession to approach at the time of the eclipse, as the theory required.

The brighter component of Algol has three times the diameter of the sun. The companion is the fainter by three magnitudes, but its diameter is twenty per cent greater than that of the brighter star. The centers of the two stars are 13 million miles apart, or slightly more than a third the average distance of Mercury from the sun. Their orbits are

inclined eight degrees from the edgewise position relative to the earth.
Once in each revolution the companion passes between us and the bright
star (Fig. 13·14), partially eclipsing it for nearly ten hours and reducing the light of the system at the middle of the eclipse to a third its
normal brightness.

More than a thousand eclipsing binaries are known. Their periods
range from 4 hours 43 minutes in the case of UX Ursae Majoris to 27

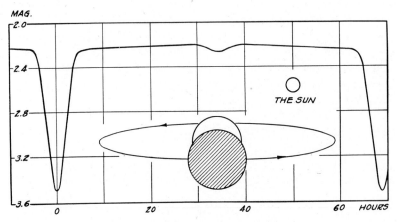

FIG. 13·14. Light Curve and System of Algol. The size of the sun is shown
on the same scale.

years for Epsilon Aurigae, and are most frequent around two or three
days.

13·15. Bright Eclipsing Binaries. The variability in brightness of six
eclipsing binaries, including Algol, can be easily observed without the
telescope. The names of these stars, the intervals between the times
of their primary minima, and their visual magnitudes at maximum and
minimum brightness are as follows:

| | | Magnitude | |
Star	Period	Max.	Min.
β Persei	$2^d\ 20^h\ 49^m$	2.2	3.5
λ Tauri	3 22 52	3.8	4.2
V Puppis	1 10 55	4.1	4.8
δ Librae	2 7 51	4.8	5.9
u Herculis	2 1 14	4.8	5.3
β Lyrae	12 21 48	3.4	4.3

If any one of these stars is compared frequently with a neighboring
star, it will eventually appear fainter than usual. The times of sub-

sequent minima can then be predicted. Several other eclipsing binaries are barely visible to the unaided eye. The majority are telescopic objects.

The bright stars Delta Orionis, Beta Aurigae, and Alpha Coronae Borealis are eclipsing binaries, but the eclipses are so slight that the diminution in light can be observed only with apparatus of high precision. Stebbins, while at the University of Illinois, discovered their variability by use of the photoelectric cell.

The light of the third magnitude star Epsilon Aurigae diminishes more than half a magnitude once in 27 years and the eclipse lasts about two years. The light remains nearly constant at minimum for nearly a year, which might mean that the bright star is totally eclipsed, except that its spectrum remains visible all that time. The explanation is that the bright star at minimum is behind a semi-transparent cloudy layer surrounding the companion star.

13·16. The Light Variations. The light curve of an eclipsing binary shows how the magnitude of the system varies through a complete revolution. Twice during a revolution the curve drops to a minimum and

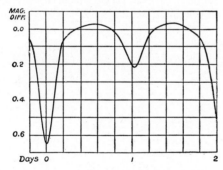

FIG. 13·16. Light Curve of u Herculis. Determined at the Lick Observatory from photoelectric observations.

rises again. The deeper minimum, or *primary minimum,* occurs when the star having the greater surface brightness is being eclipsed; the shallower one, or *secondary minimum,* occurs when that star is eclipsing its companion.

Even when the eclipses are not occurring, the light continues to vary appreciably in many of these systems chiefly because these stars are ellipsoids. They are elongated by tidal action, each of the pair in the direction of the other, a relation which is maintained by the equality of their periods of rotation and revolution. During the eclipses the stars are seen end-on; halfway between the eclipses they are presented broadside, so that their disks are larger and the stars are accordingly brighter. Thus the light of the system rises to maxima midway between the minima (Fig. 13·16). This effect of the ellipticity of the disks is likely to be conspicuous when the two stars are almost in contact.

In addition, the hemispheres of the two stars that are turned inward are brighter than those turned outward. The difference is greater for the two hemispheres of the less luminous star, so that the light curve is higher near the secondary minimum (Fig. 13·14). In the more widely

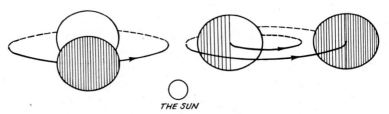

THE SUN

FIG. 13·16A. The Eclipsing Binary u Herculis at Primary Minimum and Greatest Elongation. The eclipses are partial. The stars are markedly elongated, one toward the other, by the tidal effect. They are flattened at the poles by their rotations. The hemispheres turned inward are somewhat the brighter. The size of the sun on this scale is shown.

separated eclipsing binaries both ellipticity and radiation effects are so slight that their light curves outside the eclipses are practically horizontal (Fig. 13·17).

13·17. Light Variations During Eclipses. The eclipses of binary stars, like eclipses of the sun, may be total, annular, or partial (6·5). During the total eclipse the light remains constant at the minimum (Fig. 13·17), and the duration of this phase is longest as compared with the whole eclipse when the orbit is edgewise to us and when the two stars differ greatly in size. That the light does not vanish during totality (the greatest decrease is four magnitudes) shows that the larger star is not dark, although it is usually the fainter of the two. The eclipse is annular at the opposite conjunction, when the smaller star is in front; here the light may not be quite constant because the eclipsed star, as in the case of the sun, is likely to be somewhat less bright near the edge than at its center.

When the eclipse is partial, or total, or annular only for an instant, the curve drops to its lowest point and at once begins to rise. In general, the depths and shapes of the light curve during eclipses depend on the relative size and brightness of the two stars, and on the inclination of the orbit. The secondary minimum is scarcely discernible in some systems, while in others it equals the primary minimum in depth. The fraction of the period in which the eclipses are occurring depends on the ratio between the sum of the radii of the two stars and the radius of the

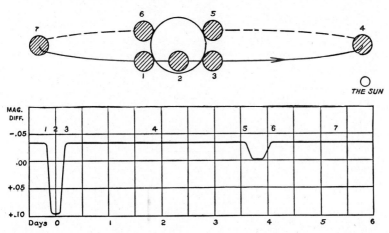

FIG. 13·17. Apparent Relative Orbit and Light Curve of the Eclipsing Binary 1 H. Cassiopeiae. The principal eclipse, of the bright star by its faint and smaller companion, is annular. The secondary eclipse, when the companion is behind the bright star, is total. Tidal and reflection effects are inconspicuous, because of the wider separation of the stars. (*Curve and orbit determined by Joel Stebbins from his observations with the photoelectric photometer at the University of Illinois*)

orbit. If the fraction is large, the stars are revolving almost in contact; examples are Beta Lyrae and the class of stars to which W Ursae Majoris belongs.

13·18. The Photometric Orbit. For any model of an eclipsing system, in which the inclination of the orbit is specified, it is possible to predict the form of the light curve. Conversely, when the light curve is determined by photometric observations, it is possible to calculate the elements of the orbit and the dimensions of the two stars in terms of the radius of the orbit.

One of the elements so determined is the inclination, i, of the orbit. If the spectroscopic orbit is also known, we can now return to it and supply the value of i in the expressions $a \sin i$, $m_1 \sin^3 i$, and $m_2 \sin^3 i$ (13·12), thus determining the radius of the orbit in miles, and the masses of the stars. Going back to the photometric orbit, in which the dimensions were derived in terms of the radius of the orbit, we have finally the absolute dimensions of the stars themselves. Thus the combination of the photometric and spectroscopic orbits permits the evaluation of the sizes and masses, and therefore the densities of the stars—data of great value in studies of the constitution of the stars.

13·19. Dimensions of Eclipsing Stars. In the study of eclipsing systems we have an example of the power of astronomical research. The greatest telescope shows any one of these systems only as a point of light fluctuating periodically in brightness. Yet the observations of this light with the photometer and spectroscope and the judicious use of analysis lead to fairly complete specifications of the remote binary system.

TABLE 13·II. DIMENSIONS OF ECLIPSING BINARIES (BRIGHTER STAR)

Name	Spec-trum	Period	Radius		Mass	Density
		days	$a = 1$	$\odot = 1$	$\odot = 1$	$\odot = 1$
HD 1337	O8	3.52	0.59	23.8	36.3	0.003
V Puppis	B1	1.45	0.42	7.5	19.2	0.04
u Herculis	B3	2.05	0.32	4.6	7.3	0.09
β Persei	B8	2.87	0.21	3.1	4.6	0.16
β Aurigae	Ao	3.96	0.16	2.8	2.5	0.11
U Pegasi	F3	0.38	0.40	0.6	0.2	0.88
W Ursae Majoris	Go	0.33	0.32	0.7	0.7	1.9
Castor C	M1	0.81	0.20	0.8	0.6	1.4

The dimensions of the brighter components of a few eclipsing binaries are given in Table 13·II. The stars are listed in order of advancing spectral class, or of increasing redness. In most eclipsing systems the stars are white (spectral classes B and A), but yellow and red stars are found as well. We notice in the Table the decrease in radius and mass and the increase in density with increasing redness of these stars.

13·20. Eclipsing Binaries Having Elliptic Orbits. Most of these stars have nearly circular orbits. In cases where the orbits have considerable eccentricity, additional effects are observed in the light curves, which follow from the law of equal areas (7·16); the stars revolve faster near periastron. Two effects are as follows:

(1) *The two eclipses are of unequal durations.* The eclipse that occurs nearer periastron is the shorter. The difference is greatest when the major axis of the orbit is directed toward the earth.

(2) *The intervals between the minima are unequal.* The interval including periastron passage is the shorter. The difference is greatest when the major axis of the orbit is perpendicular to the line of sight.

In some of these systems the major axis of the orbit rotates rapidly in the direction the stars revolve, though in most systems the period of this rotation is hundreds of thousand years. The advance of periastron is caused by the oblateness of the stars. Thus in the period of rotation of the axis the light curve exhibits a cycle of the two effects that have

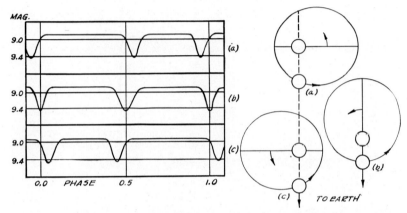

FIG. 13·20. Light Curves and Orbit of the Eclipsing Binary GL Carinae. The major axis of the orbit rotates in a period of 25 years. Notice the differences in the light curves corresponding to the three different directions of the major axis. (*From data determined by Henrietta Swope, Harvard Observatory*)

been described. As an example, the major axis of the orbit of GL Carinae rotates in a period of 25 years. The primary and secondary minima have the same depth in the light curve of this system (Fig. 13·20).

Before concluding the account of eclipsing binaries we consider the evidence of the rotations of stars, which has come partly from the studies of eclipsing stars.

13·21. Rotations of the Stars. The spectroscopic method of studying the sun's rotation, by comparing the Doppler shifts of the lines at opposite edges of the disk, is not applicable ordinarily to the stars which show no disks. It can, however, be applied to some eclipsing binary stars. Preceding the middle of the eclipse of a bright star by a much fainter one, the light comes mostly from the limb of the bright star that is rotating away from us; afterwards the light comes from the approaching

limb. Thus during the beginning of the eclipse the lines of the star's
spectrum are displaced farther toward the red, and during the ending
they are displaced farther toward the violet end of the spectrum than
can be ascribed to the revolution of the star. This effect has been
clearly observed in the velocity curves of a number of eclipsing stars.

Struve and Elvey at Yerkes Observatory have determined the rotations of single stars from the contours of the lines in their spectra. The

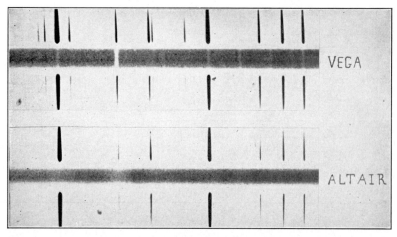

FIG. 13·21. Spectra of Vega and Altair. The widening of the lines in the
spectrum of Altair is ascribed to the rapid rotation of this star. (*Photographed
at Yerkes Observatory*)

effect of the rotation is to widen the lines, unless the axis of the star
is directed toward us. The blue stars which they have studied have
equatorial velocities up to 300 km/sec, and the suggestion is made that
the most swiftly spinning ones may not be far from the stage where
instability sets in. For the blue stars, exceedingly rapid rotation is detected in single stars about as frequently as in members of binary systems. The rotation period of the single star Altair (Fig. 13·21) is
given as around six hours. Among the cooler stars, however, rapid rotation occurs only in close binary systems.

DIMENSIONS OF THE STARS

When the angular diameter and distance of a celestial body are
known, the linear diameter is easily derived. Thus we know the diameters of the sun, moon, and certain planets. But even the largest and

nearest of the stars are so remote that their angular diameters are comparable with that of a golf ball at the distance of a hundred miles. No
telescope can show such an object as a disk. Nevertheless the sizes of
many stars are now available as the result of calculation from other data.
Given the diameters and the masses, the mean densities become known.
The following Sections summarize these matters and mention a class of
stars of remarkably high density.

13·22. Diameters of the Stars. We have seen (13·19) that the diameters of stars of certain eclipsing systems can be evaluated. Another
method of determining the diameters is available for stars whose absolute magnitudes and spectral classes are known. The total luminosity
of a star is found from its absolute magnitude. The brightness of unit
area, say of a square mile of the star's surface, can be derived from the
surface temperature which becomes known when the spectral class is
observed. Dividing the total luminosity by that of a square mile, we
obtain the area of the surface, and thus the diameter of the star.

TABLE 13·III. CALCULATED TEMPERATURES AND DIAMETERS OF
REPRESENTATIVE STARS

Star	Spectrum	Temperature	Diameter (Sun=1)	Mass (Sun = 1)	Density (Sun = 1)
Giants					
Antares	M1	3,000° K	390	10	0.0000002
Aldebaran	K5	3,200	72	4	0.00001
Arcturus	K0	4,000	30	4	0.0001
Capella A	G0	5,300	16	4	0.001
Main Sequence					
β Centauri	B1	19,000	6	4	0.02
Vega	A0	10,600	2.6	3	0.2
Sirius A	A0	10,600	1.9	2.4	0.3
Altair	A5	8,200	1.6	2	0.5
Procyon	F3	6,300	2.3	1.1	0.1
α Centauri A	G0	5,750	1.3	1.1	0.5
The Sun	G0	5,750	1.0	1.0	1.0
70 Ophiuchi A	K0	4,900	1.0	0.9	0.9
61 Cygni A	K7	3,900	0.7	0.5	1.4
Krueger 60 A	M3	3,300	0.3	0.3	9
White Dwarfs					
Sirius B	F	7,500	0.034	0.96	25,000
o$_2$ Eridani B	A0	11,000	0.019	0.44	64,000

TABLE 13·IV. DIAMETERS OF RED GIANT STARS MEASURED WITH
THE INTERFEROMETER

Star	Spectrum	Angular Diameter	Parallax	Diameter Sun = 1
Mira Ceti	M7	0″.056	0″.012	500
Betelgeuse	M2	{ .054 / .034	.011	{ 530 / 360
Alpha Herculis	M8	.030	.008	400
Antares	M1	.035	.013	290
Beta Pegasi	M5	.021	.022	100
Aldebaran	K5	.020	.062	34
Arcturus	K0	.022	.098	24

By this procedure the diameters of representative stars in Table 13·III
were calculated.

Direct measurement of the angular diameters of certain stars has been
accomplished by use of a special type of interferometer. The application of this method is limited to a few stars whose angular diameters
are exceptionally great. The angular diameters of seven giant stars
listed in Table 13·IV were measured with the 20-foot interferometer
attached to the 100-inch telescope on Mount Wilson.

The giant stars have the greatest diameters, as Table 13·III shows.
First called "giants" because of their high luminosities, these stars have
proved to be giants indeed. The red giants are the largest. Antares is
an example; its diameter is 390 (Table 13·III) or 290 (Table 13·IV)
times the sun's diameter, or something like the diameter of the orbit
of Mars. It will be understood that these figures give the order of the
linear diameter. The specified value can be no more accurate, at least,
than the adopted value of the parallax, which in the case of Antares has
a probable error of 20 per cent.

The stars of the main sequence are generally comparable in size with
the sun; the blue stars are somewhat larger, and the red ones smaller.
The great decrease in luminosity down this sequence must be ascribed
mostly to diminishing surface temperature. The smallest known stars
are the white dwarfs, such as the faint companion of Sirius; these stars
are comparable with the planets in size.

13·23. Masses of the Stars. The gravitational effect of a single star
on its neighbors is too small to give any information about its mass. It

is only when the star is a member of a binary system that the mass can be evaluated on this basis, and then only in favorable circumstances (13·7, 13·12, 13·18). In the case of visual binaries, their orbits must be determined and their distances known. Precise determinations of the masses of spectroscopic binaries require that both spectra appear, and in addition that the two stars mutually eclipse or else be separated with the telescope. Fortunately the masses of stars, whether double or single, can be derived with considerable confidence from a simple relation (13·8) which they bear to their absolute magnitudes. The masses of some representative stars are listed in Table 13·III.

The great majority of the stars for which the information is available have masses between one fifth and five times the sun's mass. Exceptionally large masses are found for the highly luminous class O stars; some of these are of the order of a hundred times the sun's mass.

13·24. Densities of the Stars.

The mean density of a star is found by dividing the mass by the volume which is derived from the linear diameter. The density is not the same throughout the star; it increases toward the center where the density is probably twenty or more times the average value.

There is great diversity in the densities of the stars, as Table 13·III shows. The lowest values are found for the red giants. Antares, for example, has a mean density two ten-millionths of the density of the sun, or *1/2000 of the density of ordinary air*. If Einstein's theory of gravitation is correct, a star as large as Antares could not have a density as great as the sun's and at the same time be visible; for gravity at its surface would be so powerful that the light could not escape.

From these amazingly low values there is a steady upward gradation along the giant sequence, from red to blue, until the densities merge into those of the main-sequence stars. Along the latter sequence, from blue to red, the density increases slowly. In the white dwarfs it has risen abruptly to *tens and perhaps even hundreds of thousands times the density of water*.

13·25. The Companion of Sirius.

By the relation which connects the mass and brightness of an ordinary star, the faint companion of Sirius (13·5) should be as luminous as the sun. This star nearly equals the sun in mass. Yet it has only 1/360 the sun's luminosity; its absolute visual magnitude is 11.3. The companion of Sirius is no ordinary star. It has the mass of a star, but a size more appropriate for a planet. The diameter, calculated from the effective temperature and absolute magnitude, is 30,000 miles—only three or four times the earth's diameter. The mean density is therefore enormous; it is of the order of 30,000 times the density of water.

Such high compression of matter would have been considered impossible a few years ago; and even now it might be regarded with some suspicion if it were not confirmed by an independent observational test. Adams at Mount Wilson Observatory observed a considerable shift of the lines in the spectrum of this star toward the red end of the spectrum, in practical agreement with the displacement predicted by the theory of relativity (7·28) for a star of this order of density.

This result is considered both a successful test of the general theory of relativity and a support of the opinion that the highly ionized material in the stars is capable of enormous compression.

The amount of the displacement of the lines in the spectrum of a star toward the red, as predicted by the theory of relativity, is directly proportional to the mass of the star and inversely proportional to its radius. In the case of the sun the predicted shift is equivalent to the Doppler effect for a radial velocity of 0.6 km/sec, which is small enough to be confused with displacements of the lines from other causes. The predicted displacement in the spectrum of the companion of Sirius is more than thirty times the shift in the solar spectrum; it is equivalent to the Doppler effect for a radial velocity of 20 km/sec.

After allowance for true Doppler effects due to the orbital motion of the companion and to the motion of the binary system as a whole, derived from observations of the spectrum of Sirius itself, Adams found the shift toward the red in the spectrum of the companion equivalent to the Doppler shift for a velocity of 19 km/sec.

13·26. Dwarf Stars. The companion of Sirius is the apparently brightest known example of the class of dwarf stars which do not conform to the mass-luminosity relation and which stand apart from the other stars in the spectrum-luminosity diagram (11·29), far below the main sequence. Their spectra also differ from the spectra of ordinary stars. About forty have been recognized. The fact that few are known does not mean that they are really scarce. Owing to their feeble light it is difficult to identify any except the nearest ones.

Recalling a current view that the source of a star's radiation is the energy released in its interior by the combination of hydrogen nuclei to form helium, we could imagine that the supply of hydrogen in the dwarf stars is nearly exhausted. The energy released is no longer sufficient to maintain the gas and radiation pressure required to keep these stars inflated. Gravity now has the upper hand, jamming together the fragments of atoms in very high concentration.

REVIEW QUESTIONS

1. How is it possible to decide whether two stars which appear very close together are a physically connected or accidental double if their revolution has not been observed?

2. Describe the discovery of the companion of Sirius before it was seen.

3. What must be known about a visual binary system in order to evaluate (a) the sum of the masses of the two stars? (b) the mass of each star?

4. Describe the mass-luminosity relation. Show that the mass of a single star can be determined by this relation.

5. Explain why the lines in the spectrum of Mizar appear double at times and single at other times.

6. If the spectrum of a star contains one set of lines, how could you determine whether it is a single star or a binary having one component much fainter than the other?

7. Explain that a very close binary cannot be detected if its orbit is presented flatwise to us.

8. Algol was definitely proved to be an eclipsing binary when observations of its spectrum showed that the radial velocity of the bright star changes from recession to approach at the time of minimum brightness. Explain.

9. Account for the following features of the light curves of certain eclipsing binaries:

(a) Brightness is constant for a time at minimum.
(b) Brightness immediately increases at end of decline.
(c) Eclipses occur during most of the period of the variation.
(d) Light continues to vary outside the eclipses.
(e) Secondary minimum is not halfway between the primary minima.

10. Repeated observations of some eclipsing binaries whose orbits have considerable eccentricity show that the major axes of the orbits are rotating. Explain.

11. What is the evidence that stars rotate on their axes?

12. Explain that the size of a star can be determined when its absolute brightness and temperature are known. Show that giant stars must be larger than main-sequence stars of the same spectral class.

13. How do the stars compare with the sun as to size, mass, and density?

14. In what respects do dwarf stars differ from ordinary stars?

PROBLEMS

1. Employing data from Table 13·I calculate (13·7) the combined mass of the binary star Alpha Centauri.

Answer: $m_1 + m_2 = (17.66)^3/(80.1)^2(0.761)^3 = 1.9$ times the sun's mass.

2. Employing data from Table 13·I calculate (13·9) the parallax of Procyon.

Answer: $p^3 = (4.26)^3/(40.2)^2(1.9) = 0.0252$; $p = 0''.293$.

3. The angular diameter of Antares is $0''.035$ and the parallax is $0''.013$. Calculate the linear diameter of this star.

Answer: Diameter $= 0''.035/0''.013 \times 9.29 \times 10^7$ miles $= 250$ million miles, or 290 times the sun's diameter.

4. Assuming that the diameter of the companion of Sirius is 1/30 of the sun's diameter, and that its mass is 0.8 the sun's mass, calculate its mean density (the sun's mean density is 1.4 times the density of water).

Answer: The density is $0.8 \times 30^3 \times 1.4 = 30,000$ times the density of water.

Yerkes Observatory, Williams Bay, Wisconsin.

CHAPTER XIV

STELLAR ATMOSPHERES AND INTERIORS

ATOMIC STRUCTURE AND RADIATION — STELLAR ATMOSPHERES — STARS WITH EXTENDED ATMOSPHERES — THE INTERIORS OF THE STARS

Like the sun, the stars are globular masses of intensely hot gas. Although they are of very great size, their vast distances prevent us from seeing them as disks even with the largest telescopes. The radiations which come to us from the stars emerge from their photospheres and filter through their atmospheres, though in some instances the atmospheres themselves are extended enough to produce their luminous impressions in the spectra. The purpose of this Chapter is to present the evidence the starlight conveys concerning the exteriors of the stars and to consider the problem of what the interiors may be like in order to produce the exterior phenomena. We notice first of all the relations between the atoms of these gases and the radiations they absorb and emit.

ATOMIC STRUCTURE AND RADIATION

14·1. Constituents of the Atom. The *atom* is the smallest particle into which matter can be divided by chemical processes. In the current understanding, it has three constituents: electrons, protons, and neutrons. The *electron* is the lightest unit and it carries unit negative charge of electricity. The *proton* is 1840 times as massive as the electron and carries unit positive charge. The *neutron* has about the same mass as the proton and is electrically neutral. The *nucleus* of the atom is a compact group of protons and neutrons. It is surrounded by electrons whose effective distances from the nucleus are thousands of times as great as the diameter of the nucleus itself.

The behavior of the atom is quite successfully represented by the equations of wave mechanics. In these the electron is not considered as a particle at a particular point in the atom, but has its mass and charge distributed symmetrically around the nucleus. While the procedure is mathematically straightforward, that sort of atom is somewhat difficult to visualize. In the description of the atom and its radiation it is proper to employ an earlier conventional model proposed by the Danish physicist Bohr, in which the electron is considered as a particle revolving around the nucleus. As an example we consider the atom of hydrogen, the simplest and also the most abundant.

14·2. Model of the Hydrogen Atom. The hydrogen atom consists of one electron and one proton. In the Bohr model the electron revolves

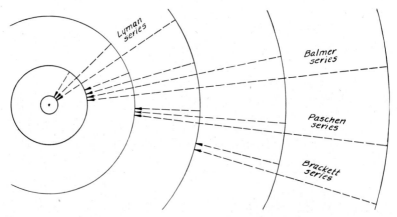

Fig. 14·2. Conventional Representation of the Hydrogen Atom, showing possible orbits of the electron around the nucleus.

around the proton, analogous to a planet revolving around the sun. The force which holds the electron in its orbit, however, is that of the attraction between the unlike electric charges which, like the gravitational force, is inversely proportional to the square of the distance between them. Moreover, the electron may be found at different times in a variety of possible orbits. The mean distances of these orbits from the nucleus are proportional to the numbers 1, 4, 9, 16, . . . , the squares of the integers. The radius of the innermost orbit is half an angstrom, or a ten thousandth the wave length of green light. In the normal state of the atom the electron remains in the smallest orbit. If the atom acquires additional energy, as from radiation that strikes it, the electron is raised to a higher orbit. Almost immediately the electron drops to a lower orbit and the atom releases energy.

The relation between the gain or loss of energy by the atom in such a transition and the frequency of the radiation it absorbs or emits is

$E_1 - E_2 = h\nu$, where E_1 is the energy of the atom when the electron is in one orbit and E_2 the energy when it is in another; h is a constant and ν is the frequency of the radiation.   Thus the hydrogen atom absorbs particular frequencies of the light that strikes it (dark-line spectrum) and emits the same frequencies again (bright-line spectrum). The atoms of the other chemical elements differ in their nuclear charges and in the arrangements of their electron orbits, and therefore produce different patterns of spectral lines.

14·3. Series of Hydrogen Lines. A prominent feature of the spectra of white stars is the series of hydrogen lines.   Beginning with the Fraun-

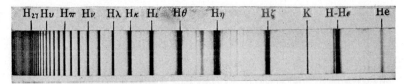

FIG. 14·3.   Hydrogen Lines in the Spectrum of Zeta Tauri.   Ultraviolet portion of the spectrum, showing the Balmer series from Hϵ to the limit of the series at the left.   (*Photographed by Curtiss, Observatory of the University of Michigan*)

hofer C line they appear along the spectrum at diminishing intervals, like a succession of telegraph poles receding into the distance, until they close up in the ultraviolet.   These lines of the *Balmer series* (Fig. 14·3) are designated in order: Hα, Hβ, Hγ, and so on.   More than thirty members of the series are identified in stellar spectra and also in the spectrum of the sun's chromosphere.

Balmer, in 1885, derived an empirical formula by which the wave length of any line in the series may be calculated.   In the more general form, which applies to other hydrogen series as well, it is

$$\nu = 109{,}678(1/m^2 - 1/n^2),$$

where $m = 2$ and n is any number greater than m.   The Balmer series is only one of the possibilities.   Three others have been observed: the *Lyman series* ($m = 1$) in the extreme ultraviolet, the *Paschen series* ($m = 3$) in the infrared, and the *Brackett series* ($m = 4$) in the far infrared.   The value of m signifies the number of the orbit (Fig. 14·2) from which the electrons are raised to produce the series of dark lines and to which they return to produce the series of bright lines.   A single hydrogen atom can have only one electron transition at any instant, but in a gas containing very many atoms all the possible transitions are likely to be in progress.

The hydrogen spectrum has been described because of the simplicity of the hydrogen atom. The lines of the other chemical elements are arranged in series as well.

14·4. The Chemical Elements. Table 14·I lists the names, symbols, atomic numbers, and atomic weights of 92 chemical elements, the only ones recognized up to very recent times. The *atomic number* is the number of positive electric charges in the nucleus, and in the normal atom the number of electrons around the nucleus. The *atomic weight* is the mass of the atom on a relative scale, based on the adopted atomic weight of 16 for oxygen. These are generally not integers because they are average weights. Most elements have two or more kinds of atoms, or *isotopes,* which differ in mass because their nuclei contain different numbers of neutrons. In chemical behavior and spectra the isotopes are practically the same.

As the number of electrons in the atom is greater, the spectrum may become much more complex. The complexity is lessened, however, by the grouping of electrons in closed *shells* where they are so firmly held that they are not easily displaced to higher levels. The shells are the same as the Bohr hydrogen orbits. Thus the two electrons of the helium atom constitute the lowest closed shell, and the eight additional electrons of neon (atomic number 10) close the second. Only the electrons in unfilled shells contribute ordinarily to the production of the spectral lines. The sodium atom (atomic number 11) has only one electron outside the closed shells. The spectrum of sodium is accordingly analogous to the hydrogen spectrum.

14·5. Neutral and Ionized Atoms. A *neutral atom* has its full quota of electrons which carry as many negative unit charges as there are positive unit charges in the nucleus, so that it is electrically neutral. The *ionized atom* has lost one or more electrons. It has absorbed energy enough to transfer these electrons successively beyond the outermost orbit. They have accordingly become *free electrons*—free to dart about independently until they are captured by ionized atoms which have positive charges and accordingly trap by their attractions stray electrons that come too close. A *singly ionized atom* has lost a single electron and has thereby acquired a single unit positive charge. A *doubly ionized atom* has lost two electrons and has an excess of two positive charges. With successive ionizations the amounts of energy required to remove the elec-

TABLE 14·I.   THE CHEMICAL ELEMENTS *

Element	Symbol	Atomic Number	Atomic Weight	Element	Symbol	Atomic Number	Atomic Weight
Hydrogen	H	1	1.008	Silver	Ag	47	107.88
Helium	He	2	4.004	Cadmium	Cd	48	112.41
Lithium	Li	3	6.94	Indium	In	49	114.76
Beryllium	Be	4	9.02	Tin	Sn	50	118.70
Boron	B	5	10.82	Antimony	Sb	51	121.76
Carbon	C	6	12.01	Tellurium	Te	52	127.61
Nitrogen	N	7	14.01	Iodine	I	53	126.92
Oxygen	O	8	16.00	Xenon	Xe	54	131.3
Fluorine	F	9	19.00	Caesium	Cs	55	132.91
Neon	Ne	10	20.18	Barium	Ba	56	137.36
Sodium	Na	11	23.00	Lanthanum	La	57	138.92
Magnesium	Mg	12	24.32	Cerium	Ce	58	140.13
Aluminum	Al	13	26.97	Praseodymium	Pr	59	140.92
Silicon	Si	14	28.06	Neodymium	Nd	60	144.27
Phosphorus	P	15	31.02	Illinium	Il	61	
Sulphur	S	16	32.06	Samarium	Sm	62	150.43
Chlorine	Cl	17	35.46	Europium	Eu	63	152.0
Argon	A	18	39.94	Gadolinium	Gd	64	156.9
Potassium	K	19	39.10	Terbium	Tb	65	159.2
Calcium	Ca	20	40.08	Dysprosium	Dy	66	162.46
Scandium	Sc	21	45.10	Holmium	Ho	67	163.5
Titanium	Ti	22	47.90	Erbium	Er	68	167.64
Vanadium	V	23	50.95	Thulium	Tm	69	169.4
Chromium	Cr	24	52.01	Ytterbium	Yb	70	173.04
Manganese	Mn	25	54.93	Lutecium	Lu	71	175.0
Iron	Fe	26	55.84	Hafnium	Hf	72	178.6
Cobalt	Co	27	58.94	Tantalum	Ta	73	180.88
Nickel	Ni	28	58.69	Tungsten	W	74	184.0
Copper	Cu	29	63.57	Rhenium	Re	75	186.31
Zinc	Zn	30	65.38	Osmium	Os	76	191.5
Gallium	Ga	31	69.72	Iridium	Ir	77	193.1
Germanium	Ge	32	72.60	Platinum	Pt	78	195.23
Arsenic	As	33	74.91	Gold	Au	79	197.2
Selenium	Se	34	78.96	Mercury	Hg	80	200.61
Bromine	Br	35	79.92	Thallium	Tl	81	204.39
Krypton	Kr	36	83.7	Lead	Pb	82	207.2
Rubidium	Rb	37	85.48	Bismuth	Bi	83	209
Strontium	Sr	38	87.63	Polonium	Po	84	210
Yttrium	Y	39	88.92			85	
Zirconium	Zr	40	91.22	Radon	Rn	86	222
Columbium	Cb	41	92.91			87	
Molybdenum	Mo	42	96.0	Radium	Ra	88	226
Masurium	Ma	43	97.8	Actinium	Ac	89	227
Ruthenium	Ru	44	101.7	Thorium	Th	90	232.12
Rhodium	Rh	45	102.91	Protoactinium	Pa	91	234
Palladium	Pd	46	106.7	Uranium	U	92	238

* Neptunium, atomic number 93, and plutonium, number 94, were produced in the construction of the atomic bomb. Plutonium also occurs naturally. Two other elements, numbers 95 and 96, have been produced in the laboratory.

trons against the increasing attraction of the nucleus become greater. The extent of the ionization of an atom is indicated by adding a plus sign to the symbol of the element for each electron the atom has lost, or else by adding a Roman number (number I designates the neutral atom). Thus singly ionized sodium is written Na+ or NaII.

The removal of an electron leaves the superstructure of the atom similar to that of the element next lower in atomic number. The singly ionized helium atom, for example, has one electron, like the neutral hydrogen atom, and the general pattern of the lines of its spectrum is similar to that of the neutral hydrogen atom, except in their wave lengths. The gain or loss of energy of the atom accompanying an electron transition from one orbit to another depends not only on the radii of the two orbits but also on the square of the nuclear charge. Since the helium charge is twice that of hydrogen, the frequency of a helium line is four times the frequency (wave length one fourth) of the corresponding hydrogen line. The lines of ionized helium ordinarily observed correspond to the Brackett series of hydrogen in the far infrared.

14·6. Other Features of Atomic Spectra. We have seen that the transitions of the electrons between the orbits of the Bohr atom corre-

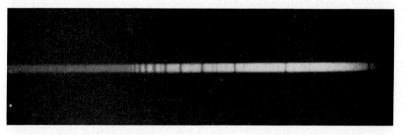

FIG. 14·6. The Hydrogen Continuum. Spectrum of π^1 Cygni showing the Balmer series of hydrogen and the continuum at the left. (*Photographed at Lick Observatory*)

spond to the absorption or emission of discrete amounts of energy by the atom. This results in dark or bright lines of definite wave lengths in the spectrum. But the removal of electrons from the atoms is effected by their absorption of any amount of energy in excess of that required to raise the electrons beyond the outermost orbit. Thus continuous absorption begins at the limit of each series of lines (Fig. 14·6). The excess energy gives various velocities to the liberated electrons. Similarly, the capture of electrons by ionized atoms produces a bright continuum.

A characteristic of the spectra that requires additional specifications in the atomic model is the splitting of the lines. This effect is conspicuous in the spectrum of sodium, as in the Fraunhofer D lines, but is observed with difficulty in the hydrogen lines. The explanation is that the electrons are spinning like tops, adding to the energy in any orbit if they spin in the direction they revolve, and subtracting from it if they spin in the opposite direction. A further division of the pairs of lines is ascribed to the rotation of the nucleus of the atom. Despite the close analogy between an electron revolving around the nucleus and a planet revolving around the sun, it is often the custom to dismiss the electron orbits entirely and to refer merely to energy levels or states of the atom.

14·7. Molecular Spectra. The complexity of the spectra increases greatly when the atoms are united in molecules. As the simplest case,

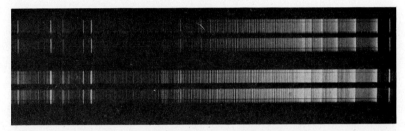

FIG. 14·7. Cyanogen Bands in the Spectrum of the Carbon Arc. (*Photographed at Mount Wilson Observatory*)

the diatomic molecule may be considered as like a dumbbell, having its two atoms connected by an elastic rod. The energy of the molecule at any instant depends on the speed of rotation of the dumbbell, the distance between the two atoms, and the positions of the spinning electrons in the orbit systems of the atoms. The result is that systems of bands replace the lines of the atomic spectra. Each *band* is composed of many fine lines whose distances apart diminish successively until they terminate sharply in the band head. These bands are conspicuous in the spectra of red stars.

We are now ready to consider how the knowledge of atomic and molecular spectra has been employed in the investigations of the atmospheres of the stars.

Stellar Atmospheres

14·8. Temperatures by the Radiation Laws. The *effective temperature* of a star is the temperature of its radiating surface calculated by the radiation laws (10·5) from the observed quantity and quality of the star's radiation. While these laws apply to a perfect radiator, the results may well represent the photospheric temperatures within ten per cent.

One procedure is similar to that employed in determining the sun's temperature from the solar constant. Another way is to find the closest match between the spectral energy curve of the star and the theoretical curves calculated for different temperatures, using the observed curve for a standard lamp as a control.

The *color temperature* is an abbreviated description of the result determined from the color index (11·25) of the star by the formula: $T = 7200/(I + 0.68)$, where T is the absolute temperature and I is

TABLE 14·II.   COLOR INDICES AND CALCULATED EFFECTIVE TEMPERATURES OF THE STARS

Spectrum	Color Index	Temperature	Spectrum	Main Sequence		Giants	
				Color Index	Temperature	Color Index	Temperature
O	....	50,000° K to 25,000	Go	0.57	5,750° K	0.67	5.300° K
			G5	0.65	5.400	0.92	4,500
			Ko	0.78	4,900	1.12	4,000
Bo	−0.33	21,000	K5	0.98	4,300	1.57	3,200
B5	−0.18	14,000	Mo	1.45	3,400	1.73	3,000
Ao	0.00	10,600	M2	....	2,870	....	2,810
A5	0.20	8,200	M8	....	.....	....	1,780
Fo	0.33	7,100					
F5	0.47	6,300					

the color index. The temperatures given in Table 14·II are calculated in this way, except that the temperatures of the reddest stars are deduced by a different formula from the heat index, that is to say, the visual magnitude minus the radiometric magnitude as determined with the thermocouple.

14·9. Temperatures of the Stars.   The surface temperatures of the stars range from 50,000° K, or more, down to somewhat less than 2000° which is about the melting point of platinum. Even the coolest star is still very hot by ordinary standards. As implied by the formula of the preceding Section, the color of the star depends on its temperature.

With diminishing temperature, according to Wien's law ($10 \cdot 5$), the most intense radiation is displaced toward the red end of the spectrum. Thus a hot star such as Spica (class B) is blue; it is brighter photographically than visually. A star of moderate temperature such as the sun (class G) is yellow. A cool star such as Betelgeuse (class M) is red; it is nearly two magnitudes fainter photographically than visually.

The temperatures diminish with advancing spectral class, from O to M. We shall see that the succession of patterns of spectral lines through the sequence is produced chiefly by change of temperature. But we notice in Table $14 \cdot II$ that the yellow and red stars of the main sequence have temperatures considerably higher than the giant stars of the same spectral class. Evidently the characteristics of the spectra are not controlled entirely by temperature.

14·10. Excitation and Ionization of Atoms. The sort of line formed in the spectrum when the atom absorbs energy depends on the state of the atom at that time. The *normal atom* is in its lowest energy state. When this atom absorbs energy, an electron is transferred to a higher level from which it immediately falls back with the emission of energy. *Ultimate lines* in the spectrum, either dark or bright, are produced by transition from or to the lowest level. In the *excited atom* the electron is already at a higher level. *Subordinate lines* are produced when the electron is raised from or falls back to that level. The ionized atom, as we have seen, has lost one or more electrons and is prepared to produce lines at other wave lengths. The states of the atoms in stellar atmospheres depend primarily on the extent of their excitation by energy from their heated environment—the process of *thermal excitation and ionization*.

As an analogy, consider the evaporation of a liquid in a closed container. The extent of the evaporation increases as the temperature is raised. It depends also on the boiling point of the liquid and the amount of vapor already above the liquid that can return to it to offset the evaporation. Similarly in a highly heated gas the fraction of ionized atoms increases with the temperature of the gas. At a particular temperature it is greater when the electrons are loosely bound to the atoms and when the density of the gas is low, so that there are fewer electrons in the neighborhood subject to capture by the atom.

14·11. The Ionization Potential is a number that is proportional to the energy required to remove an electron from a normal neutral or already ionized atom. Technically it is the energy acquired by an electron when it is accelerated across a potential drop of that number of volts. But we may here simply notice the number itself. An atom

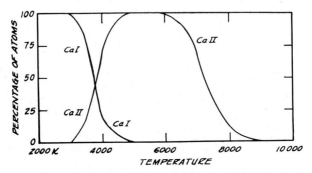

FIG. 14·11. Effect of Temperature on Calcium in Stellar Atmospheres. All calcium atoms are neutral (Ca I) at temperatures up to about 3000° K, where singly ionized atoms (Ca II) begin to appear. All these atoms are singly ionized from 5000° to 6000° where the second ionization begins.

having a low ionization potential may be ionized at a lower temperature than one having a high number.

Table 14·III gives the ionization potentials of some elements whose lines are prominent in stellar spectra. The column headed I refers to the neutral atom, II the singly ionized atom, and III the doubly ionized

TABLE 14·III.   IONIZATION POTENTIALS OF SELECTED ELEMENTS

Element	Symbol	Stage of Ionization		
		I	II	III
Helium	He	24.5	54.1	....
Nitrogen	N	14.5	29.4	47.2
Oxygen	O	13.6	34.9	54.6
Hydrogen	H	13.5	....	....
Carbon	C	11.2	24.3	47.6
Silicon	Si	8.1	16.3	33.3
Iron	Fe	7.8	16.2	30.5
Magnesium	Mg	7.6	15.0	79.7
Titanium	Ti	6.8	13.6	27.6
Calcium	Ca	6.1	11.8	51.0
Strontium	Sr	5.7	11.0	....
Sodium	Na	5.1	47.1	71.3

atom. Evidently sodium is ionized at relatively low temperature, while helium requires the highest temperature of all neutral atoms. Notice that the number is greater for successive stages of ionization. A similar tabulation could be shown of the excitation potentials which are proportional to the ionization potentials.

14·12. Effect of Temperature on Spectra. The theory of thermal ionization, originally proposed by the physicist Saha, of Calcutta, in

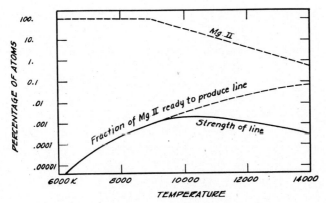

FIG. 14·12. Relative Strength of Mg II Absorption Line λ 4481 at Different Temperatures. The diagram shows the percentage of magnesium atoms in stellar atmospheres that are singly ionized (Mg II) at the different temperatures, the fractions of these that are in the proper state to produce this particular absorption line, and finally the relative strength of the line. The line is strongest at temperatures around 10,000°.

1920, has been amplified and given more precise form. For a gas at an assigned temperature and pressure, the formulae now permit the calculation of the fraction of the atoms in any stage of ionization, and of these the fractions at any level of excitation. It is accordingly possible to predict how the pattern of lines in the spectrum of a gas will change as the temperature and pressure are altered.

The strength of a line in the spectrum of a gas depends on the abundance of the gas—the number of atoms present—and on the fraction of these atoms which are in the correct state to produce the line in question. If, for example, it is a subordinate line of the singly ionized atom, the atom must have lost an electron, and have acquired sufficient additional energy to raise a second electron to the required level. When this fraction is calculated for various temperatures, and plotted against them, the curve through the plotted points shows how the strength of the line in the spectrum of the gas varies as the temperature of the gas is increased—at what temperatures the line makes its appearance, becomes strongest, and disappears (Fig. 14·12).

We have noticed (11·18) that stellar spectra fall into a single sequence, except for some branching at the red end. Along the sequence, from the red to the blue stars, the temperature increases and the patterns of lines in the spectra become less complex. It is in order to explain the spectral changes in terms of atomic processes.

14·13. Interpretation of the Spectral Sequence; the Coolest Stars. At the relatively low temperatures of the red stars the spectra show lines of neutral atoms and molecular bands. The lines are particularly those of elements such as sodium, calcium, and iron whose atoms are easily excited, as indicated by their low ionization potentials (Table 14·III). Hydrogen lines are present despite its higher ionization potential because hydrogen is a very abundant element.

The bands belong to neutral diatomic molecules, particularly carbon compounds, titanium oxide, and zirconium oxide. These provide the basis for classifying the red stars. The presence of carbon bands and the absence of titanium oxide bands characterize the spectra of classes R and N. Titanium oxide bands are prominent in the spectra of class M stars. Zirconium oxide is prominent and titanium oxide is usually absent in class S stars. Further studies are needed to show whether this division of the red stars into three groups is owing to chemical or physical differences.

14·14. Stars of Intermediate Temperature. At the higher temperatures of the yellow stars the compounds are being disrupted and bands are no longer prominent in the spectra. The titanium oxide bands have disappeared at class Ko. But the cyanogen (CN), the hydrocarbon (CH), the hydroxyl (OH), and other molecules are still present at the temperature of the sun.

The Fraunhofer H and K lines of singly ionized calcium dominate the spectra of the yellow stars. Here all calcium is singly ionized (Fig. 14·11) and the second ionization is about to begin. The hydrogen lines are becoming stronger as more of these atoms are excited. The complex patterns of neutral metals, such as iron and magnesium, are still conspicuous. These neutral lines are fading in the hotter class F stars. With the removal of an electron the atom produces a different set of lines, as we have seen; and the strong lines of many ionized metals lie in the far ultraviolet that is cut out by the earth's atmosphere. Thus with increasing temperature and degree of ionization in stellar atmospheres the spectra become less complex.

14·15. Spectra of the Hottest Stars. The hydrogen lines are most conspicuous in class Ao. They decline in still hotter stars as more of

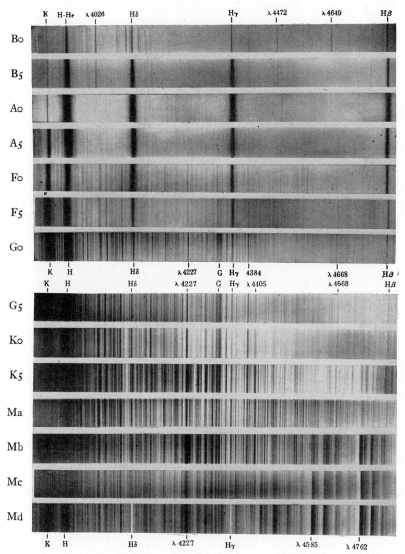

FIG. 14·15. Sequence of Stellar Spectra. Classes B to M. (*Photographed by W. C. Rufus, University of Michigan Observatory*)

their atoms become ionized. Having only one electron to lose, the singly ionized hydrogen atom cannot absorb light. But some of this abundant element remains neutral even in the hottest stars. Neutral helium, having the highest ionization potential, is latest to appear, in class B9. Its lines become strongest at B3 and quickly fade, until only its ionized lines appear in class O stars.

In addition to hydrogen and singly ionized helium the spectra of the very hot class O stars show lines of doubly ionized nitrogen and oxygen and triply ionized silicon—a simple pattern because most of the prominent lines are in the far ultraviolet. The hottest stars are of class O5. At the theoretical upper limit, class O0 (temperature 100,000° K or more), all lines should be removed from the observable region of the spectrum.

The changing patterns along the spectral sequence are therefore caused chiefly by changing temperature. At any point in the sequence the prominence of a particular series of lines is conditioned by the excitation and ionization potentials of the atoms that produce them, by the wave lengths of the lines, and by the abundance of the chemical element in stellar atmospheres. It remains to consider the effect of different densities of these atmospheres on the spectra they produce.

14·16. Spectra of Giant and Main-Sequence Stars. The effective temperatures of giant stars are lower than those of main-sequence stars of the same spectral class (Table 14·II). The reason is given by the ionization theory. According to this theory, the degree of ionization in stellar atmospheres increases with the temperature, and at any specified temperature is greater when the pressure of the gases is low. Giant stars have less dense although more extensive atmospheres than main-sequence stars. Accordingly, their atmospheres attain a particular degree of ionization, and the corresponding class of spectrum, at a lower temperature.

While the spectra of giant and main-sequence stars of the same class are the same in general appearance, certain lines are stronger for the giant stars, and some lines are weaker. The effects of diminished temperature and pressure do not entirely compensate. Elements whose atoms are easily ionized give relatively weaker lines in the spectra of giant stars; those having high ionization potentials give relatively stronger lines. The lines of the majority of the elements do not show this effect noticeably.

Giant stars are distinguished from main-sequence stars by the strengthening and weakening of certain lines in their spectra relative to the intensities of the other lines. They are distinguished by other spectral characteristics as well. Since the atmospheres of giant stars are more extensive and less dense, the lines in their spectra are generally stronger and somewhat narrower. All these effects are more pronounced in the supergiants. These and other characteristics of stellar spectra, which vary with the absolute magnitudes of the stars themselves, offer

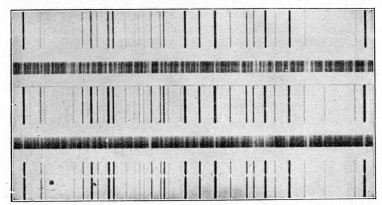

FIG. 14·16. Spectra of a Giant and a Main-Sequence Star of the Same Class. The spectrum of Polaris, a class F9 giant star, is above; the spectrum of Xi Ursae Majoris, a class F9 star of the main sequence, is below. Some lines are relatively stronger in the upper spectrum, while some are less conspicuous. The long vertical lines belong to the comparison spectrum. These are negatives. (*Photographed at the Dominion Astrophysical Observatory, Victoria*)

criteria for determining absolute magnitudes and therefore parallaxes of the stars.

14·17. Spectroscopic Parallaxes. The method of determining the parallaxes of stars from their spectra makes use of the lines that are conspicuously strengthened or weakened with increasing luminosities of the stars. From comparisons of the intensity of one of these sensitive lines with that of a neighboring line in spectra of stars of known luminosities, a graph can be drawn to show how the ratio varies with the absolute magnitude of the star. In Fig. 14·17 the intensity ratio of a sensitive strontium line to a neighboring iron line is so represented. We notice that the intensities of the two lines are equal for a star of absolute magnitude +3.4; the strontium line is four times as intense for magnitude +0.7, and eight times as intense for magnitude −2.0. Whenever such a relation has been determined for two lines, the absolute magnitude, M, becomes known for any star whose spectrum contains the lines. The star's parallax, p, can be found by the formula: $M = m + 5 + 5 \log p$ (11·27).

As an example, the strontium line λ4215 is twice as intense as the iron line λ4260 in the spectrum of a star whose apparent magnitude, m, is +7.0. Required the parallax of the star.

From Fig. 14·17 the star's absolute magnitude is +2.0. Thus log $p = (M - m - 5)/5 = (2.0 - 7.0 - 5.0)/5 = -2.0 = 8.0 - 10$. The star's parallax is 0″.01, so that its distance is 100 parsecs.

The parallaxes of several thousand stars have been determined in this way. The probable error of a spectroscopic parallax is about 15

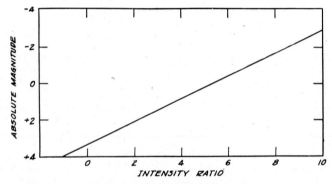

FIG. 14·17. Increasing Intensity of the Strontium Line λ4215 Relative to the Iron Line λ4260 in Stellar Spectra. When this ratio is measured in the spectrum of a star, the star's absolute magnitude becomes known.

per cent, while that of a trigonometric parallax is around 0″.008. The two methods are equally reliable for a parallax of 0″.05. The trigonometric parallax is likely to be the more dependable for stars nearer than 20 parsecs, and the spectroscopic parallax for stars more distant than this.

14·18. Relative Abundance of the Elements. There is a known relation between the intensity of a line in the spectrum of a star and the number of atoms whose absorptions have produced the line. This "number of absorbing atoms" is generally expressed as the number in a vertical column of the star's atmosphere above one square centimeter of its photosphere. Given the fraction of all the atoms of an element which are in the proper state to absorb this particular line, the total number of atoms of the element in this vertical column can be calculated. By this procedure the relative abundance of the chemical elements in the star's atmosphere become known.

TABLE 14·IV. MOST ABUNDANT ELEMENTS IN SUN'S ATMOSPHERE

Element	Per Cent Volume	Relative Mass	Element	Per Cent Volume	Relative Mass
Hydrogen	81.76	1200	Sulphur	0.003	1
Helium	18.17	1000	Carbon	0.003	0.5
Oxygen	0.03	10	Iron	0.0008	0.6
Magnesium	0.02	10	Sodium	0.0003	0.1
Nitrogen	0.01	2	Calcium	0.0003	0.2
Silicon	0.006	3	Nickel	0.0002	0.2

Table 14·IV shows the twelve elements which are most abundant in the sun's atmosphere, according to the analysis of Menzel and his associates at Harvard Observatory. It is to be noticed that 80 per cent of the atoms in the solar atmosphere are hydrogen, and that over 99.9 per cent are hydrogen and helium. There is considerable evidence that stellar atmospheres resemble the sun's atmosphere in the relative abundance of the elements. The elements most abundant in the sun and stars are also among the most abundant near the earth's surface, with the exceptions of hydrogen and helium which are the most likely to escape from the earth.

STARS WITH EXTENDED ATMOSPHERES

Stars whose spectra contain bright lines are generally hot stars of classes O and B. (The spectra of class M stars often contain bright lines.) They appear to have less stability than the normal stars we have been considering. Radiation pressure and the centrifugal effect of rapid rotation leave gravitation a precarious hold on their atmospheres which are accordingly much extended.

14·19. Wolf-Rayet Stars are named after two astronomers at the Paris Observatory who discovered the first star of this class, in 1867. They have strong continuous spectra on which broad bright lines are superposed. The bright lines are sometimes bordered at their violet edges by dark lines, as in the spectra of novae (12·16). The lines are chiefly of helium, oxygen, nitrogen, and carbon in various stages of ionization;

but in the spectra where nitrogen appears, carbon is practically absent and vice versa. Formerly included in class O, these stars are now usually grouped by themselves in class W. Having average absolute magnitude −3.4, they are about as luminous as normal class O stars. Their brightest member is the second magnitude star Gamma Velorum.

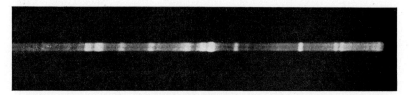

FIG. 14·19. Spectrum of a Wolf-Rayet Star. (*Photographed at Lick Observatory*)

The explanation of the Wolf-Rayet spectrum is somewhat similar to that of the nova spectrum. The model that represents it consists of a star surrounded by a rapidly expanding gaseous envelope which is supplied by material streaming out from the star. The velocity of this material is around 3000 km/sec, as determined from the widths of the bright lines. These lines are widened by Doppler displacements; their light comes from various parts of the expanding material, some of which is approaching and some receding from us. The dark lines at the violet edges of the bright ones are produced by the material in front of the star, whose motion toward us represents the full speed of the expansion. The envelope must be highly transparent, for lines of four times ionized oxygen and nitrogen, which must arise in very low and hot levels of the envelope, appear beside lines of neutral helium, which must originate in much higher and cooler levels.

14·20. The P Cygni Stars resemble Wolf-Rayet stars in their high luminosities, extended atmospheres, and spectra containing bright lines having dark lines at their violet edges. The bright lines are narrower,

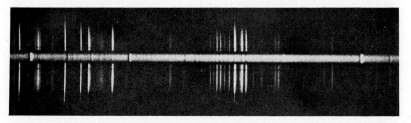

FIG. 14·20. Spectrum of P Cygni. (*Photographed at Perkins Observatory*)

showing that the velocities of expansion are more moderate. They are also less numerous, and in some cases are almost absent. These stars are mostly of class B, with a few of early A, such as Alpha Cygni.

The star P Cygni itself burst out like a nova twice in the seventeenth century and then became invariable at the fifth magnitude. The most prominent bright lines of its spectrum (Fig. 14·20) are hydrogen, in contrast with the Wolf-Rayet stars whose hydrogen lines are weak.

14·21. Class B Emission Stars. Several hundred class B stars whose spectra contain bright lines seem at first sight quite different from the ones described in the preceding Section. Gamma Cassiopeiae and Zeta Tauri are examples. Broad dark lines have narrow bright lines in the middle, and these in turn have fine dark lines in the middle. This is particularly true of the hydrogen lines. The explanation is illustrated in left diagram of Fig. 14·21A. The broad dark lines are produced in the star itself; they are widened by the rapid rotation of the star. The narrower bright lines are the light of the gaseous shell around the

FIG. 14·21.   Spectrum of B Emission Star 11 Camelopardalis.   (*Photographed at the Observatory, University of Michigan*)

star, which is rotating more slowly than the star itself and is not expanding. The fine dark lines at the centers of the bright lines are due to the absorption of the starlight by the part of the shell between us and the star. Since this part of the shell has practically no motion in the line of sight with respect to the star itself, the fine dark lines have no Doppler displacement relative to the lines on which they are superposed.

Struve at Yerkes Observatory proposes very tentatively a working model which may apply to all these stars with extended atmospheres. The model consists of: (1) a main-sequence star having a photosphere and a reversing layer; (2) a gaseous shell around the star, which is not expanding; this shell has the spectrum of narrow lines that we associate with a supergiant star; (3) an expanding gaseous shell outside the first one.

The two shells vary in optical thickness between the different types of bright-line stars. In Alpha Cygni the outer shell has little influence in the spectrum (left diagram of Fig. 14·21A); the inner shell is dominant, concealing the star itself. In the B emission stars the outer shell is ineffective, and the inner shell is transparent enough so that the lines of its spectrum appear superposed on the wide absorption lines of the star itself. In the case of P Cygni the outer shell dominates the spectrum (right diagram of Fig. 14·21A), concealing the structure inside

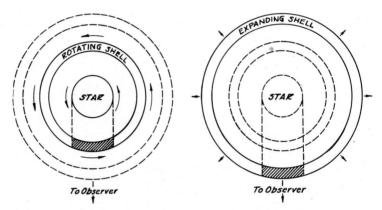

FIG. 14·21A. Working Model of Stars with Extended Atmospheres (Struve). A main-sequence star is surrounded by an inner gaseous shell which is not expanding and an outer shell which is expanding. The diagram at the left, in which the outer shell is ineffective, applies to B emission stars; the diagram at the right, in which the outer shell conceals the structure inside, applies to P Cygni stars.

it. As the author clearly points out, this working model is perhaps oversimplified.

14·22. The "Contact Binary" Beta Lyrae.

The behavior of the spectrum of this star, which has long perplexed investigators, seems to be brought near to an explanation by recent work at the Yerkes and McDonald Observatories. Beta Lyrae is an eclipsing binary having a period of 12.9 days. The brighter and larger component gives a dark-line spectrum of class B9, and these lines oscillate in the period of revolution. The spectrum of the fainter star is invisible. Bright lines and associated dark lines of class B5 vary in intensity but do not oscillate during the revolution of the binary. In addition, dark satellites to the B9 lines appear on the red side just before the eclipse and on the violet side after the eclipse.

When the components of a binary system are very close together and are also of unequal mass, according to the theory developed by Kuiper, gas streams from the more massive star in the direction of the less massive one, and forms a sort of one-streamered pinwheel enveloping both stars. The theory is in support of the physical picture (Fig. 14·22) proposed by Struve to represent the features of the spectrum.

The violet satellite lines, which are uncovered soon after the mid-eclipse, are produced by the gas streaming at the rate of 300 km/sec from the bright star toward the faint one. Part of this gas swirls around the faint star and returns to the bright one at somewhat reduced speed,

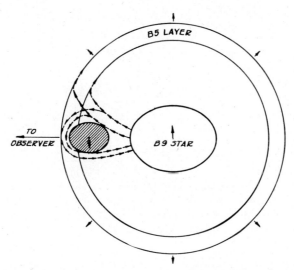

FIG. 14·22. Proposed Interpretation of the "Contact Binary" Beta Lyrae.

forming the red satellites in the spectrum. Most of it goes to form the rotating and expanding ring in which the B5 lines arise.

THE INTERIORS OF THE STARS

14·23. The Equilibrium of a Star. The exploration of the interior of a normal star proceeds on the reasonable assumption that it is everywhere in mechanical equilibrium. The weight of the gas above every point in the interior is exactly supported by the gas and radiation pressure at the point. The weight depends on the mass of the overlying gas and the acceleration of gravity. These data can be calculated at any point in a star of known mass and radius if it is also known how the density varies with distance from the star's center. The density distribution has usually been assumed, resulting in the use of different models by different investigators. It has been determined independently in the cases of a few eclipsing binaries whose periastrons are advancing conspicuously. Even so, there is no assurance that stars in general are built on the same model.

The gas and radiation pressure which balances the weight of the overlying gas depends on the temperature. Thus the problem is to evaluate the temperatures at different distances from the center of the star, which can produce the required pressures. We consider first the gas pressure.

14·24. The Gas Law. The relation between the pressure, p, the density, ρ, and the absolute temperature, T, of a gas is given by the *gas law:*

$$p = R\rho T/\mu,$$

where R is a constant and μ is the mean weight of the particles in the gas in terms of the weight of the hydrogen atom. These particles may be molecules, atoms, or the constituents of shattered atoms. This law applies ordinarily to a *perfect gas*. In the laboratory a gas compressed to a density exceeding one tenth the density of water ceases noticeably to conform to the law. But in the intensely hot interiors of the stars, where the atomic structures are disrupted, the law may continue to operate at densities exceeding that of water.

14·25. Effect of Chemical Composition. The atoms in stellar interiors must be almost completely ionized. There remains a confusion of atomic nuclei and electrons, in which each individual is a particle in the equation of the preceding Section. A neutral atom of hydrogen (atomic weight 1 and number 1) becomes two particles of average weight 0.5. A neutral atom of iron (atomic weight 55.8 and number 26) becomes 27 particles of average weight 55.8/27, or 2.1.

Consider two stars having the same size, density, and density distribution, the first star composed entirely of iron and the second entirely of hydrogen. According to the formula the temperature at a point in the first star must be 2.1/0.5, or more than four times, that at the corresponding point in the second star in order to produce the same amount of gas pressure. Thus chemical composition is an important factor in determining the interior temperature of a star.

The procedure has been to find by trial and error a composition that gives a central temperature appropriate to the observed luminosity of the star. Calculations of this sort assign to the sun a central temperature of the order of twenty million degrees and a hydrogen content a third the entire mass of the sun.

14·26. Importance of Radiation Pressure. It is well known that radiation exerts pressure on anything that obstructs its progress. Radiation pressure is proportional to the rate of the radiation which by Stefan's law varies as the fourth power of the temperature. But the gas pressure, by the gas law, varies only as the first power of the temperature. Thus with increasing temperature the ratio of radiation to gas pressure increases. In the hot interior of a star the pressure of the outflowing radiation must have a considerable share in keeping the star inflated.

The problem of the maintenance of this radiation is of great importance to an understanding of what goes on in the interior of a star. The sun, for example, is radiating away 5.08×10^{23} horsepower of energy, or 70,000 horsepower from each square yard of its surface, and presumably has been doing so for many hundred million years. What is the source of this energy that comes up from the interior to keep the stars shining?

14·27. The Source of the Radiation. The problem is to find stores of energy within the stars which can be liberated in sufficient amounts to maintain their radiations for very long periods of time. A number of proposed sources have been examined and discarded; among them the contractions of the stars, their possession of sufficient radioactive elements, and the conversion of their material into energy. The current proposals involve the transmutation of elements, in particular, the combination of hydrogen nuclei to form helium nuclei with the release of energy.

The atomic weight of hydrogen is 1.008, while the weight of helium is 4.004. If the hydrogen in the stars is combining to form helium, each combination of four hydrogen nuclei involves a release of energy equivalent to $4.032 - 4.004 = 0.028$, or seven tenths of one per cent of the original mass. Calculation shows that a hydrogen content of ten per cent of the sun's mass, if it is ultimately entirely combined into helium, can keep the sun shining at its present rate for ten thousand million years. As an example of the means by which hydrogen may combine to form helium we notice the theory proposed by the physicist Bethe of Cornell.

14·28. The Carbon Cycle. The process is represented by the following succession of formulae, in which the superscripts refer to atomic weights and the subscripts to the number of positive charges on the nuclei of the atoms. The symbol γ means the emission of a gamma ray, or high frequency radiation, and ϵ^+ denotes the release of a positron.

The positron, or positive electron, soon combines with a negative electron to produce a photon, which is a unit of radiation. The cycle is:

$$_6C^{12} + _1H^1 \rightarrow _7N^{13} + \gamma \qquad (1)$$

$$_7N^{13} \rightarrow _6C^{13} + \epsilon^+ \qquad (2)$$

$$_6C^{13} + _1H^1 \rightarrow _7N^{14} + \gamma \qquad (3)$$

$$_7N^{14} + _1H^1 \rightarrow _8O^{15} + \gamma \qquad (4)$$

$$_8O^{15} \rightarrow _7N^{15} + \epsilon^+ \qquad (5)$$

$$_7N^{15} + _1H^1 \rightarrow _6C^{12} + _2He^4 \qquad (6)$$

In the turmoil of the star's interior: (1) A carbon nucleus of weight 12 combines with a proton (hydrogen nucleus) and forms radioactive nitrogen, with the release of a γ-ray. (2) The nitrogen degenerates into carbon of weight 13 and a positron. (3) The carbon combines with a proton and forms ordinary nitrogen, with the release of a γ-ray. (4) This nitrogen combines with a proton to form radioactive oxygen, with the release of a γ-ray. (5) The oxygen disintegrates into nitrogen of weight 15 and a positron. (6) The heavy nitrogen combines with a proton to produce the original carbon nucleus and a helium nucleus.

In this cycle four hydrogen atoms combine to form one helium atom, and the excess weight of the hydrogen is liberated as radiant energy. The carbon nucleus is recovered in its original form, so that it can be used repeatedly. This mechanism seems to meet the requirements of main-sequence stars like the sun more successfully than those of giant stars. It assigns to a giant such as Capella a central temperature five times as high as would be expected if Capella is constructed on the same model as the sun. We leave these matters to the astrophysicists.

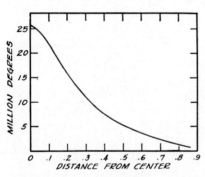

Fig. 14·29. Temperatures in the Sun's Interior. The results are subject to considerable uncertainty.

14·29. The Interior of a Star. The temperature rises rapidly with increasing depth in a star like the sun. At a quarter of the way to the center it reaches a million degrees (Fig. 14·29). The temperature near the center is of the order of twenty million degrees, while the density has risen to as much as fifty or a hundred times the density of water. Hydrogen contributes a third of the entire mass. Throughout most of the interior the atoms of all elements are completely or highly ionized; the material is a confusion of swiftly moving atomic nuclei and electrons.

Energy is liberated in the interior in the form of very high frequency radiation. It is repeatedly absorbed and again emitted by the particles, and is thus passed along and ultimately upward, until it escapes into space. Meanwhile the frequency is stepped down, so that much of the energy emerges as visible radiation. The rate of radiation of the stable star equals the rate of liberation of energy in its interior. The area and temperature of the photosphere are adjusted to meet this condition. Of two stars having the same rate of liberation of energy the larger has the lower surface temperature and accordingly the smaller rate of radiation per unit area.

The source of energy is not yet completely understood. When this problem is solved, it may be easier to understand why the majority of the stars are so remarkably stable, while some of them pulsate, some others develop extended atmospheres, and still others explode. Another problem of great interest is how the stars originate, develop, and decline. The answer to this problem is not in sight.

REVIEW QUESTIONS

1. Supply the term concerning atomic structure corresponding to each of the following definitions:

(a) Lightest constituent having unit negative charge.
(b) Constituent of nucleus having unit positive charge.
(c) Number of electrons around nucleus of normal atom.
(d) Atom which has lost a single electron.
(e) Atom normally having two electrons.

2. Explain the following features of the spectrum of hydrogen in terms of the structure of the atom:

(a) Invariable pattern of lines.
(b) Dark-line spectrum.
(c) Bright-line spectrum.
(d) Several series of lines.
(e) Balmer series in particular.
(f) Continuum beyond head of a hydrogen series.

3. Explain the relation between the surface temperatures and colors of stars. Name (a) a hot star; (b) a star of moderate temperature; (c) a cool star (remembering that these are relative terms).

4. Recalling the kinetic theory of gases, explain how the atoms of a gas may be ionized by a sufficient increase of temperature.

5. Why is the ionization potential (Table 14·III) of the singly ionized atom of a particular element greater than for the neutral atom?

6. Referring to Table 14·III, describe and account for the changes in the following features of the spectra along the sequence from the cool to the hot stars:

(a) Band spectra of molecules.
(b) Lines of neutral sodium and calcium.
(c) Lines of singly ionized sodium and calcium.
(d) Lines of hydrogen.
(e) Lines of neutral helium.
(f) Lines of ionized helium.

7. Why does a giant star have lower surface temperature than a main-sequence star of the same spectral class?

8. Explain how the distance of a star can be determined from an examination of its spectrum. Why is this method likely to be more reliable than that of direct parallax for the more remote stars?

9. The most abundant elements in stellar atmospheres are also most abundant on the earth, with the exceptions of hydrogen and helium. Assign a reason for the difference.

10. Wolf-Rayet stars were formerly included in class O. What is the reason for now grouping them in a separate class?

11. Bright lines in the spectra of Wolf-Rayet stars have dark lines at their violet edges, while those of class B emission stars have dark lines at their centers. Explain the difference.

12. Show that radiation pressure in a star's interior increases relative to gas pressure as the temperature is greater.

13. Describe the interior of a star, particularly as to its composition, temperature, and energy transfer.

14. Describe a current theory of the source of the radiation of the stars.

A Region of the Milky Way in Sagittarius. The nebula Messier 8 appears above and the Trifid nebula below. (*Photographed with the 24-inch Bruce Telescope, Harvard Observatory*)

CHAPTER XV

INTERSTELLAR CLOUDS AND HAZE

DIFFUSE NEBULAE — THE INTERSTELLAR MATERIAL

The spaces between the stars, referred to in earlier times as "empty space," contain perhaps as much material as there is in all the stars themselves. The material is in the form of fine dust and gas. Some interstellar clouds are made luminous by neighboring stars. Others are dark, but are recognized by the dimming and reddening of the stars behind them. A widespread interstellar gas makes its presence known by producing additional dark lines in the spectra of remote stars.

DIFFUSE NEBULAE

15·1. Nebulae in General. Hazy spots in the heavens, excluding the comets, have long been called *nebulae*. It was eventually noticed that one class of hazy spots is found mostly near the Milky Way, while a second class seems to avoid the Milky Way. The former came to be known as *galactic nebulae*. The latter, called *extragalactic nebulae,* later proved to be vast stellar systems outside the system to which the sun belongs. The extragalactic systems are described in Chapter XVIII.

Galactic nebulae are clouds of gas and dust. They are of two types: (1) Planetary nebulae have fairly regular forms and relatively small angular dimensions; they very often have stars at their centers. We have already (12·20) considered these in connection with the envelopes around novae. (2) Diffuse nebulae have irregular forms and often large angular dimensions. Some of them are faintly luminous. The majority are dark.

15·2. The Great Nebula in Orion is the brightest of the diffuse nebulae. Its place is marked by the middle star of the three in line in Orion's sword. Through the telescope it appears as a luminous greenish cloud around the star which itself is resolved into a trapezium of four stars.

Photographs with large telescopes bring out its filmier outskirts as well, and those with wide-angle cameras with long exposures show that it is a condensation in nebulosity that spreads over the whole region of Orion (Frontispiece).

A few other diffuse nebulae are interesting objects with the telescope; but photographs are required to do justice to most of them.

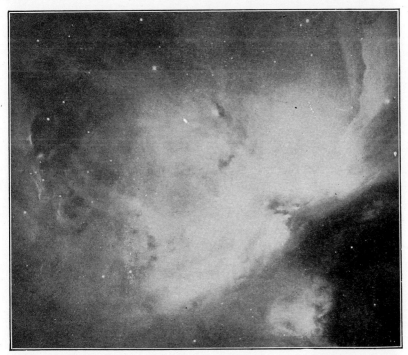

FIG. 15·2. The Great Nebula in Orion. (*Photographed at Mount Wilson Observatory*)

These nebulae are actually faint—not faint because of great distance as a star may be. Since they are extended, they have the same brightness per unit area regardless of distance. Close at hand they would still be difficult to see.

15·3. The Illumination of Nebulae. The presence of stars near or actually involved in the nebulae is responsible for their shining. In the absence of such stars the nebulae are very nearly dark. This fact was demonstrated, in 1922, by Hubble at Mount Wilson Observatory. Particular stars can be selected which are associated with practically every known bright nebula, and in each instance the extent of the illumination of the nebula is directly proportional to the apparent brightness of the star (Fig. 15·3). A star of the first magnitude illuminates the nebula to an angular distance of nearly two degrees on Hubble's photographs, while the illumination of a twelfth magnitude star extends less than a minute of arc.

The relation between the absolute photographic magnitude, M, of the associated star and the limiting distance, l, in parsecs, to which the

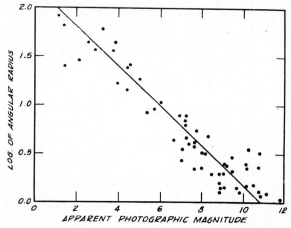

FIG. 15·3. Increase in Extent of Nebular Illumination with Increasing Bright-ness of Associated Star. (*Adapted from a diagram by Hubble*)

nebula is illuminated, as observed on the Mount Wilson photographs with an exposure of 160 minutes, is $\log l = -M/5$. Thus a supergiant star for which M is -5 illuminates a nebula to a distance of 10 parsecs, or more than the distance of Vega from the sun. A star as luminous as the sun ($M = +5.6$) can light up a nebula to a distance of only 0.08 parsecs, or 450 times the distance of Neptune from the sun.

Another important conclusion from these investigations was the relation between the temperature of the associated star and the quality of the nebular light. If the star is as hot as class B1 (temperature 18,000° K), the light of the nebula differs from that of the star. If the star is cooler than class B1, the nebular light resembles the starlight. We examine the two cases separately.

15·4. Fluorescence of Nebulae.

The density of the nebular gas is not greater than that of the best vacuum in the laboratory. In so tenuous a gas the atomic processes can differ from those in the stars. Atoms are relatively far apart and are less likely to interfere with one another; they are mostly in their lowest energy states, having their electrons at their lowest levels. In the vicinity of a very hot star such a gas becomes fluorescent. A *fluorescent substance* is one that glows with its own light when it is stimulated by high frequency radiation.

The greater part of the radiation of a very hot star is in the far ultraviolet. Any radiation of wave length less than 912 angstroms can remove the electron from a normal hydrogen atom, leaving it positively charged. When a substitute electron is finally captured by this atom, the electron may land in any one of the possible orbits. If it arrives at a high level, it then comes down by a single transition or by a series of jumps, one of which may represent a bright line of the Balmer series. While such processes may occur very infrequently in a single atom, they go on continuously in the vast assemblage of atoms of the nebula.

Thus the diffuse nebulae, such as the great nebula in Orion, having very hot stars involved in them or in their neighborhoods, are fluorescent, and their spectra contain bright lines. This is also true of all the planetary nebulae, whose central stars are of class O.

15·5. Bright-Line Spectra of Nebulae. The bright lines which characterize the spectra of the fluorescent nebulae are identified chiefly with

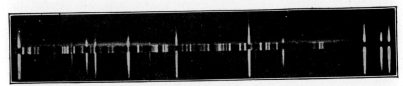

FIG. 15·5. Spectrum of the Orion Nebula. A comparison spectrum runs through the middle. The long bright lines belong to the spectrum of the nebula. The two lines at the extreme right are the green nebular lines at λ4959 and λ5007. The conspicuous line at the extreme left is the combination of the ultraviolet lines at λ3726 and λ3729. The remaining prominent lines are of hydrogen and helium. (*Photographed at Lick Observatory*)

hydrogen and helium, oxygen, and nitrogen in different stages of ionization. Prominent among them are the pair of lines at λ3726 and λ3729 in the ultraviolet, due to singly ionized oxygen, and the pair at λ4959 and λ5007 in the green, due to doubly ionized oxygen. The latter pair gives the greenish hue to the fluorescent nebulae. Neither pair has yet been observed in laboratory spectra of oxygen.

The identification of these two pairs of oxygen lines, including additional lines of oxygen, nitrogen, and some other elements, rests on theoretical evidence. They are "forbidden lines," so called because the atomic transitions producing them are much less likely to occur in a gas under ordinary conditions than the lines normally observed. But in the very rare and extended gas of the nebulae it is the other way around. The unusual lines are much more likely to appear than the normal ones.

The relative strength of the bright lines does not indicate the relative abundance of the chemical elements in the gases of these nebulae.

FIG. 15·6. Nebulosities Surrounding the Pleiades. (*Photographed by Barnard at Mount Wilson Observatory*)

Hydrogen is the most abundant, and helium is second. Oxygen and nitrogen are much rarer, but they are able to utilize greater quantities of energy in the exciting starlight.

15·6. Dark-Line Spectra of Nebulae. When the stars in the vicinities of nebulae are cooler than class B1, the nebulae are not noticeably fluorescent. Their spectra are the same as those of the associated stars, which in general are dark-line spectra. Examples are the nebulosities surrounding stars of the Pleiades (Fig. 15·6). The light of such nebulae is the starlight scattered by the dust particles which are present along with the gas. Scattered starlight, in fact, constitutes part of the light of all nebulae, but its presence in fluorescent nebulae may be unnoticed. The spectrum of the emitted light concentrated in a few bright lines is much more conspicuous than that of the scattered light which is spread over all wave lengths.

The colors of nebulae that shine mostly by scattered starlight are nearly the same as those of the associated stars. This is well shown on the photographs (Fig. 15·6A) of the remarkable region in Scorpius and Ophiuchus, where bright nebulae appear around the stars like the glow around street lamps on a foggy night. Thus the glow around the red star Antares, which is scarcely noticeable in blue light (lower photograph), becomes conspicuous in yellow light (upper photograph). The opposite is true of the nebulae around the class B stars. In general, the

22 Scorpii (B3)   BD-24° 12684 (B3)

Photovisual

Antares (Mo)   σ Scorpii (B1)

Photographic

Antares (Mo)   σ Scorpii (B1)

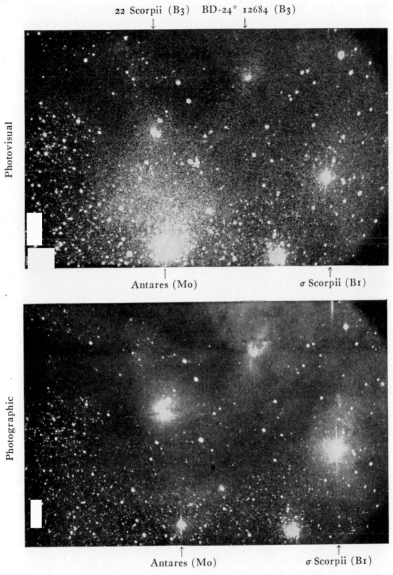

FIG. 15·6A. Reflection Nebulae in the Region of Antares. Photographed with yellow filter (above) and without filter (below). The glow around the red star Antares is more conspicuous in the photovisual exposure, while that around blue stars, such as Sigma Scorpii, is stronger in the photographic exposure. (*Photographed with a Schmidt camera at the McDonald Observatory*)

nebulae which shine by scattered starlight are slightly bluer than the stars themselves.

Thus the nebulae are composed of gas and dust. When the gas is stimulated by the radiation of a sufficiently hot star, it is fluorescent.

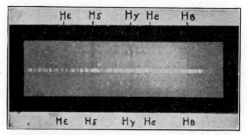

FIG. 15·6B. Spectrum of the Nebula Surrounding Merope in the Pleiades. The spectrum of the nebula resembles that of the involved star, showing dark lines, especially of hydrogen and helium. A comparison spectrum appears in the middle. (*Photographed by V. M. Slipher, Lowell Observatory*)

Otherwise the nebulae shine with the starlight scattered by their dust particles.

15·7. Dark Nebulae have no stars near by to illuminate them. They make their presence known by dimming the light of whatever lies behind

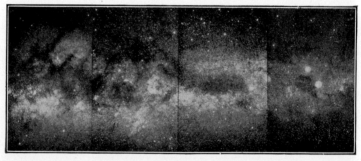

FIG. 15.7. Great Rift in the Milky Way. The southern part of the rift, from Sagittarius (left) to Centaurus (right). These extreme regions are shown on a larger scale in Figs. 17·8 and 17·3. (*Photographed at the Arequipa station of Harvard Observatory*)

them, conspicuously so in the photographs when they obscure parts of bright nebulae or bright regions of the Milky Way. Some of them are easily visible to the unaided eye and have therefore been known for a long time, though their interpretation as dust clouds instead of mere vacancies came about in fairly recent times. A succession of dark nebulae produces the great rift in the Milky Way (Fig. 15·7) which extends from Cygnus to Centaurus, nearly a third of the way around the heavens. The rift is punctuated at its two ends by a transverse dark streak north of Alpha Cygni and by the "coalsack" near the Southern Cross.

Dark nebulae are not perfectly dark, except perhaps in their central parts. Struve and Elvey at Yerkes Observatory found that several average a few hundredths of a magnitude brighter than the general background of the sky. That the contrast is not greater suggests a competitive scattering of starlight by material widely dispersed through interstellar space.

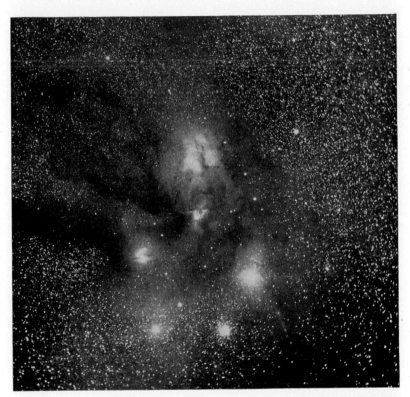

FIG. 15·7A. Dark Clouds Against the Milky Way in Scorpius. Part of this region is shown in Fig. 15·6A. (*Photographed at Yerkes Observatory*)

THE INTERSTELLAR MATERIAL

If the dust and gas between the stars were confined to the obvious nebulae, the study of the system of stars around us could proceed by

avoiding the directions of the bright and dark patches. But the interstellar material is present in all parts of the heavens. In order to allow
for its effects it is necessary to determine the distance and density of the
obscuring stuff in all directions in space. We now consider some
methods of exploring the dusty medium and the results of such inquiries.

15·8. Counts of Stars.

15·8. Counts of Stars. If the stars were of the same absolute magnitude and were uniformly distributed through space and if interstellar
space were perfectly transparent, the total number of stars brighter than
a limiting apparent magnitude would increase four times for each fainter
magnitude to which the limit is extended. Consider, for example, the
total number of stars brighter than the seventh magnitude as compared
with the total number brighter than the sixth magnitude.

Since the apparent brightness of equally luminous stars varies inversely as the squares of their distances from us, a seventh magnitude
star, which is apparently $1/2.5$ as bright as a sixth magnitude star, would
be the square root of 2.5, or 1.6, times as far away. Thus the stars
brighter than the seventh magnitude would occupy a volume of space
around us $(1.6)^3$, or nearly 4, times as large as the space occupied by
the stars of the sixth magnitude; and with the assumption of equal distribution they are four times as numerous. It is true that the stars are
not equally luminous. But the luminosity function ($11·31$) can be
employed instead of that assumption.

As a somewhat too simple example, suppose that the total numbers
of stars brighter than successive magnitudes are counted in a particular
area, and that the ratio of the numbers remains four up to the eleventh
magnitude, but at the twelfth magnitude the ratio is reduced to two.
We conclude that the stars remain uniformly distributed and that space
continues transparent out to the distance represented by the eleventh
magnitude stars. Then the stars either thin out or are dimmed by a
dust cloud, or both. Other evidence is needed for the decision.

15·9. Reddening of the Stars; Color Excess.

15·9. Reddening of the Stars; Color Excess. Interstellar dust clouds
not only dim the stars beyond, but they make them appear redder than
their normal colors by scattering their violet light more than their red
light. Similarly our atmosphere strongly reddens the light of the setting
sun. If in a particular part of the sky the stars more distant than 300
parsecs are reddened, there is a dust cloud at that distance.

The *color excess* of a star is the difference in magnitude by which
the observed color index (photographic minus visual magnitude) exceeds
its accepted value for a star of its particular spectral class (Table 14·II).

Thus the color excess of a star of known spectral class can be found by comparing its magnitudes determined on photographs of different color sensitiveness. Then the "photographic absorption," that is to say, the measure of how much the brightness of the star is reduced on ordinary blue-sensitive plates, is the color excess multiplied by the appropriate factor. The distance of the star, d in parsecs, is calculated by the formula:

$$5 \log d = m - M + 5 - K,$$

where m is the apparent photographic magnitude, M the absolute photographic magnitude of a star of this particular spectral class, and K is the photographic absorption. In determining how the photographic absorption of starlight in a particular direction increases with distance from the earth it is well to employ class A and late class B stars which have less dispersion in absolute magnitude and can generally be observed at greater distances than somewhat yellower stars.

The most accurate survey of color excesses is that of Stebbins, Huffer, and Whitford of the University of Wisconsin. They have determined the colors of 1332 class O and B stars, employing the photoelectric cell and color filters.

15·10. Dust Clouds of Auriga. As an example of current studies of the interstellar clouds by means of colors and counts of stars, we notice

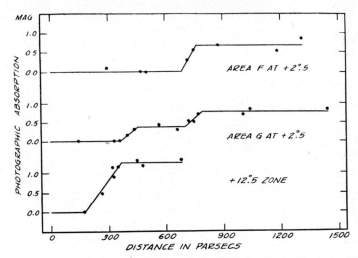

FIG. 15·10. Photographic Absorptions of Starlight by Dust Clouds in Three Areas of Auriga.

some results in the constellation Auriga. These are based on many
photographs of the region with blue and red-sensitive plates.

Fig. 15·10 shows how the photographic absorptions of the starlight
in three areas of the region vary with distance from the earth. By this
interpretation the region is veiled by clouds at distances of 300 and 800
parsecs from us. The stars of area F, seen through an opening in the
nearer cloud, are reduced 0.7 magnitude in brightness by the more dis-

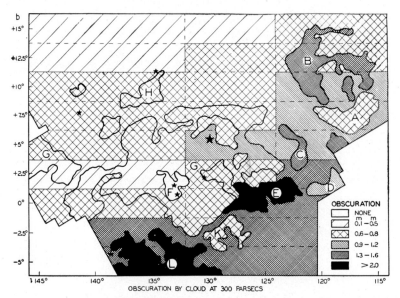

FIG. 15·10A. Irregular Density of the 300-Parsec Dust Cloud over the Region
of Auriga.

tant cloud. The stars of area G are dimmed 0.4 magnitude by the first
cloud and an equal additional amount by the second. The nearer cloud
is so dense over the +12°.5 zone that the stars behind the second cloud
do not appear in these photographs.

This two-cloud interpretation is conventional. Another way is to
represent each array of points by a straight line and to express the obscuration by a constant coefficient in magnitudes per kiloparsec.

Fig. 15·10A shows the variety in density of the 300-parsec cloud
over the Auriga region as determined by the star counts. The star near
the center is Capella. The various areas of different densities are arbitrarily lettered; some of them, such as area H, are features of the more
distant cloud.

15·11. The Size of the Dust Particles. The fact that the starlight is reddened by interstellar clouds shows that particles in the clouds are very small. If most of them were as much as a thousandth of an inch in diameter, they would obstruct the light without changing its color. If, however, the constituents of the clouds which are responsible for the observed color excesses were mostly atoms and molecules, they would cause greater reddening than is observed. The ability of a gas to scatter light varies inversely as the fourth power of the wave length of the light. Thus a gas scatters ultraviolet light of wave length 3000 A sixteen times as effectively as red light of length 6000 A. Actually the clouds reduce the ultraviolet only twice as much as the red light.

Greenstein at Yerkes Observatory concludes that the scattering of light by particles between a thousandth and a hundred thousandth of an inch in diameter can account for the observed reddening of the stars. Most of these particles could be seen only with the aid of a microscope. It is possible that much of this "dust" consists of frozen gases and even minute ice crystals.

Gas is present in interstellar space as well. We have noticed its fluorescent light in the spectra of some of the bright diffuse nebulae. In company with dust particles it forms a very widespread haze. The presence of the gas is shown by its absorption of additional dark lines in the spectra of distant stars.

15·12. Interstellar Lines in Stellar Spectra. Many years ago a "stationary" K line of calcium was observed in the spectrum of the binary star Delta Orionis; this line does not oscillate with the others in the period of the revolution, and is narrower than the lines in the spectrum of the star itself. It is an example of the narrow *interstellar lines* which are produced in the spectra of distant stars by tenuous intervening gas. The constituents of this gas now recognized are atoms of sodium, calcium, ionized calcium, potassium, iron, and ionized titanium, and also the cyanogen and hydrocarbon molecules, including ionized hydrocarbon.

Atoms of other elements are doubtless present in the gas. Since most of the atoms are in their lowest energy state, the lines they absorb are likely to be in the far ultraviolet and therefore unobservable. This is true of the hydrogen atoms, which are far more abundant in the interstellar gas than those of any other element, according to Struve. The abundance of the recognized elements varies considerably in different parts of the heavens.

Like the patchy diffuse nebulae, the tenuous haze that causes interstellar lines is patchy. Particularly due to investigations at Mount

Wilson Observatory, these lines are found to be complex, sometimes having as many as five components. This means that the starlight has passed through a succession of discrete clouds having different velocities in the line of sight. The complexity is generally the greatest near the middle of the Milky Way, but it varies here from one region to another.

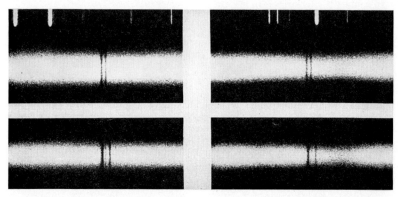

FIG. 15·12. Interstellar Lines with High Dispersion in the Spectrum of Kappa Aquilae (above) and of HD 167264 (below). The Fraunhofer K line of calcium appears at the left and the H line at the right. Notice that the lines are divided into two or three components. (*Photographed at Mount Wilson Observatory*)

Interstellar lines are easiest to recognize in the spectra of white stars whose own lines are relatively few and broad. They are likely to increase in intensity with increasing distances of the stars, and have accordingly been employed as criteria of distance.

REVIEW QUESTIONS

1. Distinguish between planetary and diffuse nebulae. Name an example of each class.

2. Why are some nebulae luminous, while others are dark? How are dark nebulae recognized?

3. Account for the bright-line spectra of some bright nebulae and the dark-line spectra of others. Give an example of a nebula having each kind of spectrum.

4. What is characteristic of the spectra of bright-line nebulae? Of dark-line nebulae?

5. (a) If counts of stars with respect to magnitude in a certain area show that the number of stars brighter than each successive magnitude is four times greater than the number down to the next brighter magnitude, what is the conclusion? (b) If the factor is considerably less than four, what are two possible conclusions?

6. (a) Explain the meaning of the term "color excess." (b) Suppose that a star having a spectrum of class A is as red as a normal star of class K. What is inferred?

7. What would you conclude about the dust in space if it dimmed but did not redden the stars beyond it?

8. Explain the following features of interstellar lines:

(a) They are more likely to be recognized in the spectra of blue stars than of yellow or red ones.

(b) They do not have the same Doppler displacements as the lines in the spectra of the stars.

(c) They are often divided into two or more components.

PROBLEM

A number of stars of Class A5 in a small area in Auriga have mean apparent magnitude 11.2 and mean color index $+0^m.58$. Stars of this class have absolute magnitude $+2.5$ and normal color index $+0^m.20$ for the particular red and blue plates employed. The photographic absorption is 3 times the color excess. Required the photographic absorption and mean distance (159) of these stars.

Answer: Photographic absorption $= 0^m.38 \times 3 \doteq 1^m.1$. Distance $= 330$ parsecs.

The Bruce Telescope at the Southern Station of Harvard Observatory, near Bloemfontein, South Africa.

CHAPTER XVI

STAR CLUSTERS

16·1. Two Types of Star Clusters. Star clusters are assemblages of stars whose members are less widely scattered than the stars in the fields around the clusters. They are not temporary congestions in the celestial traffic. The stars of each group are moving together so that the clusters will maintain their identities for a very long time. Star clusters are of two types: open clusters and globular clusters.

FIG. 16·1. Double Cluster in Perseus. (*Photographed at Yerkes Observatory*)

Open clusters, such as the double cluster in Perseus (Fig. 16·1), are not highly concentrated toward their centers. Their separate stars are usually distinguishable through the telescope and in some cases even to the naked eye. They are also known as *galactic clusters.* The nearer ones, whose proper motions are large, are sometimes called *moving clusters.*

Globular clusters are more compact and are spheroidal in form; the cluster Messier 13 in Hercules (Fig. 16·7) is an example. They are much larger, more populous, and more distant than the known open clusters.

Star clusters, nebulae, and extragalactic systems were cataloged together by earlier astronomers, owing to their frequent difficulty in distinguishing between them. They are often designated by their numbers in one of the catalogs. The great cluster in Hercules, for example, is known as NGC 6205, or as Messier 13. The first designation is its running number in Dreyer's *New General Catalogue* (1887). This catalog and its extensions in 1894 and 1908, known as the *Index Catalogue* (IC), list over thirteen thousand objects. The second designation of the Hercules cluster is its number in the catalog of 103 bright clusters and nebulae which the comet hunter Messier prepared for the *Connaissance des Temps* of 1784.

OPEN CLUSTERS

16·2. Open Clusters. The Pleiades and Hyades in Taurus are familiar examples of open clusters; their brighter stars are plainly visible to the

FIG. 16·2. Praesepe in Cancer. (*Photographed by William Henry*)

naked eye. The double cluster in Perseus, the Praesepe cluster in Cancer, the cluster of Coma Berenices, and a few others appear as hazy patches to the naked eye and are resolved into stars with very slight optical aid. The remainder are telescopic objects. Four hundred open clusters are recognized.

These clusters lie near the principal plane of the Milky Way. They accordingly appear in or near the Milky Way, except some of the very nearest ones, in particular, the Coma and Praesepe clusters. The number of stars in a cluster ranges from not more than twenty to a few thousand in the Perseus clusters. Giant stars are scarce in most and entirely absent in some clusters. The scarcity of high luminosity stars and the heavy dust clouds in the directions of the Milky Way limit the present visibility of open clusters to those within the distance of 6000 parsecs.

16·3. The Dimming of Open Clusters by Interstellar Dust provided
the first definite evidence that the dust is not confined to the conspicuous
nebulae. An investigation of these clusters by Trumpler at Lick Observatory showed in 1930 that the scattering of starlight in interstellar
space is widespread and must be allowed for.

Trumpler determined the distances of many clusters by plotting for
each the spectral classes of its stars against their apparent magnitudes
and fitting the diagram to the standard spectrum-luminosity diagram
(Fig. 11·29). The distance of the cluster is then determined by the
usual formula: $5 \log r = m - M + 5$. If, for example, the average
apparent magnitude of the class A stars in the cluster is +10.5, while
the absolute magnitude of these stars in the standard diagram is +0.5,
the distance of the cluster is 1000 parsecs. Dimming of the cluster stars
by intervening dust would make the apparent magnitude greater and
would accordingly result in a value of the distance greater than the
actual distance.

A second method of determining the distances of the clusters assumed
that the linear diameters are the same for all clusters having about the
same number of stars and degrees of concentration toward the center.
This seems to be true for clusters whose distances can be found independently. Thus the true distance of any cluster could be calculated
from its apparent diameter which would not be affected by interstellar
scattering.

The distances of the more remote clusters came out considerably
greater by the first method than by the second. The conclusion was that
clusters in all parts of the sky are dimmed by intervening dust. In any
method involving the apparent magnitude, the true distance, r, should
be found by the formula: $5 \log r = m - M + 5 - Ad$, where d is the
distance in kiloparsecs the light has passed through the dusty medium,
and A is the reduction in magnitudes per kiloparsec. Trumpler adopted
the value $A = 0.8$ photographic magnitudes per kiloparsec as a statistical constant for the correction of all cluster distances determined by
the photometric method.

16·4. "Moving Clusters"; the Ursa Major Cluster. A few star clusters so near us that their proper motions are large have been called
moving clusters. The members of such a cluster are recognized by their
common space motions. Field stars, which may appear in the cluster
but do not belong to it, are readily excluded by their discordant motions.
If the sun were a member of a cluster, its companions could be identified by their large parallaxes and zero space velocities. Such stars have

not been found. While the sun belongs to no cluster, it is in the midst of one.

It has long been known that the stars of the Great Dipper, except its end stars Alpha and Eta Ursae Majoris, have a common motion. Stars in other parts of the sky share in this motion; among them are Sirius, Alpha Coronae, and Beta Aurigae. The Ursa Major cluster contains about forty stars. The sun is in its midst though it is not a member of the moving company; that is why the stars of the cluster are so widely scattered over the sky.

The space motion of the Ursa Major cluster is directed toward a point south of the constellation Capricornus. Ultimately its members will withdraw from the sun's vicinity and converge in the distance to assume the appearance of an ordinary open cluster.

16·5. The Taurus Cluster. Just as the trails of meteors in a shower seem to diverge from the radiant, so the parallel paths of the stars in a

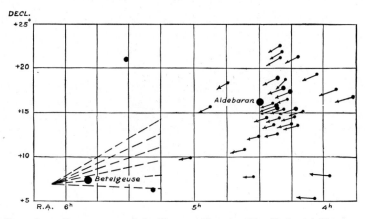

FIG. 16·5. Convergence of the Taurus Cluster. The V-shaped Hyades and neighboring stars in Taurus are converging toward a point in the sky east of Betelgeuse in Orion. Aldebaran, the brightest of the Hyades stars, is not a member of the moving cluster. The lengths of the arrows represent the proper motions of the stars of the moving cluster in an interval of 50,000 years. (*Adapted from a diagram by Lewis Boss*)

moving cluster are directed away from a divergent point if the cluster is approaching us. They are directed toward a *convergent point* if the cluster is receding from us. This effect of perspective is especially noticeable in the proper motions of the members of the Taurus cluster (Fig. 16·5).

The Taurus cluster comprises stars of the Hyades (Aldebaran is not included) and the surrounding region. The densest part of the cluster contains 140 stars. The diameter of the group is 18 parsecs and its center is 40 parsecs (130 light years) from the sun. The space motion

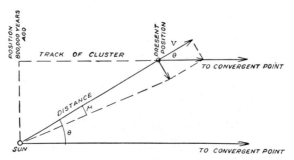

FIG. 16·5A. Track of the Taurus Cluster. The present distance of the cluster can be found when the proper motion, μ, radial velocity, V, and angular distance, θ, from the convergent point have been determined.

of these stars is eastward and away from the sun. The convergent point of their paths lies a little way east of Betelgeuse in Orion.

When the convergent point of a moving cluster is known and the proper motion, μ, and radial velocity, V, of one of its stars have been observed, the distance of that star and of any other member of the cluster with known proper motion can be calculated. The space velocity is $v = V/\cos \theta$, where θ (Fig. 16·5A) is the star's angular distance from the convergent point. The tangential velocity is $T = v \sin \theta$. The parallax can now be found from the relation (11·11): $p = 4.74\mu/T$.

As an example, the observed values for Delta Tauri in the Taurus cluster are: $\mu = 0''.115$, $V = +38.6$ km/sec, and $\theta = 29°.1$. The resulting space velocity is 44.0 km/sec, and the parallax is $0''.025$. The distance of the star is therefore 40 parsecs.

The space velocity and θ define the track of the star with respect to the sun. By means of relations easily worked out from Fig. 16·5A it can be shown that the Taurus cluster was nearest the sun 800,000 years ago at the distance of 20 parsecs.

16·6. Lifetime of the Clusters. The common motion of the stars in a cluster suggests their common origin. The maintenance of this parallelism, despite the fact that the cluster moves through regions populated by other stars, shows that the cluster stars are not often greatly diverted by collisions with or by the attractions of the field stars. While these factors may eventually break up the cluster formation, Bok at Harvard Observatory finds a cause of somewhat more rapid disintegration in the gravitational force directed toward the center of the galactic system.

In this view, the tidal force will spread the cluster in the direction of the center of the system until it goes to pieces. The time required for the disintegration of the present open clusters is estimated as of the order of 10^{10} years, depending on their compactness. Since we have no idea as to how new clusters could be formed, we might consider the

FIG. 16·6. Region of the Pleiades. (*Photographed at Yerkes Observatory*)

cluster as a vanishing species of a youthful stellar system—as lumps that will disappear when the system is more thoroughly stirred.

GLOBULAR CLUSTERS

16·7. The Brighter Globular Clusters. A hundred globular clusters are recognized in the galactic system. They can usually be distinguished from open clusters by their more regular form and their greater central concentration. Only a few are visible at all without the telescope.

Omega Centauri (Fig. 16·8) is the brightest globular cluster. Appearing to the naked eye as a hazy star of the fourth magnitude, it has a place in the star maps and a letter in the Bayer system. Owing to its low declination, −47°, this cluster is not favorably placed for observers in the United States. The cluster 47 Tucanae (Fig. 16·9), the second in order of brightness, is still farther south; it is 17° from the south celestial pole and not far from the Small Magellanic Cloud.

Messier 13 in Hercules is best known of the globular clusters to observers in middle northern latitudes where it passes nearly overhead in the early evenings of summer. This cluster and Messier 22 in Sagit-

FIG. 16·7.   Globular Cluster Messier 13 in Hercules.   (*Photographed at the Dominion Astrophysical Observatory, Victoria*)

tarius are faintly visible to the naked eye. Messier 5 in Serpens, Messier 55 in Sagittarius, and Messier 3 in Canes Venatici can also be glimpsed in favorable conditions.

16·8. Characteristics of Globular Clusters.   Globular clusters appear nearly circular. The nearest ones have apparent diameters two thirds as great as that of the moon, as measured ordinarily on the photographs, and something like twice as great as traced on the photographs with the densitometer. The slight flattening of their central parts suggests that they are slowly rotating. The greater part of the population of a cluster is contained within a globe 30 parsecs, or about a hundred light years, in diameter. The most congested region, where the stars run together in the photographs, is about ten parsecs in diameter. Here the spacing becomes more nearly planetary than stellar.

Any one of the nearest clusters contains at least fifty thousand stars bright enough to be observed, though the stars near the center are too congested to be separately visible. These are the supergiants, giants, and the bluer stars of the main sequence. Stars no brighter than the sun are quite invisible through the largest telescope at the great distance of even the nearest cluster.

FIG. 16·8. Globular Cluster Omega Centauri. (*Photographed with the 60-inch Reflector of the southern station of Harvard Observatory*)

Globular clusters are relatively scarce. Probably none exists within a radius of 6000 parsecs around the sun where the hundreds of open clusters are visible. It is the greater luminosity of the globular clusters that makes their observed number comparable with that of the open clusters.

16·9. Distances of Globular Clusters. Many globular clusters contain Cepheid variable stars chiefly of the short-period type, though there are typical Cepheids as well. With the discovery of the nearly uniform absolute magnitudes of short-period Cepheids and the period-luminosity relation for the others, the way was prepared for measuring the distances

of the globular clusters. Our knowledge of these distances is due chiefly
to the work of Shapley at Mount Wilson and Harvard Observatories.

The distances of half the clusters were determined by comparing the
observed apparent magnitudes of their Cepheid variables or of their
brightest stars with the corresponding absolute magnitudes. Experience

FIG. 16·9. Globular Cluster 47 Tucanae Near the Small Magellanic Cloud.
This cluster (near the right edge of the photograph) and Omega Centauri (Fig.
16·8) are the nearest and brightest of the globular clusters. (*Photographed at
the southern station of Harvard Observatory*)

had shown that the brightest stars in globular clusters of the same degree of compactness have about the same absolute magnitudes, between
one and two magnitudes brighter than the Cepheids. The remaining
distances were deduced from the apparent diameters and total brightness
of the clusters, on the assumption that they are uniform in linear
diameter and total luminosity. The distances, corrected for effects of
interstellar scattering of the light, are listed in the April, 1944, issue of
Proceedings of the National Academy of Sciences.

The nearest globular clusters are Omega Centauri and 47 Tucanae,
which we have already noted as the brightest; their distances are given

as 6800 parsecs, or about 22,000 light years. The distance of Messier 13 in Hercules is 10,300 parsecs, or 34,000 light years.

16·10. Distribution of Globular Clusters. Almost all the globular clusters are found in one hemisphere of the heavens having its center in the constellation Sagittarius. Fully a third are assembled in the vicinity of the great star cloud of Sagittarius. Shapley, in 1917, gave reason for the one-sided distribution. Having determined their distances he found that without correction for absorption of their light in space the globular clusters seemed to form a spheroidal system some 60,000 parsecs (200,000 light years) in diameter, having its center 16,000 parsecs distant from the sun in the direction of a point in Sagittarius.

Since the Milky Way is conspicuously brighter in that direction, Shapley reached the conclusion that the system of the globular clusters is concentric with the system of the Milky Way itself. These results brought out clearly for the first time the discrete character of the system of stars around us and the sun's eccentric position within it, and they prepared the way for the discovery of exterior systems.

16·11. Effect of Interstellar Scattering on Cluster Distances. Evidence has accumulated meanwhile, beginning in 1930 (16·3), that interstellar space in almost every direction may not be considered perfectly transparent. Starlight is dimmed in transit, so that the photometrically determined distances are greater than the actual ones. That the globular

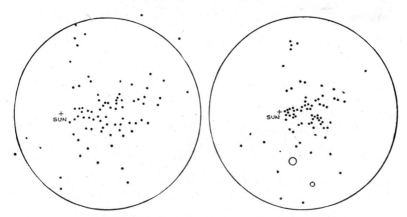

FIG. 16·11. Positions of Galactic Globular Clusters Projected on the XZ plane. The distances from the sun are corrected for optical thickness of absorbing layer of 0.46 (Baade) at the left, and 0.8 (van de Kamp) at the right. The radius of the circles is 20,000 parsecs.

clusters are themselves dimmed by the intervening material is demonstrated by the measurements of Stebbins and Whitford employing the photoelectric cell attached to the large Mount Wilson telescope. The clusters far from the Milky Way are of uniform color corresponding to spectral class F6. They become redder toward the Milky Way until they correspond in the extreme to the color of a class M star.

The interstellar material is patchy. If it were spread uniformly instead in a relatively thin layer along the principal plane of the Milky Way, the corrected distance, d', could be calculated from the original distance, d, by the formula: $\log d' = \log d - 0.1 C \operatorname{cosec} b$, where b is the galactic latitude, or angular distance from the galactic equator $(17 \cdot 4)$. C, the *optical thickness* of the layer, is the increase it would produce in the magnitude of a star if its light should pass vertically through the layer.

While it is generally agreed that the original values of the distances of the globular clusters must be reduced, no specific plan for correcting them has yet met with general approval. Tentative corrections (Fig. $16 \cdot 11$) place most of the clusters within a sphere having a radius not exceeding 20,000 parsecs and its center between 5500 and 10,000 parsecs distant from the sun. The problem of the size and form of the cluster system is further complicated by the probability that other globular clusters are hidden behind the dust clouds of the Milky Way.

Review Questions

1. State whether each of the following refers to an open or a globular cluster:

(a) Omega Centauri cluster.
(b) Praesepe cluster.
(c) "Moving cluster."
(d) Contains cluster-type variable stars.
(e) Always near principal plane of Milky Way.

2. Show that intervening dust, unless it is allowed for, is likely to make the measured distances of clusters greater than the actual distances.

3. Members of the Ursa Major cluster are found in various parts of the sky. How are the members recognized? How is it known that the sun is not a member?

4. Explain the convergence of the motions of the Taurus cluster.

5. The number of known globular clusters in the galactic system is one fourth the number of known open clusters. What is the evidence that globular clusters are actually very scarce as compared with open clusters?

6. Star clusters could be regarded as a vanishing species of a youthful galactic system. Explain.

CHAPTER XVII

THE GALACTIC SYSTEM

Just as the earth and the other planets are units in the planetary system attending the sun, so the sun and many thousand million other stars are units in the *galactic system,* or the system of the Milky Way. It is so named because in our view of the system its most striking feature is the Milky Way.

This Chapter begins with a description of the Milky Way as it appears to the naked eye and in the photographs. Its appearance suggests that the galactic system is much flattened and that the sun is not at its center. We next examine the progress that has been made in investigations of the structure and extent of the system. Finally we consider some effects of the rotation of the galactic system in addition to its centrifugal flattening.

THE MILKY WAY

17·1. The Milky Way of Summer. The *Milky Way* is the luminous girdle of the sky formed by the combined light of vast numbers of stars. Viewed in a clear moonless sky from a place removed from artificial lights it is one of the grandest of natural spectacles. Its general features are best displayed to the unaided eye. The central line of the Milky Way is nearly a great circle of the celestial sphere inclined 62° to the celestial equator. Owing to this high inclination its course across the sky is quite different at different hours of the night and at the same hour through the year.

At nightfall in the late summer in middle northern latitudes the Milky Way arches overhead from the northeast to the southwest horizon. It extends through Perseus, Cassiopeia, and Cepheus as a single band of varying width. Beginning in the fine region of the Northern Cross overhead, it is divided into two parallel bands by the Great Rift

FIG. 17·1. The Milky Way in Cygnus. The bright star to the right of the North America nebula is Alpha Cygni. The other stars of the Northern Cross appear in the photograph, except Beta Cygni at the foot of the Cross, which is out of the picture at the lower right. (*Photographed by F. E. Ross, Yerkes Observatory*)

which is conspicuous as far as Sagittarius. The long dark rift is not exactly in midstream. The western branch of the Milky Way is the broader and brighter one through Cygnus. Farther south, in Ophiuchus, it fades and nearly vanishes behind the dense dust clouds, appearing again in Scorpius. The eastern branch grows brighter as it continues southward, and gathers into the great star clouds of Scutum and Sagittarius. Here, in Barnard's words, "the stars pile up in great cumulus masses like summer clouds."

17·2. The Milky Way of Winter. In the evening skies of the late winter in middle northern latitudes the Milky Way against passes nearly overhead, now from northwest to southeast. The stream is thinner here and undivided. From Cassiopeia to Gemini it is narrowed by a series of near-by dust clouds which cause a pronounced obscuration north of Cassiopeia and angle down through Auriga to the southern side of the Milky Way in Taurus. The Milky Way is broader, weaker, and less noticeably obscured as it passes east of Orion and Canis Major down toward Carina.

The part of the Milky Way nearest the south celestial pole is either quite out of sight or else too near the horizon for a favorable view anywhere in the United States. This part is brilliant as it passes through Centaurus, Crux, and Carina. The Great Rift continues from Scorpius on through Centaurus, though it is less conspicuous here. There is a fine star cloud in Norma and another in Carina, and there is, of course, the celebrated coalsack near the Southern Cross.

17·3. Photographs of the Milky Way. The details of the Milky Way are well shown in the photographs with wide-angle telescopes. Barnard was a pioneer in this field. Fifty of his finest photographs are contained in his *Photographic Atlas of Selected Regions of the Milky Way.* These were made with the 10-inch Bruce telescope at Mount Wilson and Williams Bay. A more recent collection is available in the *Atlas of the Northern Milky Way,* by Ross and Miss Calvert. These photographs were taken with a 5-inch Ross camera at Mount Wilson and Flagstaff.

The photographs reproduced in this Chapter illustrate the variety in different parts of the Milky Way. Fig. 17·1 shows the region of the Northern Cross which passes nearly overhead in middle northern latitudes. Fig. 17·3 shows the fine region containing the Southern Cross and the coalsack, which cannot be seen in these latitudes. Fig. 17·8

shows the most spectacular part of the Milky Way, from Scutum to
Scorpius. The Scutum and great Sagittarius star clouds and the Ophi-

FIG. 17·3. The Milky Way in Centaurus and Crux. The Southern Cross
and the "coalsack" are near the center of the photograph. The two bright stars
at the extreme left are Alpha and Beta Centauri. The globular cluster Omega
Centauri (Fig. 16·8) appears near the upper left corner. (*Photographed by
Margaret Harwood at the Arequipa station of Harvard Observatory*)

uchus dark cloud are prominent features. The heavy veiling by dust
clouds of regions of the Milky Way is shown in another way in Fig.
17·9A.

17·4. Galactic Longitude and Latitude. In problems relating to the galactic system it is often convenient to denote the position of a celestial body with reference to the Milky Way. For this purpose we define an additional system of circles and coordinates of the celestial sphere.

The north and south *galactic poles* are the two opposite points which are farthest from the central line of the Milky Way. They are situated respectively in right ascension $12^h 40^m$, declination $+28°$, in Coma Berenices, and $0^h 40^m$, $-28°$, in Sculptor, both referred to the equinox of 1900.

The *galactic equator* is the great circle halfway between the galactic poles; it runs about a degree north of the central line of the Milky Way, which suggests that the sun lies north of the principal plane of the galactic system. The galactic equator is inclined $62°$ to the celestial equator, crossing it from south to north in the constellation Aquila and from north to south at the opposite point east of Orion. It passes nearest the north celestial pole in Cassiopeia and nearest the south celestial pole in the vicinity of the Southern Cross.

Galactic longitude is reckoned in degrees from the intersection of the galactic equator and celestial equator in Aquila (R. A. $18^h 40^m$) toward the north along the galactic equator. Viewed from the north galactic pole it increases in the counterclockwise direction. *Galactic latitude* is measured perpendicularly from the galactic equator.

STRUCTURE OF THE GALACTIC SYSTEM

17·5. Development of the Problem. As long as the stars were supposed to be set on the celestial sphere there was no problem of the structure of the universe of stars; the important problem related to the movements of the planets within the sphere. Copernicus' doctrine of the earth's rotation permitted the sphere of the stars to be imagined larger than before, since it was no longer required to rotate daily around the earth.

With the expansion of the sphere and its eventual disappearance as a tangible thing, the stars came to be regarded as remote suns. Then it was that astronomers began to look beyond the planetary system to survey the star fields, and the question arose: Do the stars extend indefinitely into space, or is the system of stars limited? If so, what is the form and extent of the system?

William Herschel in England was the pioneer in these inquiries. His first attempt to determine the structure of the stellar system was described by him in 1784. It was based on counts of the numbers of stars visible in the field of his telescope when it was directed toward various parts of the heavens. He assumed that the extension of the system in any direction was proportional to the cube root of the number of stars counted in that direction.

Herschel's procedure was too simple. But the analysis of star counts has remained a promising method of investigation. We are concerned here with some of the recent results of this statistical approach.

17·6. The Plan of Selected Areas. Herschel's method of determining the distribution of stars in all parts of the heavens by counts of stars in small areas was elaborated by the Dutch astronomer Kapteyn in his plan of Selected Areas inaugurated in 1906. He chose 206 areas scattered uniformly over the whole sky, and invited astronomers to determine photographically the magnitudes and other data for the stars in these areas. The counts were now to be made with respect to magnitude.

Two noteworthy contributions to this project are the *Mount Wilson Catalogue* and the *Bergedorfer Spectral-Durchmusterung*. The former, published in 1930, contains the photographic magnitudes to around $18^m.0$ in 139 of the Areas as far south as declination $-15°$; they are squares $15'$ or $20'$ on a side. The latter, which is still incomplete, contains the photographic magnitudes and spectral classes of stars to around $13^m.0$ in fields $3\frac{1}{2}°$ on a side centered in the original Areas. Counts of stars from the former catalog and from other sources were employed by Seares at Mount Wilson and van Rhijn at Groningen to derive the surface distribution of the stars over the whole sky. Two results of these studies are the following.

17·7. Flattening of the Galactic System. The stars crowd toward the Milky Way. This is one of the most obvious features of the galactic system as we look out from within the system and see it spread over the face of the sky. From the dull regions near the galactic poles, around the constellations Coma Berenices and Sculptor, the numbers of stars in equal areas of the sky increase as the galactic latitude decreases; and the amount of the increase becomes greater for the more distant stars. Thus the naked-eye stars are three or four times as numerous near the galactic equator as they are near its poles. For stars visible with the largest telescopes the factor exceeds forty.

The high galactic concentration of the fainter and in general more distant stars shows that the main body of the galactic system is much flattened in the direction of its poles and widely extended in the direction of its equator. The similarity of the counts in the same latitudes north and south of the galactic equator indicates that the sun's position is not far from the plane of this equator.

In the Milky Way   Near the Galactic Pole

FIG. 17·7. Concentration of Stars Toward the Milky Way. Two regions of the same size, in the Milky Way and near the galactic pole. The faintest stars shown in both regions are of the eighteenth magnitude. (*Photographed at Mount Wilson Observatory*)

17·8. Eccentric Position of the Sun.

While the sun is near the principal plane of the galactic system, it is far from the center. The center is distant some 30,000 light years from the sun in the direction of the great star cloud of Sagittarius, in galactic longitude 325°, latitude 0° (right ascension $17^{\mathrm{h}} 33^{\mathrm{m}}$, declination $-29°$).

The eccentric position of the sun was first inferred from the distribution of the globular clusters (16·10), and the inference seemed to be supported by the greater brightness of the Milky Way in the neighborhood of Sagittarius and its duller aspect near Auriga and Taurus in the opposite part of the heavens. Further evidence is given by the star counts; the faint stars are most numerous around Sagittarius. This is the case with particular types of celestial objects as well, such as open clusters, novae, and planetary nebulae. The same direction of the center results from studies of the rotation of the galactic system, as we shall notice later.

The extreme flattening of the system and the eccentric position of

FIG. 17·8. Toward the Center of the Galactic System. The Milky Way from Scutum to Scorpius. The Scutum cloud is near the upper left corner. The great cloud in Sagittarius is just below the center of the photograph. To the left of this cloud the inverted bowl of the "Milk Dipper" is conspicuous; to the right are the dark nebulosities of southern Ophiuchus. The pair of stars marking the sting of the Scorpion is near the lower right corner. (*Photographed at Mount Wilson Observatory*)

the sun seem well established.   But the details of the structure are not yet known.   Most astronomers will probably be surprised if it does not turn out to be a spiral like the many extragalactic spirals.   The problem is difficult because we are inside the system and because so much of the system is concealed by the dust clouds.

17·9. Obscuration by Dust Clouds.   A good indication of the total amount of obscuring material in the galactic system in any direction is

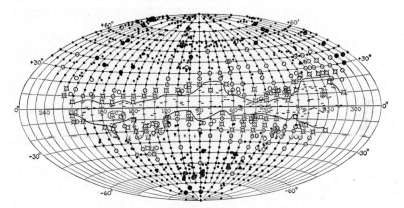

FIG. 17·9.   Obscuration of Exterior Systems near the Milky Way.   In this representation of the celestial sphere the numbers around the edge are galactic latitudes.   Full dots indicate regions where the exterior systems are more numerous than average, circles where they are less numerous than average, and dashes where they are not seen at all.   The obscuration is complete in an irregular band along the galactic equator, aside from a few "windows," and is partial for some distance north and south of the "region of avoidance."   (*Diagram by Edwin Hubble, Mount Wilson Observatory*)

given by the visibility of things outside our system.   Fig. 17·9 shows the results of a photographic survey of the extragalactic systems by Hubble with the Mount Wilson telescopes.   The numbers of systems visible in each of 1283 sample areas were counted over 75 per cent of the heavens. The numbers are greatest around the galactic poles; they become fewer with decreasing galactic latitude, until near the equator there are almost none at all.   Thus the "extragalactic nebulae" seem to avoid the Milky Way.

There is reason for supposing that the extragalactic systems are more or less uniformly distributed in all directions.   Thus, as in the case of uniformly distributed stars (15·8), the number of systems to a particular limiting magnitude should be four times as great as the number

FIG. 17·9A. Heavily Veiled Region in the Vicinity of the Cluster NGC 6553 in Sagittarius. Photographed with nearly equal exposures with plates sensitive to blue light (above) and red light (below). This heavily veiled region is shown more clearly in red light. (*Photographed at Mount Wilson Observatory*)

to the next brighter magnitude if the intervening space is transparent. Hubble's counts near the galactic poles average about eighty systems per unit area. Obscuration of one magnitude would redeuce the number to twenty, two magnitudes to five, and three magnitudes to not much more than one visible system per area. We conclude that the total obscuration is not less than three magnitudes in practically every direction near the galactic equator.

Here we have a difficult obstacle to the determination of the structure of the galactic system. Moreover, the obscuring material is patchy, as indicated by the "windows" near the equator, through which a few exterior systems can be glimpsed. The use of Selected Areas alone in low galactic latitudes is accordingly likely to be misleading. More extensive star counts are required, and these are now being made and analyzed.

17·10. The General Star Counts. The immediate program undertaken by Bok at Harvard Observatory and his associates in the enterprise is based on counts of stars down to the fifteenth magnitude on photographic plates covering the entire course of the Milky Way. The counts are made with respect to magnitude, so that it can be determined for a particular area how many stars per square degree are brighter successively than magnitude nine, ten, and so on to magnitude fifteen.

The areas into which each region is divided are such that the surface distribution of the stars in each area seems reasonably uniform and different from those in adjacent areas. An example of such division has been shown in Fig. 15·10A. Thus arranged, the star counts provide the data for the space analysis of each area. An important step in the analysis is to determine the distances of intervening dust clouds and the amounts in magnitudes that they dim the stars behind them. Color excesses of stars and counts of extragalactic systems give valuable evidence at this point.

When the details of the obscuration are determined, the analyst can then sweep the dust away and can set down for each area the numbers of stars that would be observed per square degree to each limiting magnitude if the intervening space were perfectly transparent. If the ratio between successive numbers is always four ($15·8$), with allowance for the luminosity function, the stars are uniformly distributed. If the ratio at any distance becomes greater than four, the stars are more congested there than near the sun; if it becomes less than four, the stars are more scattered. This is the end product of the analysis. In the present program it should reveal the structure of the galactic system within a radius of from one to two thousand parsecs around the sun.

17·11. The Local Structure.

The analysis of the general star counts in low galactic latitudes has progressed far enough to give a tentative view of the galactic system in the neighborhood of the sun.

The star density around the sun is relatively high. The stars thin out in most parts of the Milky Way with increasing distance from the sun. Toward Cygnus and Carina, however, which are at right angles

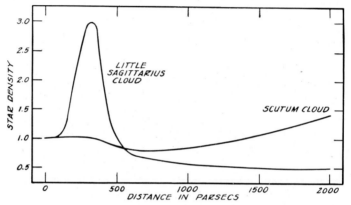

FIG. 17·11. Star Density Gradients in the Directions of the Little Sagittarius and Scutum Star Clouds.

to the direction of the galactic center, there is no considerable decrease in star density. As far as it goes, the evidence could mean that the sun is included in an arm of a spiral.

The "star clouds" of the Milky Way are mostly partial openings in the dust clouds. When the effects of the obscuring material are removed in the analysis, the surface star-density increases smoothly toward the central line of the Milky Way. There are some exceptions.

Some star clouds are really congestions. An example is the little Sagittarius cloud. In this area, and in neighboring ones which are more heavily obscured, the star density (Fig. 17·11) at the distance of 300 parsecs is three times as great as in the sun's vicinity. The Scutum cloud is another example. At 2000 parsecs the star density is nearly half again as great as it is around the sun and is still increasing.

The variety we see in the Milky Way is largely determined by the local structure. The most extensive dust clouds, including those which produce the Great Rift, are within range of the counts to the fifteenth magnitude. To an observer in another part of the galactic system the Milky Way would have a different aspect.

ROTATION OF THE GALACTIC SYSTEM

The flattening of the main body of the galactic system indicates its rotation. Other effects of the rotation are found in the two star streams, in the trend of the space velocities of the globular clusters, and in the systematic radial velocities of distant stars in different galactic longitudes. We examine these effects in the order of their discoveries.

17·12. The Two Star Streams. Up to the beginning of the present century no evidence of systematic motions of the stars had been presented aside from parallactic effects of the solar motion toward the standard apex in Hercules and the common motions of stars in binary systems and clusters.

In 1904 the Dutch astronomer Kapteyn announced that the peculiar motions of the stars (from which the effects of the solar motion are eliminated) around us are not random; there are two streams of stars moving in opposite directions in the plane of the Milky Way with a relative speed of 40 km/sec. With something like the convergence of the stars of the Hyades cluster the stars of the two streams are closing in toward two opposite points of the heavens. The convergent point of one stream is in right ascension $6^h 15^m$ and declination $+12°$, in Orion; the other is in right ascension $18^h 15^m$ and declination $-12°$, in Scutum. The line joining them is in the plane of the galactic equator and not much different from the direction of the galactic center (right ascension $17^h 33^m$, declination $-29°$).

This preferential motion of the stars is a consequence of the rotation of the galactic system, as the Swedish astronomer Lindblad has shown. Most of the stars move in the rotation in slightly eccentric orbits around the center. The effect for us is the star streaming.

17·13. Asymmetry in Stellar Motions. Another effect of galactic rotation was discovered by Stromberg at Mount Wilson in 1923. The stars around us having moderate space velocities are drifting away from the standard apex of the sun's way in Hercules at the average rate of 20 km/sec, as we have seen. But practically all stars whose space velocities exceed 60 km/sec are going another way. Their motions are directed toward the part of the Milky Way that is centered in galactic longitude $243°$ which is practically at right angles to the direction of the galactic center. Not a single high-velocity star is moving in the opposite direction. The short-period Cepheid variable stars are speeding toward longitude 243° at the rate of 100 km/sec. The globular clusters have the greatest speeds, around 250 km/sec.

This evidence shows that the sun, in addition to its moderate movement among the stars around it, is rushing in the whirl of the highly flattened body of the galactic system at the rate of the order of 250 km/sec. Its direction is at present toward galactic longitude 63° in Cepheus. The less flattened array of short-period Cepheids is rotating with the lower speed of 150 km/sec, and is therefore falling behind us at the rate of 100 km/sec. The still less flattened assemblage of globular clusters is rotating so slowly that its apparent progress to the rear is not far from the sun's speed in the rotation.

17·14. Systematic Effect in the Radial Velocities of the Stars. If the material is more concentrated around the center of the galactic

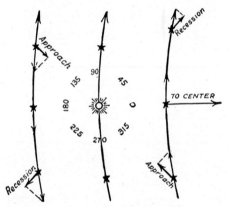

Fig. 17·14. Effect of the Rotation of the Galactic System on the Radial Velocities of the Stars. Stars nearer the center than the sun's distance are revolving faster, and are therefore passing by the sun. Stars farther from the center are revolving slower, and are falling behind the sun. Accordingly, stars whose longitudes differ by 45° and 225° from that of the center are receding from the sun, while stars at 135° and 315° are approaching.

system, then, at least in the suburbs of the system where we are, the stars should have smaller speeds in the rotation as their distances from the center are greater. The stars between the sun and the center should move around faster than the sun, so that they overtake and pass by us. The stars farther from the center than the sun's position should move more slowly and therefore fall steadily behind us.

Evidence that this is the case is found in the radial velocities of the stars in different parts of the Milky Way, when these velocities are freed from other effects.   Stars of low galactic latitudes whose longitudes are 45° and 225° greater than the longitude of the center (Fig. 17·14) are receding from us with the greatest speed.   Stars whose longitudes are 135° and 315° greater are receding with the greatest speed.

Plaskett and Pearce, at the Dominion Astrophysical Observatory, Victoria, made an extensive study of this differential effect, employing their radial velocities of many class O and B stars whose remoteness renders them specially useful for this purpose.   They located the galactic center in longitude 324° and estimated the diameter of the system as 30,000 parsecs, or nearly 100,000 light years.   The speed of the galactic rotation at the sun's distance from the center is 275 km/sec, according to these authorities, and the period of the rotation at this distance exceeds 200 million years.

FIG. 17·15. The Extragalactic System Messier 33, in Triangulum. One of the nearest of the spiral systems, it is selected tentatively as an example of the appearance of the galactic system to a very distant observer. (*Photographed at Mount Wilson Observatory*)

17·15. The Present View of the Galactic System.

In its general structural relations the galactic system is often pictured as a vast flat spiral resembling the extragalactic system Messier 33 in Triangulum, though considerably larger. In this view, our system consists of a massive nucleus surrounded by a double-armed spiral of stars, groups of stars, and much interstellar dust and gas. Globular clusters and scattered stars form a considerably less flattened structure than the main body of the system.

The diameter of the system is estimated as 100,000 light years and the thickness of the nucleus is a tenth as great. The mass of the system is given as from one to two hundred thousand million suns. If we adopt the larger number and suppose that half the total mass is that of the interstellar material, the system contains 100,000 million stars.

The sun is some 30,000 light years from the center of the system which lies in the direction of the great Sagittarius star cloud. Some features of our environment suggest that the sun may be included in a spiral arm extending from Cygnus toward Carina. In the rotation of the system the sun is moving at the rate of 250 km/sec in the direction of Cepheus.

Review Questions

1. Why does the Milky Way have different positions in the sky during the year? At what seasons does it pass near the zenith in the early evening in middle northern latitudes?

2. Name some constellations that lie along the course of the Milky Way.

3. Give evidence that the galactic system is a flattened structure.

4. What is the evidence that the sun is not near the center of the system? State the direction of the center with respect to the constellations.

5. Why are extragalactic systems scarce in the vicinity of the Milky Way? What important conclusion is drawn from the detection of a few extragalactic systems near the galactic equator?

6. Show that the amount of obscuring material in different directions through the galactic system can be determined from counts of extragalactic systems.

7. While many "star clouds" of the Milky Way are simply partial openings in the dust clouds, some of them are actually congestions of stars. How is this determined?

8. What evidence from the star counts might mean that the sun is in an arm of a spiral?

9. Explain that the observed high speeds of globular clusters result from the rotation of the galactic system.

10. Give additional evidence that the galactic system is rotating.

11. Describe the galactic system according to the current view, and the sun's place in it. Which features seem well established and which are conjectural?

CHAPTER XVIII

EXTRAGALACTIC SYSTEMS

TYPES OF EXTERIOR SYSTEMS — THEIR RESOLUTION AND DISTANCES — THEIR DISTRIBUTION — THEIR RADIAL VELOCITIES — CONCLUSION

We have already noticed that objects originally called nebulae, excluding those that were found to be star clusters, were eventually divided into two classes. These were named galactic nebulae and extragalactic nebulae. The former are concentrated toward the Milky Way; they are clouds of gas and dust in the star fields. The latter seem to avoid the region of the Milky Way because they are generally obscured by the dust clouds which congregate there. Finally, in 1924, they were established as systems exterior to the galactic system. Some authorities continue to designate the extragalactic systems as *extragalactic nebulae*. Others prefer to call them *exterior galaxies,* or simply *galaxies.*

Types of Exterior Systems

18·1. Elliptical, Spiral, and Irregular Systems. Extragalactic systems are divided into two general groups, depending on whether or not they have rotational symmetry. *Regular systems* are in the great majority. They are characterized by rotational symmetry around a nucleus, and are of two types: (1) *Elliptical systems* have indefinite boundaries and no conspicuous structural detail; they have various degrees of oblateness, from the globular to the lenticular form. (2) *Spiral systems,* the most numerous of all, are characterized by a spheroidal nucleus surrounded by a flatter spiral structure. In the edgewise view there is some resemblance to a wheel with a rather conspicuous hub. The spirals are of two kinds: *normal spirals* and *barred spirals. Irregular systems* have neither nuclei nor any apparent rotational symmetry.

The following descriptions of the different types of extragalactic systems are based on Hubble's classification which is especially useful for the nearer systems as they appear on photographs with large telescopes.

18·2. Elliptical Systems comprise twenty per cent of the extragalactic systems whose forms can be distinguished. The separation of the stars at their centers is estimated as of the order of a hundredth of a parsec, or scarcely more than half of one per cent of the separation of the stars around the sun. The light of these objects fades from bright nuclei to indefinite edges, so that their diameters in the photographs increase with the exposure times.

FIG. 18·1. Regular Extragalactic Systems. The spiral NGC 4647 and the elliptical system NGC 4649 in Virgo. (*Photographed at Mount Wilson Observatory*)

Degree of flattening of the disks provides the only mark of distinction between the members of this type. Elliptical systems are designated by the symbol E followed by a number which is ten times the ellipticity of the disk. The ellipticity is the difference between the major and minor axes divided by the major axis. The complete series runs from class E0, having practically circular disks, to E7 whose members appear like convex lenses viewed edgewise.

If all elliptical systems really had the lenticular form, their disks would have the observed range of ellipticity depending on how they are presented to the earth. Hubble finds, however, that the frequencies of the different classes are not consistent with this supposition. Some are actually globular, although it is impossible to decide for any individual except one of class E7 whether it is more flattened than it appears to be.

Extreme types of elliptical systems, Eo and E7, are represented in Fig. 18·2. NGC 4649 (Fig. 18·1) and one of the two companions, Messier 32, of the great spiral in Andromeda (Fig. 18·4) are examples of slightly flattened, class E2, elliptical systems.

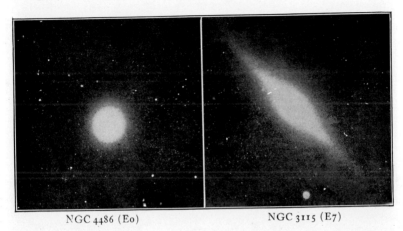

NGC 4486 (Eo)   NGC 3115 (E7)

FIG. 18·2. Extreme Types of Elliptical Systems. NGC 4486 in Virgo has a nearly circular disk. NGC 3115 in Sextans is among the most flattened elliptical systems. (*Photographed at Mount Wilson Observatory*)

18·3. Normal Spirals. All regular systems having ellipticities greater than that represented by class E7 are spirals, and no spirals presented edgewise to us have ellipticities less than this limit. If they appear more nearly circular, it is because they are not presented edgewise. The circular spirals are those whose equatorial planes are perpendicular to the line of sight.

Spirals of the normal type have central nuclei, from opposite sides of which two spiral arms emerge and coil in the same sense in the same plane. The nuclear regions are generally much brighter than the arms; they are in many cases easily visible with the telescope. But the arms, especially with respect to their spiral character, can be seen to advantage only in the photographs with long exposures.

Normal spirals are divided into three classes: *Class Sa* comprises spirals having large nuclear regions and closely coiled arms. An example is NGC 4594 (Fig. 18·5). In *class Sb* the nuclei are smaller and the arms are wider open. The great spiral in Andromeda (Fig. 18·4) is typical of the group. In *class Sc* the nuclei are the least conspicuous, the arms are most loosely coiled, and the structural details are most pronounced. Messier 33 in Triangulum (Fig. 17·15) is representative of this class.

FIG. 18·3. The Spiral Messier 51 in Canes Venatici. (*Photographed at Mount Wilson Observatory*)

18·4. The Great Spiral in Andromeda, Messier 31, is the brightest of the spiral systems. A hazy patch to the naked eye, it was placed on some of the star charts before the telescope came into use. To the eye at the telescope it remains an indefinite glow like that of "a candle shining through horn," as an early observer described it. It is the nucleus that appears to the naked eye and for the most part to the eye at the telescope. Fainter surrounding parts come out clearly in the photographs where the object is shown in its true character as a flat spiral inclined 15° from the edgewise position.

In the photographs with large telescopes the spiral in Andromeda appears as an oval 2° 40′ long and 40′ wide. At the distance of 800,000 light years the linear diameter of the more conspicuous part of the system is accordingly nearly 40,000 light years. The gradual fading at the edges in the photographs suggests that the dimensions may be considerably greater. Measurements with the photoelectric cell increase the diameter fully 25 per cent. Even so, the great spiral in Andromeda, which appears to be a giant among the extragalactic systems, seems to be inferior in size to the galactic system.

FIG. 18·4. The Great Spiral in Andromeda. (*Photographed with the 24-inch Schmidt-Type Telescope, Warner and Swasey Observatory*)

18·5. Edgewise Spirals. Many spirals are presented edgewise, or nearly so, as would be expected. They show clearly (Fig. 18·5) the polar flattening of the nucleus and the fidelity with which the material keeps to the principal plane. Characteristic of the edgewise spirals is the dark streak which sometimes seems to cut them completely in two. Just as the dust clouds near the equatorial plane of the galactic system almost completely prevent us from looking out along this plane, so the dust of these extragalactic systems obstructs the view of their equatorial regions.

FIG. 18·5. Edgewise Spirals. (Above) NGC 4565 in Coma Berenices. (Below) NGC 4594 in Virgo. (*Photographed at Mount Wilson Observatory*)

18·6. Barred Spirals. Seventy-five per cent of all extragalactic systems whose structures can be identified are spirals. More than two thirds of these are normal spirals. Most of the others are barred spirals. The arms of barred spirals do not emerge directly from the nucleus. Instead, they begin rather abruptly from the extremities of a luminous bar which extends from opposite sides of the nucleus. Barred spirals are arranged in a series paralleling the normal type, in classes SBa, SBb, and SBc. Large nuclear regions and undifferentiated arms characterize the members of the first class; aside from the nucleus they resemble the Greek letter θ. At the other extreme are the small nuclei and wide open arms of the S-shaped spirals represented by NGC 7479.

Hubble's classification of elliptical and spiral systems, which we have employed, is generally adopted as the most convenient. Some astronomers have viewed the combined series as representing possible stages of development. In this view the globular system becomes flatter

FIG. 18·6.   Barred Spiral NGC 5383 in Canes Venatici.   (*Photographed at Mount Wilson Observatory*)

until it reaches an unstable figure where the spiral superstructure of one type or the other begins to emerge.

18·7. The Magellanic Clouds. Nearest of all extragalactic systems, the two Magellanic Clouds are plainly visible to the naked eye, although they are too close to the south celestial pole to be seen north of the tropical zone. Early voyagers into the southern hemisphere brought back reports of these two "white clouds" in the heavens. Magellan observed them, and in his honor they are named. The Large Cloud is in the constellation Dorado, having its center of figure in right ascension $5^h 26^m$, declination $-69°$, and $33°$ from the galactic equator; the angular diameter of the main body is about $7°$. The Small Cloud is in Tucana, in right ascension $0^h 50^m$, declination $-73°$, and $44°$ from the galactic equator; its angular diameter is half that of the other.

The distance of the Large Cloud is 23,000 parsecs, or 75,000 light years, and the diameter of the main body is 10,000 light years. The Small Cloud is somewhat farther away, at the distance of 85,000 light years; its corresponding diameter is 6000 light years, and its center is

30,000 light years from that of its neighbor. The two Clouds may be considered as satellites of the galactic system. It is not improbable that they are within its thinly populated suburbs as well.

The Magellanic Clouds lack the rotational symmetry that is characteristic of most exterior systems. They are examples of the ragged assemblages of stars which are classed as irregular systems.

FIG. 18·7. Large Magellanic Cloud. (*Photographed at the Union Observatory, Johannesburg, South Africa*)

18·8. Irregular Systems. Two or three per cent of the extragalactic systems whose forms can be observed show no evidence of rotational symmetry. Their actual frequency may be greater than it seems to be, because the irregular systems are smaller and less brilliant than the spirals, and must therefore be nearer us in order to attract equal attention. NGC 6822 (Fig. 18·8), near the northern border of Sagittarius, is a typical irregular system. It closely resembles the Magellanic Clouds, but is smaller; its greatest diameter is not much more than 3000 light years.

Two relatively near-by but very dim exterior systems seem to stand apart from the usual types. One of these is in the constellation Sculptor at the distance of 300,000 light years. It is a globular assemblage of stars considerably concentrated toward its center and exceeding the moon in angular diameter. It is very much larger than the globular clusters and differs from the elliptical systems in its easier resolution into

FIG. 18·8. The Irregular System NGC 6822 in Sagittarius. (*Photographed at Mount Wilson Observatory*)

stars. A similar assemblage is twice as far away in the constellation Fornax. A photographic search with a special camera at Harvard Observatory has failed to find additional systems of this sort.

18·9. The Brightest Extragalactic Systems. Table 18·I lists the twenty photographically brightest exterior systems, according to a photometric survey by Shapley and Miss Ames at Harvard Observatory. All except the Magellanic Clouds rise above the horizon of latitude 40° north, though three or four are never high enough to be well observed. The diameters in the Table are as measured on photographs with reflecting telescopes. The magnitudes refer to the integrated brightness.

The brightest extragalactic systems include examples of all recognized types and their subdivisions except the barred spirals. Normal spirals of different degrees of concentration appear among them, from the highly condensed NGC 4594 to the loosely knit Messier 33. These spirals have various degrees of orientation, ranging from the flatwise Messier 101, which appears circular, to NGC 4631 which is presented so nearly edgewise that its major diameter exceeds the minor diameter ten times.

TABLE 18·I. THE BRIGHTEST EXTERIOR SYSTEMS

Name		Right Ascension	Declina-tion	Diameter Major Minor		Photg. Mag.	Type
Large Magellanic Cloud		$5^h 26^m$	$-69°$	$432'$	$432'$	0.5	I
Small Magellanic Cloud		0 50	-73	216	216	1.5	I
NGC 224 Messier	31	0 40	$+41$	160	40	5	Sb
253		0 45	-26	22	6	7.0	Sc
5128		13 22	$+30$	10	8	7.2	I
598	33	1 31	-43	60	40	7.8	Sc
55		0 12	-40	25	3	7.8	S
5236		13 34	-30	10	8	8.0	Sc
4826	64	12 54	$+22$	8	4	8.0	Sb
4594		12 37	-11	7	2	8.1	Sa
3031	81	9 52	$+69$	16	10	8.9	Sb
5457	101	14 01	$+55$	22	22	9.0	Sc
4736	94	12 49	$+41$	5	4	9.0	Sb
4945		13 02	-49	12	2	9.2	S
3034	82	9 52	$+70$	7	2	9.4	I
221	32	0 40	$+41$	3	2	9.5	E
4631		12 40	$+33$	12	1	9.6	Sc
7793		23 55	-33	6	4	9.7	S
3115		10 03	-7	4	1	9.8	E
3627	66	11 18	$+13$	8	2	9.9	Sb

Messier 31 in Andromeda is the brightest of the spirals. The Magellanic Clouds are by far the brightest of the irregular systems. It is interesting that one fifth of the brightest systems are of this apparently infrequent type. Messier 32, companion of the Andromeda spiral, is the brightest of the elliptical systems.

THEIR RESOLUTION AND DISTANCES

The fact that the spirals and associated objects are outside the galactic system was established in 1924 by Hubble at Mount Wilson Observatory. His photographs with the 100-inch telescope showed the outer parts of Messier 33 and of some other spirals partly resolved into stars.

Many of the stars proved to be Cepheid variables whose distances could be determined and accordingly the distances of the spirals that contain them. So the "extragalactic nebulae" came to be recognized as extragalactic systems.

18·10. The Period-Luminosity Relation Again. The clustering of celestial objects is a fortunate characteristic for the investigator. Often

FIG. 18·10. Resolution of the Andromeda Spiral into Stars. Individual stars in the arms of the spiral are clearly seen. This is the upper portion of the spiral as it appears in Fig. 18·4, except that it is reversed in the east and west direction. (*Photographed at Mount Wilson Observatory*)

the differences in the distances of the individuals in a group are so small in comparison with the distance of the group as a whole that they can be neglected. Under these conditions relations of apparent brightness and of absolute brightness are practically identical. This is true of the extragalactic systems.

The discovery at Harvard Observatory of a nearly linear relation between period and median apparent brightness of Cepheid variable stars in the Small Magellanic Cloud led to the establishment of the period-luminosity relation (12·6). This relation is supposedly the same for these stars wherever they are found. Having identified many Cepheid variables in the spiral system Messier 33, Hubble demonstrated that the curve representing the logarithms of their periods plotted against their median apparent magnitudes has the same form as the standard log (period)-absolute magnitude curve (Fig. 12·6). All that remained was to notice the *modulus*, the difference of magnitude $(m - M)$ between corresponding ordinates of the two curves. The distance of the system, d in parsecs, could then be found by the useful formula: $\log d = (m - M + 5)/5$. In this way the spirals were established as systems exterior to the galactic system.

18·11. Measurements of Distances.

The distances of extragalactic systems can be determined (1) when the systems are sufficiently near and loosely knit enough to be partly resolved into stars. Cepheid variables, which give the most reliable distances, are not the most luminous stars; they are not definitely found thus far in the photographs beyond the distance of a million light years. Novae of the ordinary type at their maxima and certain irregular variable stars and giant blue stars, which provide fairly dependable distances, are more luminous than the Cepheids and are accordingly observed in systems somewhat more remote.

The very brightest stars in the more open spirals are around absolute photographic magnitude −6.1, or 50,000 times as luminous as the sun; they are still visible at apparent magnitude 20.6 in some members of a great cluster of systems in Virgo. Thus the modulus, $m - M$, of the cluster is 26.7 and its distance is around 2,200,000 parsecs, or seven million light years.

(2) The many members of the Virgo cluster provide statistical criteria of absolute magnitude and surface brightness, which can extend the measurements of distance with less individual dependability to the far more numerous unresolved systems. The distances of the most remote extragalactic systems recorded in the photographs with present telescopes are of the order of five hundred million light years.

(3) In addition, the distances of systems whose spectra have been photographed can be deduced with considerable confidence by a relation between radial velocity and distance, which will be described later.

18·12. Dimensions of Extragalactic Systems.

Since these systems fade out gradually at their margins, their published diameters depend on exposure conditions and methods of measurement. The diameters as given by Hubble refer to the "main body" of the system, that is to say, the part of the system readily visible on well-exposed photographs with the large Mount Wilson telescopes.

The mean maximum diameters increase along the sequence of elliptical systems from 600 parsecs for type Eo to 1500 parsecs for type E7. Corresponding diameters of normal spirals are: Sa, 2000 parsecs; Sb, 2400 parsecs; Sc, 3000 parsecs. Barred spirals of the different types are slightly smaller. On the other hand, the main body of the galactic system is of the order of 25,000 parsecs, or 80,000 light years. The angular diameters of some bright systems measured on 3-hour exposure photographs with the Bruce telescope at the Harvard southern station exceed those of the main body by 60 per cent for the elliptical type and 220 per cent for the spiral type.

The average mass of the extragalactic systems whose rotations have been studied is 2×10^9 times the sun's mass, or a hundredth of the estimated mass of the galactic system. Some of the largest approach but seem not to equal our system in mass.

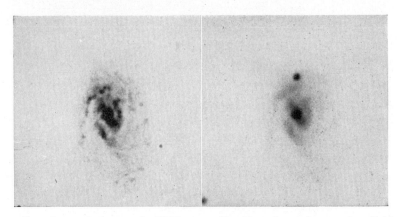

FIG. 18·13. Supernova in NGC 4273. Negatives from photographs: (left) by Mayall, May 10, 1931; (right) by van Maanen, Feb. 16, 1936, with poor seeing, showing supernova 29″ above nucleus of spiral. (*Photographed at Mount Wilson Observatory*)

18·13. Novae in Extragalactic Systems. The novae that flare out in the exterior systems and then gradually fade away are of two kinds:

(1) *The normal novae* which resemble the galactic novae in the order of their luminosity at maximum and in the character of the light variation. More than a hundred of this familiar type have been ob-

served in the great spiral in Andromeda. It is estimated that as many as 25 or 30 novae appear yearly in this system. Their absolute photographic magnitudes at maximum average −5.5 which is not far from the average for galactic novae. Since the distance factor is eliminated, the relations between the novae in Messier 31 are more clearly shown than those of galactic novae whose relative distances are often not so well known.

(2) *The supernovae* whose luminosities at maximum are considerable fractions of, or may even exceed, the total luminosities of the systems in which they appear. The first known supernova burst out in 1885 near the nucleus of the great spiral in Andromeda. At maximum brightness it shone as a star of apparent magnitude 7.2, one tenth the combined light of this vast system.

18·14. Supernovae. Knowledge of supernovae has been increased in recent years particularly by a systematic search for them by means of

Fig. 18·14. Spectrum of Supernova in NGC 4273 (Negative). Wide emission bands are shown. (*Photographed by M. L. Humason, Mount Wilson Observatory*)

photographs of clusters of extragalactic systems with the 18-inch Schmidt telescope of the Palomar Observatory, and the further study of the many discovered supernovae at the Mount Wilson Observatory. These spectacular outbursts occur in all types of extragalactic systems at the average rate of one per system per 400 years. They fall into two groups:

Group 1. These supernovae are around absolute photographic magnitude −14 at maximum, or 100 million times as luminous as the sun. If one of them were placed at the distance of ten parsecs from us, where the sun would be barely visible to the unaided eye, it would appear four times as bright as the full moon. The spectra show extremely broad emission bands from the start, while in the spectra of normal novae the bright bands do not appear until after maximum brightness of the stars. The light variations resemble those of most normal novae; there is a rapid rise to maximum, followed at first by a rapid and later by a slower decline.

An example of the first group is the supernova that appeared, in 1936, 29″ north of the nucleus of the spiral NGC 4273 (Fig. 18·13). Emission bands in its spectrum (Fig. 18·14), some 200A wide, suggest a velocity of expansion of the order of 6000 km/sec. Still wider bands have been observed in other supernovae.

Group 2. The members of this group reach a maximum luminosity equal to ten million suns. After maximum they fade more slowly at first than do the members of the other group. The series of changes in their spectra resemble that of normal novae, except on a greater scale. Supernovae of this group are probably more numerous than those of the first group, but being fainter they are less readily detected.

Three recorded novae within the galactic system are supposed to have been supernovae. These are the nova of 1054, associated with the Crab nebula, and those of 1572 and 1604.

18·15. Globular Clusters in Extragalactic Systems.   On photographs of the great Andromeda spiral there are 140 objects having the appearance of nebulous stars projected against or near the borders of the system. Their distribution (Fig. 18·15) shows their association with the spiral. One of these objects examined spectroscopically has a radial velocity of approach of the same order as that of the spiral itself.

They are globular clusters of stars, ranging in diameter from 4 to 16 parsecs. Their absolute photographic magnitudes average −5.3, which is somewhat fainter than the corresponding integrated magnitudes of the galactic globular clusters. But in no respect do they differ widely enough from these clusters to cast doubt on the identification. The cluster system of Messier 31 has a diameter of 100,000 light years.

Eight globular clusters appear near the elliptical system NGC 205, the fainter companion of Messier 31; but none is seen in the vicinity of its brighter companion, Messier 32, also an elliptical system. A few clusters are associated with the spiral Messier 33 in Triangulum, Messier 81 and 101 in Ursa Major, and perhaps with the irregular system NGC 6822. A considerable number are recognized in the Magellanic Clouds. Thus the globular clusters are connected with elliptical and irregular systems as well as with the spirals.

18·16. Comparison with the Galactic System.   The extragalactic systems, so far as they have been resolved, bear a close resemblance to the galactic system in the kinds of objects they contain. Their brightest stars have the same order of luminosity as in our system. They contain variable stars of the familiar types, including the novae. Patches

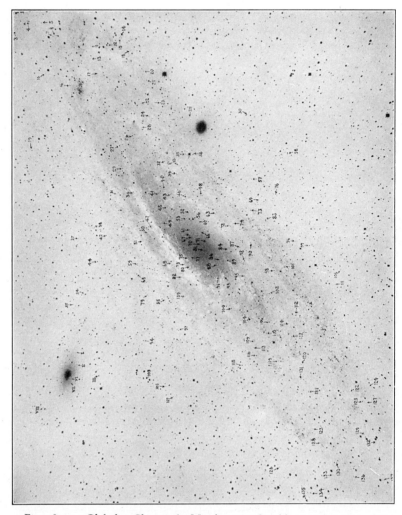

FIG. 18·15. Globular Clusters in Messier 31. On this negative of a photograph of the great nebula in Andromeda Hubble has marked the positions of
140 "nebulous objects" which he identified as globular clusters. Eight of these
objects are associated with NGC 205, in the lower left corner, and none at all
with Messier 32, directly above the nucleus of the large system. (*By courtesy
of Mount Wilson Observatory*)

of bright diffuse nebulosity are observed in some of the systems, or make their presence known by their spectra. Large dark nebulae are abundant in the spirals, and are especially noticeable in the edgewise spirals.

What is already known about the organization of the galactic system is often interpreted by analogy with the spiral nebulae of the type of Messier 33. To an observer situated halfway out from the center of that system, a milky way would be a striking feature of the heavens,

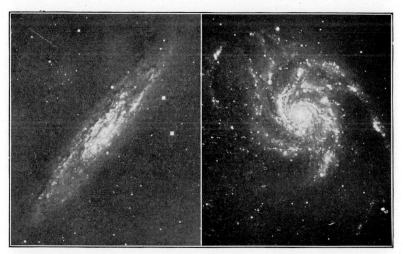

FIG. 18·16. Spirals at Different Inclinations. (Left) NGC 253 in Cetus. (*Photographed at Lowell Observatory.*) (Right) Messier 101 in Ursa Major. (*Photographed at Mount Wilson Observatory*)

brightening in the direction of the nucleus. Doubtless it would be divided into two branches along part of its course, and marked with other dark rifts caused by smaller obscuring clouds, a region generally avoided by exterior systems.

The outstanding discrepancy between the exterior systems and the galactic system is in their dimensions (18·12). The average spiral of type Sc, generally the largest of the exterior systems, seems to have not more than one eighth the diameter of the galactic system. Even Messier 31, a giant among the spirals, does not certainly equal our system in stature. Is our own system, then, a continent among the "island universes"? It is proper to look with suspicion on a conclusion which makes the observer's position in the universe conspicuous in any way. The discrepancy between the dimensions of the exterior systems and the galactic system is now considerably reduced; the exterior systems are larger and the galactic system is smaller than in the earlier estimates. Yet the question remains.

THEIR DISTRIBUTION

18·17. The Local Group. The galactic system is a member of a group of a dozen or more systems which occupy an ellipsoidal volume of space

FIG. 18·17. The Spiral NGC 6946 in Cepheus. A near-by system which may be a member of the local group. (*Photographed at Mount Wilson Observatory*)

whose longest diameter is of the order of 300,000 parsecs, or a million light years. Our system is toward one end of the group. The long axis of the ellipsoid is in the direction of Messier 31.

TABLE 18·II. THE LOCAL GROUP OF EXTERIOR SYSTEMS

Designation	Galactic Longi- tude	Galactic Lati- tude	Type	Uncorrected Distance in Parsecs	Diameter of "Main Body" in Parsecs
LMC	247°	−33°	I	26,000	3,300
SMC	269	−45	I	29,000	1,800
NGC 6822	354	−20	I	200,000	1,000
M 31			Sb		12,000
M 32	89	−21	E2	250,000	250
NGC 205			E5p		500
M 33	103	−31	Sc	250,000	4,000
IC 1613	99	−60	I	300,000	1,300

This congestion of systems in our neighborhood is a fortunate arrangement for the investigator; all are nearer us than any one might be expected to be on the basis of the average separation in the general field. The members of the local group are the only extragalactic systems

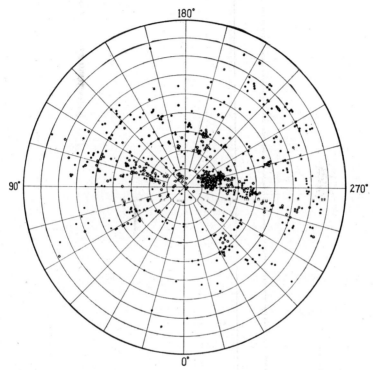

FIG. 18·18. Distribution of Exterior Systems Brighter than Photographic Magnitude 13 in the Northern Galactic Hemisphere. The positions of 538 systems are indicated by dots. The outer circle represents the galactic equator. The Virgo cluster is seen at the right of the center which marks the north galactic pole. (From *Harvard College Observatory Annals*)

which can be sufficiently resolved with present telescopes to show their Cepheid variable stars distinctly. Presenting every type of system except the barred spiral to relatively close examination, they are important as samples of extragalactic structure. Their preference for low galactic latitudes, however, subjects them to effects of absorption, and therefore introduces some uncertainty in their distances and diameters.

In addition to the list of Table 18·II which should include the Sculptor and Fornax systems (18·8), the type Sc spirals NGC 6946

(Fig. 18·17), IC 342, and IC 10 and some other systems as well may be members of the local group. A third named, only 3° from the galactic equator, seems to be partly obscured. Other members may be entirely hidden behind the dark nebulae along the Milky Way.

18·18. The Nearer Extragalactic Systems. There are 1025 exterior systems whose integrated light is brighter than photographic magnitude 13, according to a survey at Harvard Observatory. They comprise all systems of normal luminosity within a distance of ten million light years. Excluding 78 of undetermined type, 23 per cent are elliptical, 66 per cent are normal spirals, 8 per cent are barred spirals, and 3 per cent are irregular systems. Thus three fourths of the nearer systems are spirals.

The apparent surface distribution of the nearer systems is far from uniform (Fig. 18·18). Almost none is found within 10° of the galactic equator; their absence here is owing to their obscuration by the dust clouds of the galactic system. Even above galactic latitude 30°, where the obscuration within our system is slight, their distribution is patchy; there are relatively vacant areas, and regions much richer than average where definite clusters of systems are found.

18·19. Clusters of Extragalactic Systems, as distinguished from the smaller groups such as the local group (18·17), contain around five hundred members. They do not vary greatly in size, so that their relative distances are reliably shown by their apparent diameters. In their slight concentration toward the center they are analogous to the open rather than the globular star clusters. They appear to include a greater percentage of elliptical systems than is found in the general field. Otherwise it is as if they had been swept together from an originally uniform distribution, leaving the surrounding regions more sparsely populated than the average.

The Virgo cluster is the nearest of the clusters, at the distance of 2,200,000 parsecs. Its several hundred members are spread over an area some ten degrees in diameter, having its center in right ascension 12^h 24^m, declination +12°. Open spirals are exceptionally numerous as compared with the clusters generally, and some of these can be resolved in photographs with large telescopes, so as to show their brightest stars. The following notes refer to some other clusters.

The Cancer cluster contains at least 150 members. It occupies an area about a degree square.

The Coma cluster, only three degrees from the north galactic pole, has 800 members, and its diameter is 1°.7.

The Leo cluster, east of Regulus, has at least 300 members within an angular area slightly larger than that of the full moon.

The Perseus cluster (Fig. 18·19), east of Algol, has a membership of 500, mostly elliptical systems distributed over an area two degrees in diameter.

The Ursa Major cluster (No. 1), in the bowl of the Great Dipper, contains at least 300 members.

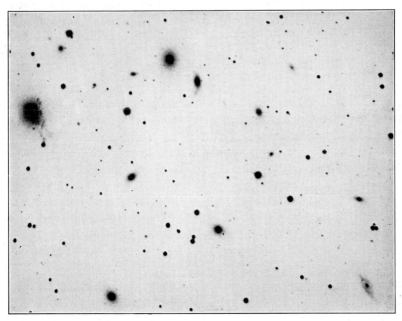

FIG. 18·19. Part of the Perseus Cluster of Extragalactic Systems. A negative. (*Photographed at Mount Wilson Observatory*)

18·20. Distribution of Extragalactic Systems.

Two extensive surveys of the exterior systems have already given much information as to their distribution over the face of the sky and through space:

(1) A survey is in progress at Harvard Observatory of all systems to about the 18th photographic magnitude. Three-hour exposure photographs with the 24-inch Bruce telescope near Bloemfontein, South Africa, provide the material in the southern hemisphere. Each plate covers effectively 25 square degrees of the sky. (2) A survey at Mount Wilson Observatory employs photographs with the large reflecting telescopes. The usable field of the 100-inch telescope equals the apparent

area of the full moon and shows extragalactic systems down to magnitude 20 in the center of the field. Counts in 1283 such sample areas have been made over 75 per cent of the heavens.

The distance of the faintest systems shown in the photographs with the 100-inch telescope is 500 million light years, and the total number of systems within this radius is 100 million, according to Hubble. He finds the distribution uniform in the long run; the average separation of the systems is two million light years.

In regions of the sky unobscured by the dust clouds of our own system the total number of extragalactic systems per square degree brighter than a specified magnitude is nearly four times the number of systems brighter than the next lower-numbered magnitude. This ratio, which is expected (15·8) if the space distribution is uniform, continues to the faintest systems observed. There is no certain evidence as yet of any thinning out of the systems toward the boundary of the visible universe, which might give a clue as to the dimensions of the vast aggregate of the extragalactic systems.

These counts of exterior systems are also useful in the explorations of the galactic system; this is especially the case in latitudes high enough so that any dust encountered is likely to be fairly near by. If in such a region the exterior systems are one fourth as numerous as might be expected, the analyst of star counts may well allow for dust that dims the stars behind it a full magnitude.

THEIR RADIAL VELOCITIES

18·21. Spectra of Extragalactic Systems. The first photograph of the spectrum of the great Andromeda spiral, in 1899, showed a dark-line pattern of about the solar type, from which it was concluded that this spiral must be a system of stars. Similar photographic evidence is now available for many other exterior systems.

It is not a simple matter to secure such photographs except of the brightest systems. The low surface brightness of these objects makes it a slow process. The exposure on a remote system is likely to be prolonged through the available time of several nights, though speed is increased to the limit, at the expense of dispersion, by the use of a very short-focus camera behind the prism.

The spectra of the extragalactic systems are composites of class G, as would be expected from an aggregation of stars of all spectral classes. Open spirals are somewhat bluer than closely coiled ones. The dark lines are wide and rather weak; evidently they are spread by the different radial velocities of the individual stars in the system. In addition, the occasional appearance of bright lines in the spectra shows the presence of bright nebulosity.

18·22. Rotation Shown by the Spectra. The flattened forms of elliptical systems and of the nuclei of spiral systems suggest that they are rotating. Evidence of the rotation is found in the spectra of the spirals whose equatorial planes are not perpendicular to the line of sight. When the slit of the spectroscope is placed along the major axis of the

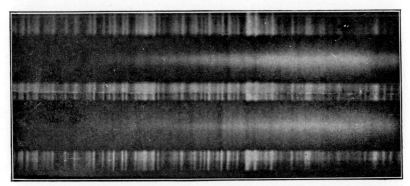

FIG. 18·22. Spectra of Two Spiral Systems. (Above) Spectrum of NGC 4594 in Virgo (Fig. 18·5). (Below) Spectrum of Messier 31 in Andromeda (Fig. 18·4). The dark lines resemble those in the solar spectrum. They are displaced toward the violet in the lower spectrum, and toward the red in the upper one. In the upper spectrum the dark lines slant noticeably, showing that the system is rotating. Bright comparison lines of vanadium and iron appear above and below the spectra of the spirals. (*Photographed at Lowell Observatory*)

inclined system, the lines of the spectrum slant (Fig. 18·22) at an angle which depends on the speed of the rotation. It is the same Doppler effect that appears in the spectra of rapidly rotating planets (Fig. 8·33).

As an example of the investigations of the rotations of spirals by means of their spectra we notice a recent study of Messier 33 by Mayall and Aller at Lick Observatory. This spiral has been frequently cited as possibly resembling the galactic system except on a smaller scale. The inner part of the spiral, 18′ in radius, rotates like a solid in a period of 59 million years, which suggests fairly uniform distribution of its material. In the outer parts, between 18′ and 30′ from the center, the period increases with increasing distance, from 60 to 200 million years.

The sense of the spectroscopic rotation, that is to say, which end of the major axis of the projected image of the tilted spiral is approaching us, can be determined from the spectrum. The sense of the spiral pattern as it is presented to us is seen in the photographs. Thus the direction of the rotation with respect to the spiral figure becomes known if it is possible to decide which side of the minor axis is the nearer.

Hubble gives reason for supposing that the nearer side is the one in which the dark nebulosity is the more conspicuous. On the basis of his conclusions from the study of a number of spirals he proposes the working hypothesis that the arms of all spirals are trailing behind the nucleus in the rotation. The spiral shown in Fig. 18·17 is accordingly rotating in the clockwise direction.

18·23. The Velocity-Distance Relation. In addition to the slant produced by the rotations of exterior systems, the lines in their spectra are usually much displaced from their normal positions. Part of the displacement is owing to the swift speed of the sun, and the earth, in the rotation of the galactic system. When this effect is allowed for, the displacement is always toward the red end of the spectrum. If these are Doppler displacements, the radial velocities of the exterior systems are velocities of recession. Having corrected the observed velocities for the solar motion, Hubble showed, in 1929, that the resulting velocities vary directly as the distances. The velocities of recession of extragalactic systems increase at the rate of 560 km/sec per million parsecs of their distance from the earth (Fig. 18·23).

TABLE 18·III. DISTANCES AND RADIAL VELOCITIES OF EXTRAGALACTIC SYSTEMS (HUBBLE AND HUMASON)

Cluster	Right Ascension	Declination	Distance in Million Parsecs	Velocity in km./sec.
Virgo	$12^h 25^m$	$+ 12°$	2	1,200
Pegasus	23 17	$+ 8$	7	3,800
Perseus	3 15	$+41$	11	5,200
Coma	12 56	$+28$	14	7,500
Ursa Major No. 1	11 43	$+ 57$	26	15,000
Leo	10 24	$+11$	32	20,000
Gemini No. 1	7 4	$+ 35$	35	23,000
Boötes	14 30	$+ 32$	70	39,000
Ursa Major No. 2	10 55	$+ 58$	72	42,000

The validity of this remarkable relation is supported by the more recent data (Table 18·III). With increasing distance of the systems

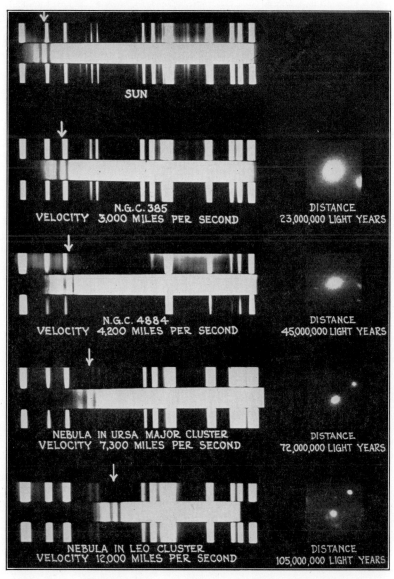

SUN

N.G.C. 385
VELOCITY 3,000 MILES PER SECOND
DISTANCE
23,000,000 LIGHT YEARS

N.G.C. 4884
VELOCITY 4,200 MILES PER SECOND
DISTANCE
45,000,000 LIGHT YEARS

NEBULA IN URSA MAJOR CLUSTER
VELOCITY 7,300 MILES PER SECOND
DISTANCE
72,000,000 LIGHT YEARS

NEBULA IN LEO CLUSTER
VELOCITY 12,000 MILES PER SECOND
DISTANCE
105,000,000 LIGHT YEARS

FIG. 18·23. The Red Shift in the Spectra of Distant Extragalactic Systems. Arrows point to the H and K lines of calcium. Direct photographs of the systems are shown at the right. (*Photographed at Mount Wilson Observatory*) the velocities became enormous. Clusters of systems are employed in these determinations so far as possible, so that each distance and radial velocity may be the average for a number of objects. Departures from precise linearity can be partly ascribed to peculiar motions of the systems of the order of 200 km/sec, which appear to be independent of distance.

18·24. Significance of the Velocity-Distance Relation. The question has been raised as to whether the enormous shifts to the red in the

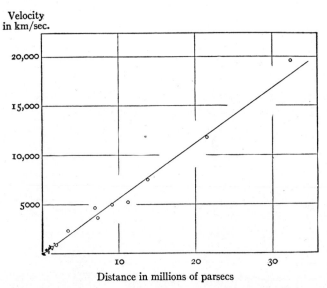

FIG. 18·24. The Velocity-Distance Relation. The small circles represent mean values for clusters or groups of extragalactic systems. (*Contributions from the Mount Wilson Observatory,* No. 427)

spectra of extragalactic systems are really Doppler effects representing equally enormous velocities of recession. As an alternative it might be imagined that the energy quanta are diminished in their journey through space, but so gradually that the effect is appreciable only for very remote sources of light. The effect would be a reduction in the frequency of the light, producing a shift to the red of its spectrum, which could be proportional to the distance. That the speed of light is not altered through these great distances is demonstrated by the observation that the aberration constant (2·15) is the same for a system in the Ursa Major cluster No. 1 at the distance of 85 million light years as for near-by stars.

As an unexpected effect the velocity-distance relation requires interpretation. As an empirical relation it has great importance as a means
of determining the distances of exterior systems, particularly of the
more remote ones whose separate stars are invisible. The procedure is
to photograph the spectrum of the system, to measure the shift of the
lines, and to calculate the corresponding radial velocity. When the
velocity has been corrected for the solar motion, the distance of the
system is obtained by the rule: distance in parsecs = 1790 times velocity
of recession in kilometers a second.

FIG. 18·25. A Group of Extragalactic Systems. A small region in Pegasus,
showing several extragalactic systems of different types. (*Photographed at
Mount Wilson Observatory*)

18·25. The "Expanding Universe." Viewed as a velocity effect the
red-shift in the spectra of extragalactic systems lends additional interest
to the theoretical inquiries concerning properties of space which have
been made since the formulation of the theory of relativity. In 1917,
Einstein added to his law of gravitation a small "cosmical term"; it was
equivalent to adding to the Newtonian law a repulsive force varying
directly as the distance from the sun. Negligible in its effect on the

nearer bodies, it becomes overwhelmingly predominant for the remote extragalactic systems. In the interest of stability the repulsive force was compensated by the assumption of a spherical universe filled with a medium of uniform density, which produced an attractive force varying directly as the distance.

As the other extreme, de Sitter in Holland studied the properties of an empty universe, in which the repulsive force operates uncontrolled. Lemaitre, in Belgium in 1927, published an intermediate solution. He showed that Einstein's model is unstable, so that it may expand or contract, and discussed the former case. In his solution the universe is expanding, like a balloon in the process of inflation, and approaching the de Sitter model as the limit. From any point of observation whatever, the exterior systems should retreat with velocities proportional to their distances, as they are observed to do.

Conclusion

18·26. The Physical Universe. The unfolding of knowledge of the physical universe reveals a picture of ever increasing grandeur. It begins, in Chapter I, with the homocentric view of the universe. The observer is the central figure. Around him is the earth, and over him bends the sky full of stars which rise and set, and march westward with the changing seasons.

In the geocentric view, upheld by Hipparchus and Ptolemy, the central earth is the dominating feature. The other members of the solar system, revolving around it, are now set distinctly apart from the more distant sphere of the "fixed stars." Next, the heliocentric view, dating formally from the time of Copernicus, establishes the solar system on an approximately correct basis, leaving the sphere of the stars, at first, unchanged.

Then emerges gradually the realization that the sun is only one of the stars; and the attention turns to the system of the stars, with the sun still occupying a central position, by virtue of tradition and from the lack of any information to the contrary. With William Herschel, the founder of sidereal astronomy, details of the stellar system begin to appear. The sun's motion in the stellar system, the existence of physically related pairs of stars, the vast numbers of star clusters and of nebulae, some of them "not of a starry nature," the first attempts to survey the galactic system—all these developments aroused interest in the regions beyond the solar system. For the successful exploration of these remote regions, the greatest ingenuity has been required. The spectroscope, photographic plate, photoelectric cell, and other devices have been called upon to supplement the eye at the telescope.

In recent years, as we have seen, the picture of the universe has developed with spectacular rapidity. The galactic system, with the sun no longer central, now stands out sharply. The hitherto mysterious spirals and associated objects, altogether perhaps as numerous as a hundred million within the reach of present telescopes, are established as exterior systems; and many of them are gathered into greater systems.

Whether all these extragalactic systems and clusters of systems are organized into a super-system which is again a unit in a still more gigantic structure we can for the present only imagine.

REVIEW QUESTIONS

1. Describe three classes of extragalactic systems, naming an example of each.

2. On the hypothesis that spiral systems evolve from elliptical systems, show that the subclasses Sa, Sb, and Sc of the spirals could represent stages of advancing age.

3. Distinguish between the structures of normal and barred spirals.

4. By what means is it determined that extragalactic systems are outside the galactic system?

5. In what ways do supernovae differ from ordinary novae? In what respects do the two groups of supernovae differ?

6. Mention several points of resemblance and one conspicuous difference between the galactic system and the spiral systems.

7. Name some members of the local group of extragalactic systems. What is the distinction between a group and a cluster of systems?

8. What is the evidence that the extragalactic systems, aside from their clustering, are fairly uniform in their distribution as far as they can be seen?

9. Describe the rotation of the spiral Messier 33. Show that it is consistent with the rotation of the galactic system in the sun's vicinity.

10. Explain that the distance of an extragalactic system can be determined from the displacement of the lines in its spectrum.

11. Account for the velocity of approach of the great spiral in Andromeda although most of the exterior systems have velocities of recession.

PROBLEMS

1. The period of a Cepheid variable star in the spiral system Messier 31 is 20 days and its median apparent photographic magnitude is 19.5. Required the distance of this system.

Answer: $M = -2.5$ (Fig. 12·6); log (distance) = $(19.5 + 2.5 + 5)/5$. The distance is 250,000 parsecs.

2. In the spectrum of an extragalactic system in Ursa Major the K line of calcium, whose normal wave length is 3934 angstroms, is displaced 197

angstroms to the red. Calculate the distance of the system by the velocity-distance relation.

Answer: The radial velocity (11·9) is 15,000 km/sec. The distance is 26 million parsecs.

Astronomical Constants

		Section
Constant of aberration.....	$20''.47$	2·15
General precession.........	$50''.2564 + 0''.000222(t - 1900)$	2·20
Constant of nutation.......	$9''.21$	2·20
Obliquity of the ecliptic....	$23° 27' 8''.26 - 0''.4684(t - 1900)$	1·18
Constant of gravitation.....	6.670×10^{-8} cgs units	7·22
Sidereal day..............	$23^h 56^m 4^s.091$ of mean solar time	3·2
Synodic month............	$29^d 12^h 44^m 2^s.8$	5·8
Sidereal month............	$27^d 7^h 43^m 11^s.5$	5·8
Tropical year.............	$365^d 5^h 48^m 46^s.0$ (31,556,926.0 seconds)	2·23
Sidereal year.............	$365^d 6^h 9^m 9^s.5$	2·23
Earth's mass.............	5.98×10^{27} grams, or 6.6×10^{21} tons	2·4
Sun's mass...............	1.983×10^{33} grams	10·1
Sun's diameter...........	1,390,600 km, or 864,000 miles	10·1
Velocity of light..........	300,000 km/sec, or 186,300 miles/sec	4·1
1 astronomical unit.......	149,500,000 km, or 92,900,000 miles	7·17
1 light year..............	9.46×10^{12} km, or 5.88×10^{12} miles	11·3
1 parsec.................	3.258 light years, or 1.92×10^{13} miles	11·3
1 radian.................	$57°.30$, $3437'.7$, or $206,264''.8$	11·3
1 statute mile............	5280 feet, or 1.609347 km	2·1
1 nautical mile...........	6080 feet, or 1.1516 statute miles	2·1
$x°$ Centigrade (C).........	$(9/5 \times x° + 32°)$ Fahrenheit (F)	
Absolute temperature (K)..	Centigrade temperature (C) $+ 273°$	

REFERENCE BOOKS

The following books are representative of the many which are useful for supplementary reading and reference. They are listed in order of the chapters in this book to which they are more particularly associated.

CHAPTER I

Allen, Richard H., *Star-Names and Their Meanings*. Stechert, New York, 1899. A useful reference on star names and their derivations.

Baker, Robert H., *Introducing the Constellations*. The Viking Press, New York, 1937.

Barton, Samual G. and William H., *A Guide to the Constellations*. McGraw-Hill Book Company, New York, 1928.

Norton, Arthur P., *A Star Atlas*. Fifth edition. Gall and Inglis, London, 1933.

CHAPTER II

Jeffreys, Harold, *The Earth. Its Origin, History and Physical Constitution*. Cambridge University Press, Cambridge, 1924.

CHAPTER III

Ageton, Arthur A., *Dead Reckoning Altitude and Azimuth Table* (H.O. 211). U. S. Navy Hydrographic Office, Washington. Primarily for the solution of the astronomical triangle.

Ageton, Arthur A., *Manual of Celestial Navigation*. D. Van Nostrand Company, 1942. Tables for working sextant sights from both assumed and dead reckoning positions.

The American Air Almanac. Superintendent of Documents, U. S. Government Printing Office, Washington. Intended for air navigation, but also useful for marine navigation. A volume is published for each four months.

The American Ephemeris and Nautical Almanac. Superintendent of Documents, U. S. Government Printing Office, Washington. A volume is published for each year.

The American Nautical Almanac. Superintendent of Documents, U. S. Government Printing Office, Washington. Intended for marine navigation. A volume is published for each year.

Bok, Bart J., and Frances W. Wright, *Basic Marine Navigation*. Houghton Mifflin Company, Boston, 1944. A useful text, clearly written and well illustrated.

Dutton, Benjamin, *Navigation and Nautical Astronomy*. Eighth edition. U. S. Naval Institute, Annapolis, 1944. The standard text on marine navigation for use in the U. S. Navy.

Mattingly, Charles, *American Air Navigator*. Ziff-Davis Publishing Company, Chicago, 1945. Written by the Chief Navigator of the Consolidated Vultee Aircraft Corporation, this book is remarkable for the clarity of the text and the excellence of the illustrations.

Stewart, John Q., and Newton L. Pierce, *Marine and Air Navigation*. Ginn and Company, Boston, 1944. Another good example of the recent textbooks in navigation.

Tables of Computed Altitude and Azimuth (H.O. 214). U. S. Navy Hydrographic Office, Washington. In nine volumes, one for each ten degrees of latitude.

CHAPTER IV

Dimitroff, George Z., and James G. Baker, *Telescopes and Accessories*. The Blakiston Company, Philadelphia, 1945. The design and uses of astronomical instruments.

CHAPTER V

Goodacre, Walter, *The Moon*. The author, Bournemouth, England, 1931. Contains maps, photographs, and descriptions of the surface formations.

CHAPTER VI

Dyson, Frank, and R.v.d.R. Woolley, *Eclipses of the Sun and Moon*. Oxford University Press, Oxford, 1937.

Mitchell, S. A., *Eclipses of the Sun*. Columbia University Press, 1923.

CHAPTER VII

Dreyer, J. L. E., *History of the Planetary Systems from Thales to Kepler*. Cambridge University Press, Cambridge, 1906.

Moulton, Forest Ray, *An Introduction to Celestial Mechanics*. Second edition. The Macmillan Company, New York, 1923.

Williams, Kenneth P., *The Calculation of the Orbits of Asteroids and Comets*. Principia Press, Bloomington, Indiana, 1934.

CHAPTER VIII

Whipple, Fred L., *Earth, Moon and Planets*. The Blakiston Company, Philadelphia, 1941. An authoritative and very readable book.

CHAPTER IX

Russell, Henry Norris, *The Solar System and Its Origin*. The Macmillan Company, New York, 1935.

Watson, Fletcher G., *Between the Planets*. The Blakiston Company, Philadelphia, 1941. A good reference for additional reading about asteroids, comets, meteors, and meteorites.

CHAPTER X

Abetti, Giorgio, *The Sun. Its Phenomena and Physical Features*. D. Van Nostrand Company, New York, 1938.

White, Harvey E., *Classical and Modern Physics*. D. Van Nostrand Company, New York, 1940.

CHAPTER XI

Morgan, W. W., Philip C. Keenan, and Edith Kellman, *An Atlas of Stellar Spectra,* with an Outline of Spectral Classification. University of Chicago Press, Chicago, 1943.
Schlesinger, Frank, and Louise F. Jenkins, *Catalogue of Bright Stars*. Second edition. Yale University Observatory, 1940. "Containing all important data known in January, 1940, relating to all stars brighter than 6.5 visual magnitude, and to some fainter ones."

CHAPTER XII

Campbell, Leon, and Luigi Jacchia, *The Story of Variable Stars*. The Blakiston Company, Philadelphia, 1941. How variable stars are observed and the important results derived from their study.
Merrill, Paul W., *The Nature of Variable Stars*. The Macmillan Company, New York, 1938.

CHAPTER XIII

Aitken, Robert G., *The Binary Stars*. Second edition. McGraw-Hill Book Company, New York, 1935. A standard reference on this subject.

CHAPTER XIV

Goldberg, Leo, and Lawrence H. Aller, *Atoms, Stars and Nebulae*. The Blakiston Company, Philadelphia, 1943. An informative and clearly written account of astrophysics.

CHAPTER XVII

Barnard, Edward E., *A Photographic Atlas of Selected Regions of the Milky Way*. The University of Chicago Press, Chicago, 1927.
Bok, Bart J., *The Distribution of the Stars in Space*. The University of Chicago Press, 1937.
Bok, Bart J., and Priscilla F., *The Milky Way*. The Blakiston Company, Philadelphia, 1941. An up-to-the-times account of the galactic system and the methods of investigating it.
Ross, Frank E., and Mary R. Calvert, *Atlas of the Northern Milky Way*. University of Chicago Press, Chicago, 1936.

CHAPTER XVIII

Hubble, Edwin, *The Realm of the Nebulae*. Yale University Press, New Haven, 1936. An authoritative and well illustrated account of the extragalactic systems.
Shapley, Harlow, *Galaxies*. The Blakiston Company, Philadelphia, 1943. An authoritative account of our knowledge of the extragalactic systems.

Current contributions to the literature of astronomy appear in the publications of the various observatories and in the astronomical periodicals such as:

The Astronomical Journal. Published by The American Astronomical Society. Yale University Observatory, New Haven 11.

The Astrophysical Journal. An International Review of Spectroscopy and Astronomical Physics. Published bimonthly. The University of Chicago Press, Chicago 37.

The Journal of the British Astronomical Association. Published ten times a year.

The Journal of the Royal Astronomical Society of Canada. Published monthly. 198 College Street, Toronto 2B, Ontario.

Monthly Notices of the Royal Astronomical Society. Published monthly. Burlington House, London, W. 1.

The Observatory. Published monthly. The Editors, Royal Observatory, Greenwich, London S.E. 10.

Popular Astronomy. A Review of Astronomy and Allied Sciences. Published monthly (except July and September) by Goodsell Observatory, Northfield, Minnesota.

Publications of the Astronomical Society of the Pacific. Published bimonthly by the Society. San Francisco.

Sky and Telescope. Published monthly. Sky Publishing Corporation, Harvard Observatory, Cambridge 38.

INDEX